ARCHITECTURE & ASSEMBLY LANGUAGE

Third Edition

Barry Kauler

KARDA PRINTS
Narrogin, Australia

SIGMA PRESS
Wilmslow, England

Cover Design by: Design House, Marple Bridge, Stockport

First published by

Karda Prints, 10 McCormick Way, Narrogin, WA 6312, Australia

This edition published by

Sigma Press, 1 South Oak Lane, Wilmslow, Cheshire SK9 6AR, UK

First printed 1992

ISBN: 1-85058-304-8

British Library Cataloguing in Publication Data

A CIP catalogue record for this book is available from the British Library.

Printed by: Interprint Ltd, Malta.

CONTENTS

ACKNOWLEDGEMENTS:

A textbook is not something you "knock off" in a few weekends. It is a project that seems to have no end point, yet at some stage the decision must be made that "enough is enough and let's go to print!"

Unfortunately I cannot stop, and the third edition has made its appearance only six months after the second.

Thanks to family members who tolerated my eccentric behaviour.

Thanks also to staff of the Departments of Computer Science & Computer Engineering, Edith Cowan University, Perth, Western Australia, for their active encouragement.

All wordprocessing, page layout and most illustrations for this book were done using the superb Ami Professional software from Lotus Development Corporation. Master artwork was printed on a Hewlett Packard LaserJet III.

B.Kauler Jan. '92

HOW TO READ THIS BOOK:

Without difficulty, hopefully. The main feature about its structure that you will find slightly unusual is the hypertext "hotlinking". You will quickly pick up how to utilise this and will find it to be a boon while studying.

INTRODUCTION

This textbook, together with the Companion Disk, form a complete environment for learning Assembly Language and the inner workings of the PC.

A purchase voucher for the Companion Disk is at the back of the book, with a description of its contents. Basically it provides ''pop-up'' hypertext access to most of the reference material contained in this book, on your screen at any time. The disk also contains example programs and an Assembler and Debugger.

All you will need in addition to the book and disk, is a text editor or word processor, and you are ready to embark upon the adventure of learning Assembly Language and the hardware of the IBM-compatible family of PC's.

The chapters are organised in a suggested chronological sequence for the presentation of the lectures, or for self-study with a matching hands-on workshop at the end of each chapter.

Prerequisites

Of course an in-depth book of this nature must assume some prior knowledge, and in this case a basic familiarity with operation of the IBM-PC and MSDOS is assumed. It would be helpful to understand MSDOS to the extent of being able to use it on a day-to-day basis, including an understanding of the files CONFIG.SYS and AUSOEXEC.BAT. In case you do feel a bit rusty, Chapter One contains some revision exercises.

It is also assumed that you have a basic familiarity with number systems, including decimal, binary, hexadecimal, and ASCII character coding, plus basic Boolean AND, OR & NOT logic. Again, some revision notes are in Chapter One - sufficient even if you are relatively new to these topics.

Objectives/Justification Of/For this Book

The Main Contents on page iii show the overall content of the book, however, the schedule of presentation and the objectives may be defined by the instructor or lecturer. Note that due to the hypertext nature of this book, only headings are given on page iii: turn to the referenced page for a chapter-index.

The material attempts to provide a balance between hardware and software, though again the emphasis is up to the lecturer, or student in the case of self-study.

This course gives Computer Studies students the opportunity to learn more about the nuts and bolts level of computers, and this should be seen as a guiding philosophy in its design.

Assembly language and the architecture of the PC should be viewed by students as a vital aspect of their program of study. To understand the nuts and bolts helps enormously with comprehending higher levels and adapting to new developments. The x86 CPU family was chosen as this is the major standard and there is no doubt that this situation will consolidate. PC's in general will continue to encroach upon mainframes and will become an increasingly important part of your accumulated knowledge.

MSDOS is here to stay for quite some time and is the logical operating system to use as a basis for study in the PC environment. Although we are moving toward MSWindows and OS/2 with Presentation Manager, DOS can be considered as a stepping stone - all three operating systems have originated from Microsoft and one finds common philosophies intertwining them.

This textbook progresses in a most natural manner through DOS and into OS/2 (& Windows) and with DOS principles ingested the student will feel surprisingly at home with the OS/2 kernel.

Also the shear momentum of 40 million DOS systems currently in use in the world will require graduates to have some familiarity with DOS programming.

The '386 and '486 CPU's are becoming a major standard, supplanting mainframes, and a knowledge of Assembly language programming of this family is a sound choice. Take note of the new NCR System 3000 family, that uses '386 and '486 CPU's in mainframe architectures.

Do not look down upon Assembly language - it is an essential part of your toolbox of knowledge. Even if you do most of your programming in a high level language such as Pascal, still you will find it convenient to insert some Assembly code on occasions. Some programmers by choice program entirely in Assembly, for very sound reasons. Assembly code is much faster and compact than code written in high-level languages, though Assembly is a high-level when used with an adequate library.

Note that the "browser" program developed for viewing the on-disk hypertext database was written by the Author in Assembly code. It is very tight coding indeed and the total program is a TSR (resident, or "pop-up") program of about 10K bytes. Another similar but inferior commercial program written in C, is 50K.

A final note is that you should understand Assembly code simply to be able to read books and articles in which example Assembly coding is given. This is a very common occurrence and sufficient reason on its own to justify a course of study in Assembly language.

1

REVIEW DOS, INTRO. PC ARCHITECTURE

Well here we are at the first chapter, which can also be considered as the first lesson in a PC architecture course. One step at a time will turn you into a master of the PC. Here are the main headings for this lesson--

PREREQUISITES:

Refer back to the Introduction to this book for more details.

You should have a few clues on how to use a PC, such as navigating around directories and basic file management. To make sure you are up to scratch, Worksheet-(MSDOS) consists of a number of basic exercises. I have only given some background on this material in this textbook, so if you have any problem with Worksheet-(MSDOS), refer elsewhere. If Worksheet-(MSDOS) is no problem for you, there's no need to do it.

BACKGROUND STUFF:

THE MEAT OF THIS LESSON:

INTRO to the BROWSER:

The Companion Disk available with this book has most of the reference material from the book on-disk in hypertext form, with a BROWSE program to access it.

This printed textbook is also in hypertext form -- "hotwords" in the text are linked to elsewhere in the book by "hotlinks" in the right margin. These hotlinks are simply page numbers that point to reference material related to the hotword.

BROWSE's disk-based hypertext technique marks hotwords as intense characters on the screen and it's simply a matter of moving the cursor onto the hotword and pressing the <enter> key, to move to the referenced part of the database.

Since BROWSE is a TSR (resident) program, it is very convenient to load it, perhaps at power-on, by a suitable line in the AUTOEXEC.BAT file, and pop it up at any time. Note also that BROWSE does general text searches and is context-sensitive. While working away using DEBUG or any text editor or other program, BROWSE can be popped up for quick reference. Look at the README.1ST and MICRO.HTX files on the Companion Disk for full details on loading & using BROWSE, however here are a few clues on usage:

Using BROWSE is simplicity itself really --- a hypertext database is just like a book, that you could read from beginning to end by using the up/down arrow keys, & PgDn/PgUp keys, but the power of hypertext is that you can zoom into whatever portions take your fancy very quickly. Wherever a word appears in intense letters, by using the <TAB>, <SPACEBAR> key, or arrow keys you can move onto that word, then by pressing <ENTER> you can jump to another portion of the text file linked to that word.

In this manner you can jump around -- each <ENTER> takes you down another "level" into the file, while <ESC> will backtrack --- by pushing <ESC> you can go back to the Main Contents, and since it's not possible to backtrack any further, another <ESC> will exit from the program.

More little notes--- pushing <q>, meaning "quit", does just that, with the advantage that the program remembers where you quit from in the data file, so next time you pop-up the program, there you are at the point you left off. Very handy. In case you can't remember which key to press, make sure the cursor is at the top left corner of the window and then press <ENTER> to pop up a menu. <F10> will also pop-up the menu.

PAUSE:

Now is a time to reflect. Do you need to do Worksheet-(MSDOS)? If so, go to **Worksheet-(MSDOS)**. *20* The section that follows is some background material for the worksheet. If you feel that you're already familiar enough with DOS, then skip the worksheet, but do look through the next couple of pages of this book as they contain important information about how the CPU & DOS start up. The second half of this chapter introduces the **architecture of the 8086** *9*

SOME BACKGROUND THEORY,
for WORKSHEET-MSDOS:

One thing you will notice about Worksheet-(MSDOS) is that it is sprinkled with "hot words", that is, words that are displayed as intense, and are linked to some other part of the text, to which you can jump. This is really nice, as it means that as you do the worksheet you can jump out to look up particular points as required, then immediately jump back to where you were.

Most of the background text linked to the hot-words of Worksheet-(MSDOS) is below, to save you the trouble of searching through reference books.

BACKGROUND THEORY HEADINGS:

POWER-UP OF THE IBM-PC:

To boot up the PC with DOS requires --

Turn-on

Bootstrap program at address FFFF0 in BIOS ROM

Loads another bootstrap program from the "boot record" on the disk

... which loads the system files

Finally COMMAND.COM executes and the DOS-prompt appears.

FIGURE 1.1

A.

A DOS system diskette in drive A: or the system files on drive C: The operating system files are IBMIO.COM, IBMDOS.COM and COMMAND.COM.

(to find out how to make a **"bootable" floppy disk** >>>) *109*

B.

The system "boot" sequence is initiated by powering up the computer, or by pressing ALT-CTRL-DEL simultaneously.

C.

The default drive prompt, A> or C> will indicate a successful loading of the operating system.

INITIALISATION OF THE CPU:

NOTE:
Some of the points made below may be a little unclear ... in which case don't worry ... the cart has been placed before the horse ... loose-ends should be tied-up in further reading, but if any particular point really troubles you, look at its hotlink.

When powering up the IBM-PC you are also powering up the 8088, 8086, 80286 or 80386 CPU, whichever your particular computer has. The CPU has **internal registers** that are initialised to certain values at power-up. Two of them, the Code Segment register, and the Instruction Pointer, are initialised as follows: 17 11

The CPU combines these two in a certain way to produce an address on the **address-bus**: 9

CS = FFFF (**hex**)
IP = 0000
CS:IP = FFFF0

Note that this address refers to the **8088 and 8086**, that have a 20-bit address bus. The '286 & '386 have **larger address buses**, but only use 20-bits in start-up "real mode". 15 130

At power-on, the CPU will put this address onto the address bus and fetch the first instruction from this address. (By the way, what does **FFFF0 hex** actually mean? >>>) 11

Thus, the program that takes control when the computer is switched on, must start at address **FFFF0**. Furthermore, it must be in ROM so that it is there at power-on. This program has a special name --- it is part of the **BIOS** -- Basic Input/Output System. 9 6

The BIOS routine with the start address of FFFF0 takes control of the boot procedure. This routine looks for the **"Boot Record"** on system diskette in drive A: or C:. The Boot Record is a small program, with certain important system information, that is then loaded from disk and executed. 216

THE SYSTEM-DISK FILES:

To boot DOS requires a **Boot Record** to be on the system disk. When loaded and executed, the Boot Record checks to see if DOS is stored on the disk. It looks for and loads into RAM the following three files: 216

Once DOS has been loaded it then checks the disk for these two files. They help to configure the system and create a personalised environment for the user:

File	
IBMIO.COM	5
IBMDOS.COM	6
COMMAND.COM	6
CONFIG.SYS	6
AUTOEXEC.BAT	7

IBMIO.COM:

This file contains extensions to the ROM-BIOS. These extensions may be changes or additions to the basic I/O operations, and often include corrections to the existing ROM-BIOS, new routines for new equipment or customised changes to the standard ROM-BIOS routines.

IBMDOS.COM:

This file contains all the DOS service routines. The IBMDOS.COM routines are more sophisticated and we can think of them as the next level up from the BIOS routines.

WHAT THE BIOS & DOS ROUTINES ARE FOR:

Note that the BIOS and DOS service routines are there for us to use when writing programs. There is a simple method for us to call any one of these "subroutines" from our program. Basically, these routines enable us to interface with the hardware of the computer, such as the keyboard, screen, printer, disk drives and serial port.

There is a **later chapter** that will take you into how to do this. *61*

COMMAND.COM:

This file contains the routines that interpret the commands from the keyboard when we are in the DOS command mode.

Internal commands;

DIR, RENAME, ERASE, TIME, DATE, COPY.

External commands;

FORMAT, DISKCOPY, ASSIGN, TREE.

Note that there are two classes of commands -- internal, and external.

The internal commands are contained within COMMAND.COM, while the external commands are kept on disk. FORMAT.COM for example is the program for the FORMAT command.

The reason that some of DOS's commands are kept as separate programs on disk is due to space constraints in the RAM. Obviously there is limited RAM, so it makes sense to keep the less-used portions of DOS on the disk, bringing them in as needed.

CONFIG.SYS:

"System" files have an extension of .SYS and may be programs or text files. A major group of .SYS files are what is known as device drivers

-- these are programs that load and become semi-permanently resident in memory.

CONFIG.SYS is a system text file that is read from disk and incorporated into DOS during DOS's startup procedure. CONFIG.SYS can be created by any text editor, and consists of a number of commands -- here is an example of a CONFIG.SYS file:

```
FILES=20
BUFFERS=20
DEVICE=ANSI.SYS
DEVICE=GMOUSE.SYS *21
COUNTRY=061
```

Refer to your DOS User's Manual for more details. An important point to note here is that DEVICE= is a command that allows you to load more device drivers into the system. GMOUSE.SYS for example is driver software for a mouse, and loading this driver will allow any program that can utilise a mouse, to do so.

Refer to the lesson on **device drivers** for more details. *273*

The chapter on Assembly language discusses **setting up the working environment** for development, including CONFIG.SYS and AUTOEXEC.BAT. *124*

AUTOEXEC.BAT:

After DOS has loaded CONFIG.SYS, it then looks on the disk for AUTOEXEC.BAT. Any file with an extension of .BAT is known as a "**batch**" file, and AUTOEXEC.BAT is a special batch file that DOS looks for at power up.

In a nutshell, a batch file is created by any text editor and contains DOS commands, as well as special batch commands, that enable you to automate the operation of DOS. Instead of having to type in the same DOS commands every time you start the computer, by putting them into the AUTOEXEC.BAT file, DOS will execute them automatically for you every time. Here is an example of an AUTOEXEC.BAT file:

```
@echo off
PATH C:\;C:\SYSTEM\DOS;C:\GALAXY
PROMPT $p$g
CD \DATA
DIR
```

Refer to your DOS User's Manual for more details on batch files, though note that they are discussed further in this book in relation to **semi-automating** the assemble-link development cycle. *111*
The AUTOEXEC.BAT file is also discussed in the documentation files

on the Companion Disk, in relation to automatically loading BROWSE at power-up.

NOTE:

The power-up sequence of the PC is quite involved, and many references are made to it throughout this book. Of particular interest is the **configuration RAM**, that the BIOS uses during the Power On Self Test (POST) sequence.

174

ANOTHER NOTE: K's & M's

You are probably already familiar with spec's like 640K, 1M or 120M, but you might like to pause here and think about it a little more. We are accustomed, with the metric numbering system, of thinking of "K" to mean x1000 the base unit of measurement, and "M" to mean x1,000,000 the base unit, however in binary numbering this is not quite right. Since memory chips are made with storage capacities measured in powers of 2, K and M have these weights:

K = x1024
M = x1024 x1024 = x1,048,576

Thus, when we say that a PC has 640K bytes of RAM, we actually mean 640 x 1024 = 655,360

Or, if the RAM is 4M, then it is actually 4 x 1,048,576 = 4,194,304

INTRO:
IBM-PC ARCHITECTURE

The first part of Chapter One was background, which may be consolidated by doing Worksheet-(MSDOS) if you feel the need.

Now we are moving ahead. Go through each one of these...

MEMORY MAP OF THE PC

The **8088 and 8086** have a 20-bit address bus, which means that they can address $2^{20}-1$ = FFFFF (**hex**) = 1Megabytes (dec). The 80286 has 24 bits, and the 80386 has 32 bits. *12* *7*

A good starting point is at the beginning. For the 8088/6 the memory organisation on the PC looks like **Figure 1.3**. You know the specification given for the PC, of 640K bytes of RAM --- this RAM exists in the memory map from address 00000 up to the **640K** shown in brackets. You can see that the first 140K or thereabouts is occupied by various things, which leaves about 500K free for user programs. Of course this free memory is a very variable thing, depending on a number of factors. *13* *8*

For example, if the CONFIG.SYS file specified some device drivers, they would be loaded into the memory and kept there. If you wanted to run a graphical user interface such as Microsoft Windows, that too would have to be loaded. Same for any Resident "pop-up" programs such as Sidekick. All of these will reduce your free memory.

Figure 1.3 is simplified and in practice there will be a lot more functions occupying the memory space. The example of **Figure 1.4** shows some possibilities. *13*

AN OVERVIEW OF NUMBERS

All data is stored in the computer's memory as binary 1's and 0's. Each memory "location" contains an eight-bit binary content:

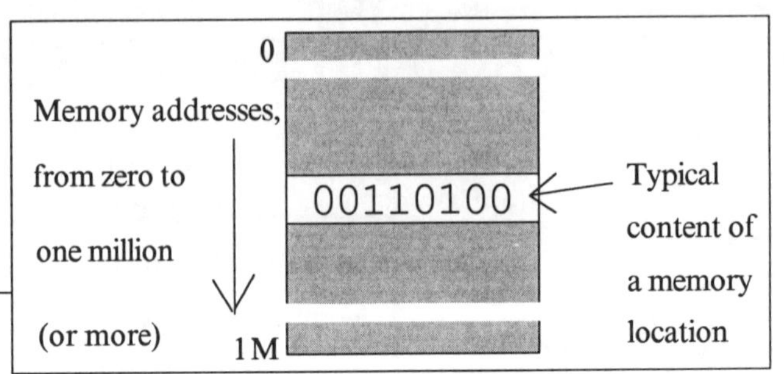

00110100

OTHER CODES, FLAGS, ETC

2's COMPLEMENT BINARY NUMBER

Positive numbers in 2's complement representation look just like unsigned straight binary numbers. They are distinguished as +ve by the most significant bit (MSB, ie the left-most bit) being 0.

A negative number is distinguished by the MSB being 1. The value 00110100 is 52 decimal (see alongside) ... so how does -52 look? The rule is, invert all bits to the left of the first-bit-from-the-right-set-to-1. Thus: 11001100

UNSIGNED /SIGNED MAGNITUDE BINARY

00110100 could be treated as a magnitude only, "straight" binary number, or the MSB could be a sign, leaving 7 bits for the magnitude -- this is not the same as 2's complement.

Considering it as the former:
00110100 = 0x2^7 + 0x2^6 + 1x2^5 + 1x2^4 + 0x2^3 + 1x2^2 + 0x2^1 + 0x2^0 = 52 decimal.

i.e. 52 decimal is represented in the memory by 00110100 binary.

BINARY CODED DECIMAL (BCD)

BCD is another way of storing decimal values in the computer. The bits are grouped into lots of four, and each group converted to decimal:

0011	0100
3	4

i.e. 34 decimal is represented in the memory by 00110100.

AMERICAN STANDARD CODE FOR INFORMATION INTERCHANGE (ASCII)

The code does not represent a number at all, but a character. From an ASCII table (look on page 253), 00110100 represents ASCII character 4.

A "character" is any single symbol, such as a numeric digit, letter, punctuation symbol, etc. Each key on the keyboard represents one character. The "4" key for example, when pressed, is stored inside the computer not as the binary value 00000100 but as the ASCII code 00110100.

The example shows "00110100" stored at a memory location ... but what value does this content represent? **Always be aware that the meaning of this data is up to the programmer** ... look at some examples of what 00110100 can represent.

HEX NUMBERS -- In this book you'll get a gut-full of these, starting from page 9, with references to register contents like FFFF and an address FFFF0. Hexadecimal numbers have base-16, i.e. are based upon a number system with 16 digits, rather than the 10 in decimal or the 2 in binary. They are:

H	0	1	2	3	4	5	6	7	8	9	A	B	C	D	E	F
D	0	1	2	3	4	5	6	7	8	9	10	11	12	13	14	15
B	0000	0001	0010	0011	0100	0101	0110	0111	1000	1001	1010	1011	1100	1101	1110	1111

The first row are the hex digits, followed by decimal, then binary -- note that hex numbers are just a shorthand notation for binary, which is why they're used. Each hex digit represents 4 binary bits, and FFFF0 hex is the same as 1111 1111 1111 1111 0000 binary. Note that hex is not BCD.

INSTRUCTION OPERATION CODE

The data does not represent a character or a value, but an instruction operation code. Machine language instructions are stored in memory as an op-code followed by zero or more operands, depending upon the instruction -- the interpretation of this code is up to the CPU.

So, 00110100 binary stored inside the memory, represents 52 decimal in 2's complement, 52 decimal in magnitude-only, 34 decimal in BCD, character 4 in ASCII, or an op-code, or some other code or status flags. Note that the shorthand **hex notation** for 00110100 is 34 also (see above).

Another possibility is that 00110100 represents only part of a number. For example a number could be represented in 32 bits, which means that it would occupy two memory locations, and 00110100 could be the low or high half of the number. The Intel standard is that the half at the lower address is also the lower half, or least significant byte.

FIGURE 1.2

THE CPU & SUPPORT CHIPS:

This first lesson will consider the architecture of the **8088** only. 14

The 8088 is the Central Processing Unit (CPU) of the PC. It executes instructions contained in RAM or ROM memory.

The CPU and a few support chips produce various signals known as the BUS, which can be broken down into:

- Address bus,
- Data bus,
- Control lines.

These are physical lines (wires) going to and from the CPU & support chips, shown in Figure 1.4. Don't worry about the exact details of the support chips at this stage.

The bus goes to all the memory and I/O chips in the computer, and is the means by which everything communicates. The only way in which more advanced CPU's differ from this is the size of each of these buses --- the 80386 for example has 32 address-lines and 32 data-lines.

MEMORY & I/O CHIPS

There are many chips in the PC, that you will be learning about in this course, including:

Chip	Page
RAM/ROM chips	*130*
8253 Programmable Timer	*167*
8255 Peripheral Interface	*136*
8237 DMA Controller,	*142*
8259 Interrupt Controller	*137*
8087 Maths Coprocessor	*177*
6818 Real Time Clock	*167*
6845 CRT Controller	*76*
8250 Serial Controller	*160*

These are the standard chips used in the IBM-PC XT models, and later models may have other chips. Often however the more advanced chips are upwards compatible with their predecessors, so learning about these chips is not wasted effort.

This upward compatibility also applies to the CPU's, so that Assembly language programs you learn to write for the 8088 CPU will also work on an 80386 CPU.

Precise details on how these buses are connected to the individual chips are given later in the course, when interfacing is gone into.

FIGURE 1.3
Memory map of the PC.

ADDRESS	CONTENTS
00000h	Interrupt service routine Address Table.
00400h	BIOS data.
00500h	DOS data.
	Resident part of DOS.
	Free memory.
	Transient part of DOS.
640K(dec)	
A0000h	Colour display RAM.
B0000h	Monochrome display RAM.
B8000h	Colour display RAM.
F0000h	ROM extensions.
F4000h	User ROM space.
F6000h	ROM BASIC (maybe).
FE000h	ROM BIOS.
FFFFFh (1Meg)	

FIGURE 1.4
Possible extensions to the map.

Address	Contents
C0000h	EGA BIOS (16K bytes).
C6000h	PGA communication(256bytes)
C8000h	Hard disk BIOS (16K bytes).
D0000h	Cluster adaptor BIOS (32K).

The functionality of the original chips, incorporated into later **VLSI** designs, is discussed at various points through the book. The **upwards compatibility** of the CPU's is also discussed, though note that the '386 has more instructions and different architecture to the 8088 so '386-specific software may not work on a 8088.

130 *196*

INSIDE THE CPU (Architecture)

This first lesson looks at the 8088 CPU only. The internal architectures of the **'286 & '386** are covered later. *196*

So what does it look like inside? We can get a block-diagram appreciation, without getting lost in the complexity of the many thousands of transistors on the chip. Refer to Figure 1.6.

It is worth spending a few moments to contemplate this diagram. To speed things up, instructions are fetched from memory whenever the CPU gets a chance, and queued in the Instruction Stream Byte Queue. This is a simple form of "pipelining".

When it's ready to execute the next instruction, the Execution Unit takes the first waiting instruction off the queue, and executes it.

The Adder is used to generate a 20-bit physical address, which it does by combining two register values. This is necessary, since all of these registers are only 16 bits.

The CPU may generate an address to fetch the next instruction, or in response to the execution requirements of the currently executing instruction, for example to store a value contained in a register at some memory location.

In the case of fetching the next instruction, the address of this is obtained from the Code-Segment (CS) register, and the Instruction Pointer (IP). To see how these two are combined to produce the actual physical address, **jump-out** to the hotlink. *54*

The Arithmetic Logic Unit executes the various **arithmetic or logical** operations as demanded by the instruction currently executing. It gets its operands from the General Registers, and will also return the answer there. *43*

Note also that the result of the arithmetic or logical operation will also set certain **flags**, which may have a bearing on the next instruction to be executed. *22*

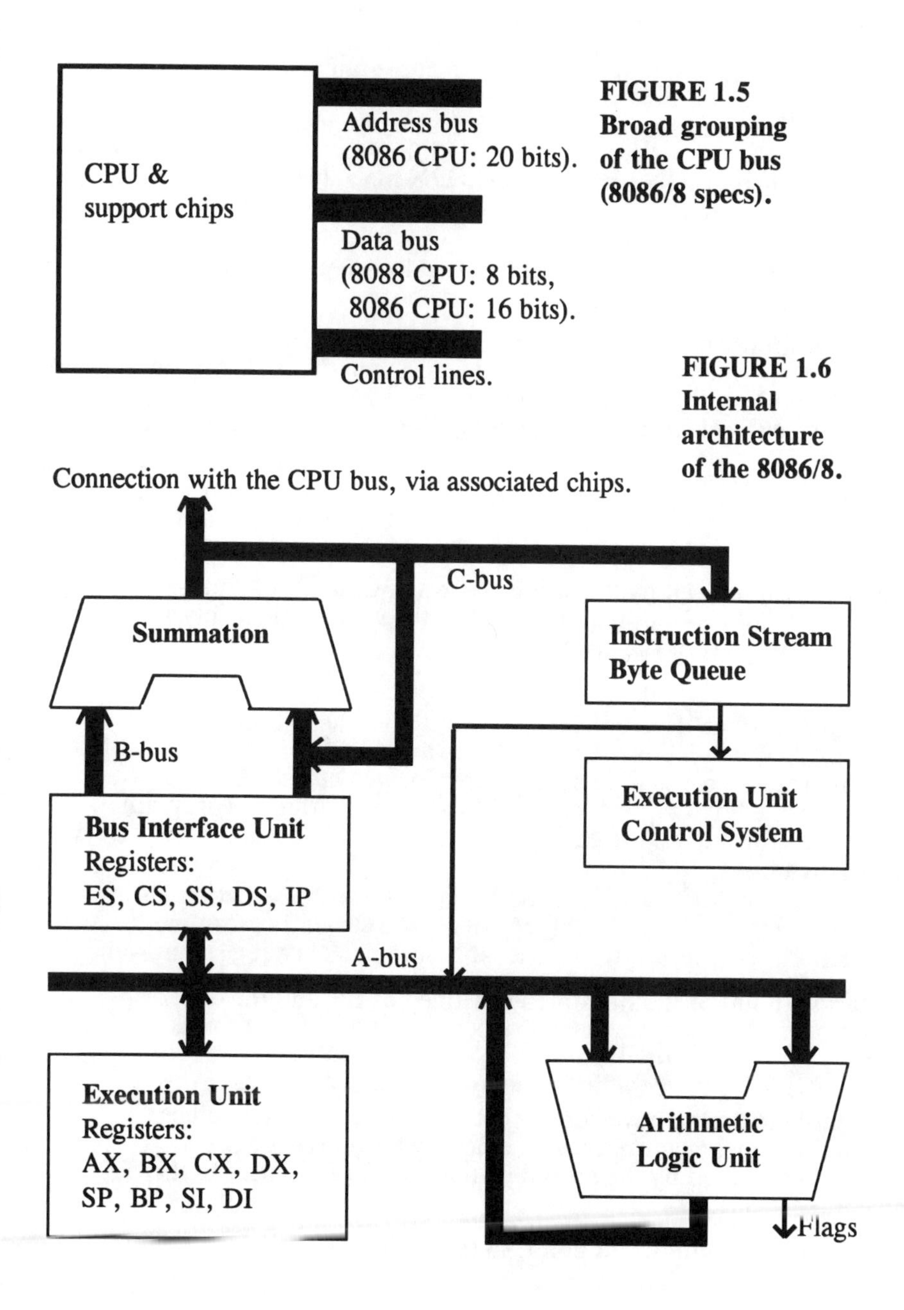

FIGURE 1.5 Broad grouping of the CPU bus (8086/8 specs).

FIGURE 1.6 Internal architecture of the 8086/8.

CPU REGISTERS

SEGMENT REGISTERS & ADDRESSING:

Just what are these segment registers? Basically, they enable your program to load from disk, anywhere in memory.

Your program will consist of code (instructions), data, and a stack, and there is a segment register allocated for each of these. **Jump out** here to the hotlink if you need clarification on how the physical address is calculated from the segment register value -- but here is an outline --

54

CODE:

Your code is addressed by the **combination** of CS and IP, that is, CSx16+IP = 20-bit physical address. Thus the value in IP is only an offset from the start of the program.

19

DATA:

Your program is able to access a data area located at a starting address specified by DS. Addressing of data from within the program will be in the form of an offset. Again, the physical address is DSx16+offset.

STACK:

The starting point of the stack area is defined by SS, and the offset is SP.

The overall picture we have here is that the segment register values (x16) are the starting addresses in memory, while the addresses maintained and used by the program are only offsets relative to those segment registers.

This is a very very important point, so think about it.

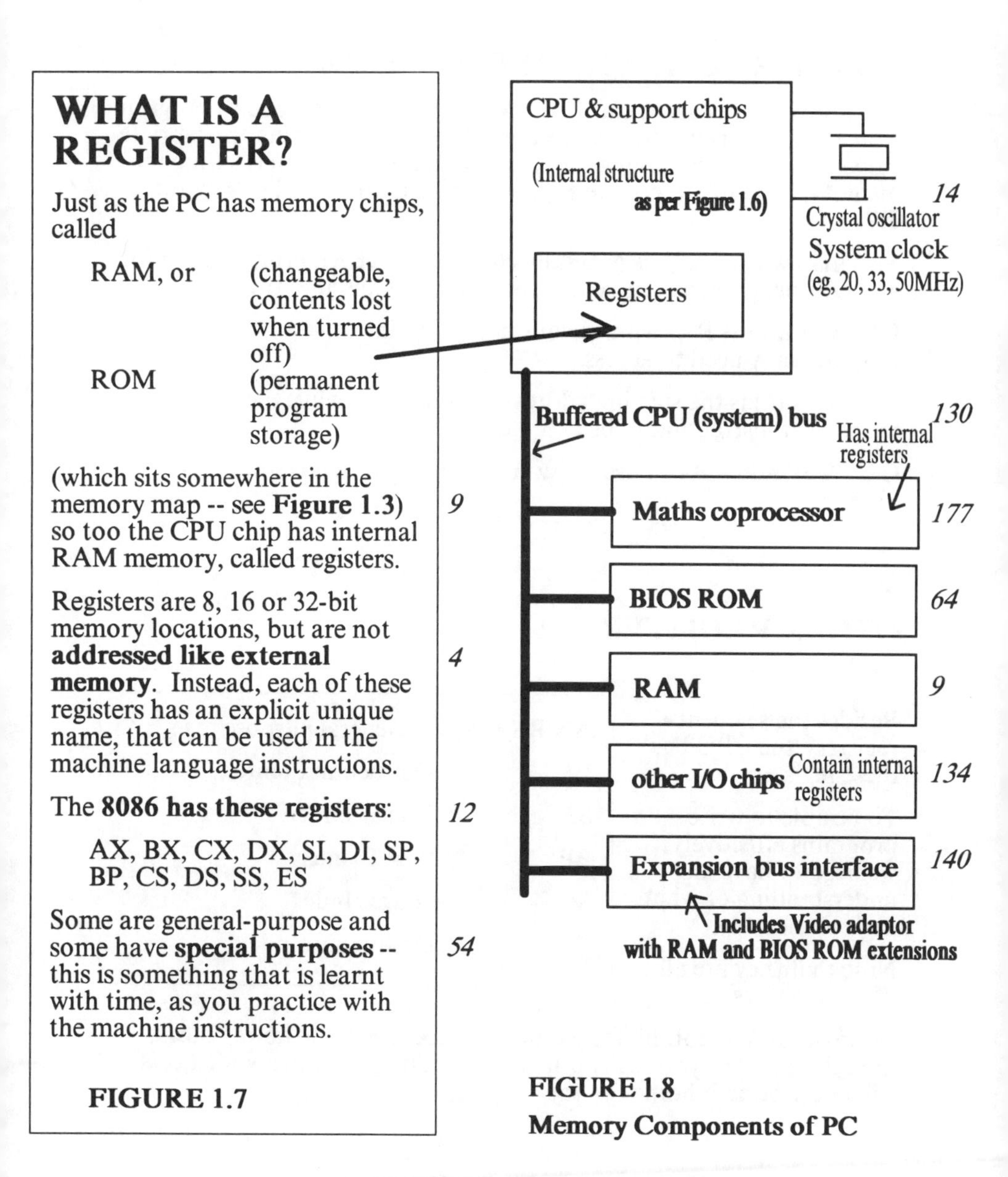

WHAT IS A REGISTER?

Just as the PC has memory chips, called

RAM, or	(changeable, contents lost when turned off)
ROM	(permanent program storage)

(which sits somewhere in the memory map -- see **Figure 1.3**) so too the CPU chip has internal RAM memory, called registers. 9

Registers are 8, 16 or 32-bit memory locations, but are not **addressed like external memory**. Instead, each of these registers has an explicit unique name, that can be used in the machine language instructions. 4

The **8086 has these registers**: 12

AX, BX, CX, DX, SI, DI, SP, BP, CS, DS, SS, ES

Some are general-purpose and some have **special purposes** -- this is something that is learnt with time, as you practice with the machine instructions. 54

FIGURE 1.7

FIGURE 1.8
Memory Components of PC

Actually, the video-adaptor circuitry need not be a plug-in card on the expansion bus. The PS/2's for example have it on the motherboard. The video card may have ROM extensions to the BIOS and RAM video memory, plus I/O ports to program the adaptor. Ditto for the hard disk interface.

LOADING A PROGRAM FROM DISK:

The above point can be clarified. When the computer loads a program from disk, it puts it into free memory. The computer puts appropriate values into the segment registers, thus when the program is sitting in memory, all ready to go, the segment registers will look like **Figure 1.9**. *19*

This map will vary. It is generally correct for a .EXE program, but for a **.COM** program all segment registers are initialised to the same value. *96*

DOS sets up the PSP with various important information that your program may need to access.

The CS (x16) is the starting address of your code, while the IP points to the next instruction to be executed.

OS/2 & Windows both use "**new .EXE**" format, that is somewhat different. *300*

OTHER REGISTERS:

Besides the segment registers, the CPU has these registers

AX,BX,CX,DX	General purpose reg's.
IP	Instruction Pointer.
SP	Stack Pointer.
BP	Base Pointer.
SI	Source Index.
DI	Destination Index.

To be able to write programs effectively, we need to have an understanding of what each of these do.

Note that they are all 16-bit registers.

Jump out to the hotlink for a quick **appreciation of the registers**, though note that you really only learn by doing, and the worksheets will really bring it home for you. *54*

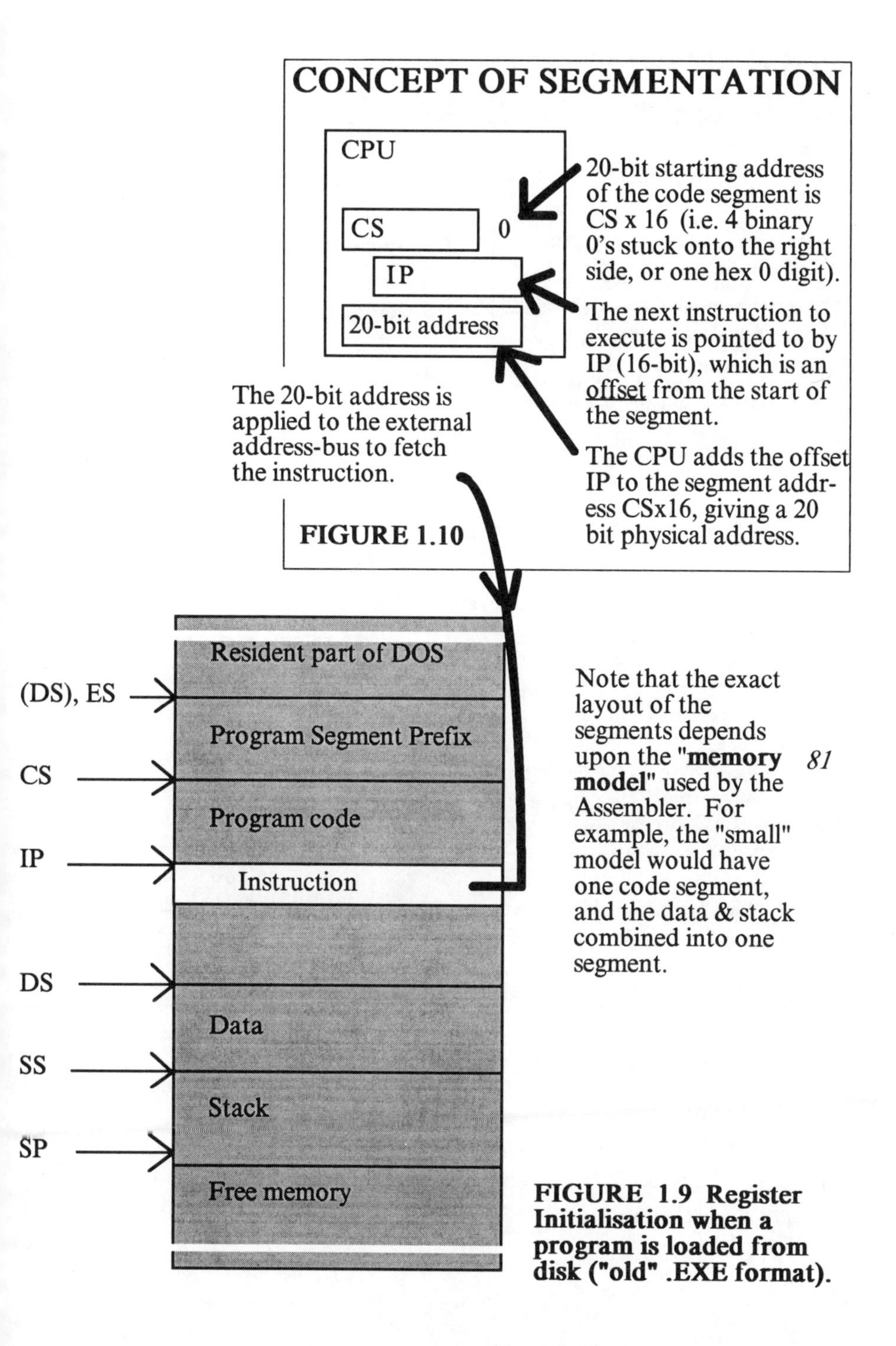

FIGURE 1.10

Note that the exact layout of the segments depends upon the "**memory model**" used by the Assembler. For example, the "small" model would have one code segment, and the data & stack combined into one segment.

81

FIGURE 1.9 Register Initialisation when a program is loaded from disk ("old" .EXE format).

WORKSHEET: MASTERY OF MSDOS

NOTE:

This is the prerequisite knowledge, from the MSDOS aspect, required for this course. Go through it if need be. A suitable reference is the shareware tutorial disk TUTOR.COM (PC-SIG #403). Also information can be obtained from your DOS User's Manual, and some background notes provided in this book -- in the latter case a "hot word" will indicate the presence of linked text.

Consists of three sections---

SECTION A: BASIC MSDOS

Reference: TUTOR.COM, Section 6

1. The three main DOS files (including hidden) on your system disk are:

COMMAND.COM 5

IBMIO.COM 5

IBMDOS.COM 5

Describe the sequence of actions these DOS programs go through after power-on.

2. What is the CONFIG.SYS file, and what part does it have to play in the sequence of **powering-up** of the PC? 4

3. Explain the use of "?" and "*" (wildcard) in specifying filenames.

4. What do the following DOS commands do (default drive is A:)

(i) VER	(ii) FORMAT /S
(iii) VOL	(iv) DEL *.*
(v) CLS	(vi) COPY B:*.*

5. Describe how the COPY command can be used to create a text file directly from the keyboard.

6. How do you think the COPY command could be used to print a text file to the printer?

7. How would you do a DISKCOPY with only a single floppy drive (A:)?

SECTION B: ADVANCED MSDOS

Reference: TUTOR.COM, Section 7

1. Explain the difference between a pathname and a filename.

2. Explain this:

```
C:> COPY A:*.* \WORDPROC\GALAXY
```

(If WORDPROC and GALAXY are directories).

3. What DOS command will change the current (default) directory from the root to GALAXY?

4. If the directory GALAXY did not exist, explain how you would create it, as a subdirectory of WORDPROC.

5. What would the DOS command be to do the same as that in Question-2, if the current (default) directory is GALAXY?

```
C:\WORDPROC\GALAXY>
```

6. If DOS is currently in the GALAXY directory, explain the effect of these DOS commands

```
(i)   DIR ..
(ii)  CD ..
(iii) CD \
```

7. What does the DOS TREE command do?

SECTION C: DOS BATCH FILES

References:
1. TUTOR.COM Section 8, 7
2. **Environment.** 124

1. Briefly, what is the purpose of the **AUTOEXEC.BAT** file and how does it differ from other .BAT files?

2. This is a typical AUTOEXEC.BAT file. Explain what each line does:

(where SYSFILES, UTILITIE, SHELL, INSTANT and COMMANDO are directories. DESK is a program).

```
PATH C:\;C:\sysfiles;C:\utilitie\shell
PROMPT Current directory = $p$_$g
CD \INSTANT\COMMANDO
DESK
cd \
```

3. Explain these batch commands:

(Note; GALAXY is a wordprocessing program that accepts a path & filename argument on the **DOS command-tail**, and in this example is located in a directory also called GALAXY).

221

```
@ECHO off
ECHO insert GALAXY data disk in A:
PAUSE
CD \WORDPROC\GALAXY
GALAXY A:*.*
```

4. If this is a batch file called GO.BAT

```
ECHO OFF
:START
ECHO %1
GOTO START
```

Typing GO MAN at the command-line would cause what to happen? Note: CTRL-C may be useful here!

5. Explain the effect of this batch command (this one is for the masochists):

```
FOR %%A IN (*.*) DO IF EXIST A:\%%A ECHO %%A IS ON A: & C:.
```

Notes: *.* will select all files in the current directory. Syntax here is critical -- don't forget the spaces, exactly as shown -- and the "." on the end.

WORKSHEET: DEBUG

This is a hands-on lesson with DEBUG.COM, a program supplied free on your DOS system disk.

It enables you to enter Assembly language programs, examine and alter memory, and debug programs by tracing through them and displaying registers.

DEBUG is an Assembler and a Debugger, but a very unsophisticated implementation. For serious work it would be far better to use tools such as the Microsoft Assembler and Microsoft Codeview Debugger, or the Borland Turbo equivalents. Another simple yet nice debugger is D86 supplied with the A86 Assembler.

These more advanced tools are described in Chapter Five.

DEBUG.COM REFERENCE:

DEBUG.COM is a program supplied free with your DOS system disks. It is very useful for preliminary fiddling with the instruction set. Select one of these...

1. REGISTER & FLAGS DISPLAY

To invoke DEBUG at the DOS command-line;

A> DEBUG

You should be greeted with "-", which is DEBUG's prompt.

To learn what DEBUG can do, a good approach is to go through the single-letter commands available. Go through the exercises, taking time to understand each command.

Firstly, we should know how to quit the program:

Try it, then reload DEBUG. Now try these:

Note that anything after ";" is a comment only and not to be typed in by you.

```
-Q          ;quit

-R          ;displays registers & flags of CPU

-R CX       ;display CX reg only
 CX 0000    ;DEBUG displays value of CX.
 : 1234     ;you can type in a new value,
            ;such as 1234, or just hit
            ;<enter> for no change.

-R F        ;to display only flags.
 NV UP DI PL NZ NA PO NC
            ;DEBUG responds with flags.
```

******WARNING******

If you change any segment registers, be sure to change them back again, so as not to potentially mess up further exercises with DEBUG.

MAKE A NOTE RIGHT NOW OF THEIR VALUE, AND CHECK THEM BEFORE GOING ONTO EACH SUCCESSIVE STEP.

These **flag statuses** do need some explanation. As with any CPU, the '86 has various flags that are set or cleared depending on the last instruction result. For example if the last result was zero, the Zero flag would be set.

367

This instruction is an example of one that would set the Zero flag:

CMP AX,AX

44

To understand DEBUG's response, refer to this table --

Now have a go at changing some flags. It is simply necessary to type in new statuses at the end of the line---

```
-R F
 NV UP DI PL NZ PO NC - OV CY
```

The overflow flag is changed from NV to OV, and the carry flag is changed from NC to CY.

FLAG	**DESCR.**	**SET**	**CLEAR**
overflow	y/n	OV	NV
direction	decrem/incr	DN	UP
interrupt	enable/dis	EI	DI
sign	negative/pos	NG	PL
zero	y/n	ZR	NZ
aux.carry	y/n	AC	NA
parity	even/odd	PE	PO
carry	y/n	CY	NC

TABLE 1.1

2. TO DISPLAY AN ADDRESSED LOCATION (Enter)

The Enter command is used for putting data into the **data-segment**. You have specified offset 100 in the data segment, and DEBUG responds with **0959:100**, which is the full address. Note that the value of DS in this example is 0959 but may be different in your machine.

35

52

DEBUG also responds with the contents of this address, in this case 00, and just pushing <enter> will leave it unchanged, or you can type in a new value and then press <enter> -- in this case 00 is replaced by hex 49.

This puts a new value of 49 hex into location DS:100 (offset 100 in the data segment). Note that DEBUG always works with hex numbers.

```
-E 100          ;you type this.
 0959:100 00    ;DEBUG responds with this.

-E 100
 0959:100 00.49        ;changing a value.

-E 100 49 F3 "X" "Y" 78
                ;doing it all on one line.

-E 100          ;verify that it worked.
 49 F3 58 59 78
```

Another option with the Enter command is to do it all on one line, and multiple consecutive locations may be changed. Typing values on the same line as the command will put them straight into the memory, starting from DS:100.

Try it, then verify that it worked, by using the same command again, as shown above (you can get DEBUG to display successive contents just by pushing the space-bar).

3. DUMP COMMAND

```
-D 1000 100F
      ;Dump range of mem.
-D ES:1000 100F
      ;segment override.
```

This command is similar to the Enter command, in that it displays the contents of a portion of memory. The difference is that it is display only, and contents cannot be changed. The second address is optional, and specifies a range.

One point to note with the E and D commands is that although they default to the data segment, an **over- ride** can be specified. This example means display the contents at offset 1000 to 100F in the extra segment. *35*

4. ASSEMBLE COMMAND

DEBUG does have a primitive assembler capability, however it must be emphasised that this is not adequate for **serious work**. DEBUG facilities are useful as a learning tool, and often convenient for very small jobs. *95*

An executable program sits in memory as machine code, but it started life when a programmer wrote the source code, maybe in Pascal, C, Fortran, or Assembler. Assembly code is machine code, just represented in a symbolic form that is more readable than 1's and 0's. An "Assembler" is a program that converts the symbolic "source code" into the machine code. The listing here is how to enter a simple Assembly language program.

```
-A 100
MOV AX,1000
MOV DS,AX
INT 3
```

33 *61*

Just hit <enter> one more time when you're finished, to get back to the "-" prompt.

"MOV" and "INT" are Assembly language instructions, and are explained in more detail in the next chapter and **Worksheet-(Addressing Modes)**. *57*

The "100" following the Assemble command specifies the offset into the code **segment** at which the program will start. Incidentally there is a **reason** why 100 is chosen. *16* *103*

Enter this little program before continuing.

5. UNASSEMBLE COMMAND

```
-U 100
```

After a program has been entered using the Assemble command, you will of course want to see if it is in there correctly. This example will unassemble 32 bytes of memory, from offset 100h. If your program is longer than that, just typing <U> followed immediately by <enter> will display the next portion of the program. Note that the U command references the **code segment**. Go ahead and try it. *16*

6. GO COMMAND

```
-G=100
```

The next logical step is to run the program. The program will be executed from CS:100, and will keep on going until an **INT 3** instruction is encountered; so don't forget that INT 3! *341*

ively you can specify a stop address

nk has more on the **Go** command.

-G=100 108

74

cute the little program, and after doing so examine the registers. This hanges DS, so before continuing with this workshop, change it back to the L VALUE. ****IMPORTANT****

ACE COMMAND

Of course just letting the program run right through may not be what you want. DEBUG is an educational tool that you can use to examine program execution instruction by instruction, and for that you need the Trace command.

This example will execute the first instruction in your program only, then DEBUG will display all the registers so you can examine what the instruction did.

This is most useful for both learning and for debugging a program.

```
-T=100      ;trace at IP=100.

;Typing <T> <enter>
;without specifying
;any address, will execute the next
;instruction, and so on through the
;program.
```

******WARNING******

Poor old DEBUG has some pitfalls. Do NOT trace into the **INT 3** instruction, as everything may hangup. Notice that each time you type <T><enter> the register values are also displayed. Stop when you see that the next instruction is INT 3.

341

You cannot Trace into an INT instruction but you can Go from wherever you currently are in the program, so typing:

-G

will continue execution until the end of the program. A useful note here is that if the INT instruction was not the end of the program, and you wanted to Go through it but stop immediately after it to continue tracing, this can be done by typing:

-G 106

where 106 is the address immediately AFTER the INT instruction --- of course you would need to know what this address is -- it won't necessarily be 106 of course -- typing "U" for Unassemble wherever you are in the program will give you the address.

8. EXAMPLE PROGRAM

Put all of these commands to work! I want you to enter this program using E for the data and A for the assembly code, U to verify entry, G to run it, and T to examine how it works.

DON'T expect to understand all the instructions, as they are to be covered in the next chapter --- the point of the exercise here is to master DEBUG.

Firstly, these hex values must be put into the **data segment** DS, at offset 200 hex---

35

06 42 55 40 50 45 52

Next, the program is to be assembled into the code segment CS at offset 100 hex.

Don't type in the comments.

The example program is shown here --

Next, unassemble the program and make sure it's correct.

This example causes a message to be displayed on the screen.

Note that the B800 moved into ES is required to correctly address a Colour Graphics Adaptor (CGA). If your computer has a monochrome adaptor, use B000.

Type G=100 to execute the program.

```
mov   cx,0          ;clear counter register
mov   ax,B800       ;display-RAM address.       78
mov   es,ax         ; ... or B000               77
mov   di,06B0       ;  /
mov   si,200        ;source offset.
mov   cl,[si]       ;get number of bytes.
mov   ah,0F8        ;setup attribute byte.
cld                                             39
mov   al,[si+1]     ;retrieve next character.
inc   si            ;incr. source pointer.      47
stosw                                           42
loop  113                                       39
int   3                                         61
```

Note that when bytes are sent to the screen they are treated as ASCII (American Standard Code for Information Interchange, by the way) characters, so you will need an **ASCII** table to verify that the data you entered has appeared correctly on the screen. *370*

Finally, use Trace to single-step through the program, making careful notes on the effect of each instruction. Note that **STOSW** is the instruction that sends the character to the screen, but as DEBUG immediately displays the registers and scrolls the screen upwards, the character might not appear in the position you expect. *42*

That's the end of this Worksheet, but note that there are some more DEBUG commands we haven't covered --- refer to your DOS User's Manual if interested in these.

SAVING TO DOS....

A footnote to this worksheet may be of interest. Yes, programs that you write within DEBUG can be saved to disk as executable files, and can also be reloaded by DEBUG. Assuming that you assembled your code at CS:100, and left DS = CS = SS, then the program can be saved as .COM type.

Here's how--- Calculate the size of your program, from CS:100 to wherever the code AND data end. In the previous example program the size is 206 - 100 = 106 bytes. Put this value into the 32-bit register-pair, using the "R" command.

Then name the file, using the "N" (Name) command.

Then save it, using the "W" (Write) command.

To start DEBUG and load your file, type both directly on the DOS command-line.

Note that the program won't execute properly from the DOS command-line, as the terminating INT 3 will not return control to DOS. Instead, before saving the file, replace INT 3 with--

```
mov ax,4C00h
int 21h
```

```
-R BX
 : 0
-R CX
 : 106

-N [A:][path]filename.COM

-W  CS:100

C:> DEBUG filename.COM
```

357

2

'86 INSTRUCTION SET

This lesson introduces the instruction set of the 8086 (which is a subset of the 80286 and 80386 chips).

STACK INSTRUCTIONS

The computer maintains a stack somewhere in memory. DOS will set the Stack Segment register SS when your program is loaded, and the Stack Pointer SP will be initialised to FFFEh, or some value to mean that the stack is empty. The **stack** is used by the computer and by your program. For example, whenever an interrupt occurs the CPU pushes the IP, CS and flags onto the stack, so that when the interrupt routine is finished (terminated by an IRET instruction) the CPU will pop these values back into the respective registers and continue from where it left off. *18*

Thus the stack is used to hold register values to enable the CPU to return from an interrupt, and also from a procedure CALL.

However you can make use of the **stack** in your program, by means of PUSH, which pushes a 16-bit value onto the stack, and POP, which *29* pops the top value off the stack into a register or memory location. Also PUSHF and POPF can be used to push the flags onto the stack and pop them off.

Be very clear that **CALL**, which is the instruction to call a procedure or subroutine, pushes IP and CS (if FAR) onto the stack, and is terminated by RET, which pops them off. *31*

Interrupts can be of two types, hardware or software. The INT instruction generates a software interrupt. The INT instruction is gone into in more detail in the **next lesson**, so don't worry too much about it here. Sufficient to say that the INT instruction will cause the CPU to go to an interrupt-handling routine, and in the process push IP, CS and flags onto the stack. The routine is terminated by IRET, which pops them off again. Okay, so how to use the PUSH & POP instructions? --- This **example** shows it all. The instruction mnemonic is followed by a register or memory location. In this case AX is pushed onto the stack (but not changing the value of AX) and the value in AX will then be also on top of the stack. POP BX will remove the top value from the stack and put it in BX. So what we have actually done is copy the value of AX to BX. *61* *29*

```
PUSH AX
POP  BX
```

> WARNING --- you can use the stack, but be sure that at the end of a procedure or interrupt routine (terminated by RET or IRET) that you have popped off exactly what you pushed on --- you can guess why.

TRANSFER OF CONTROL

This topic does need some careful thought. Any CALL, RET, or JMP instruction can be a FAR or NEAR jump. What this means is that if the jump is NEAR, the jump is only within the current code segment -- that is, only the IP is altered.

```
JMP PROCEDURX
 ....
PROCEDURX:
```

A FAR jump however can be to anywhere in the entire 1Mbyte address range, as both **CS and IP** are altered. This is an example of a JuMP instruction, that transfers control to some part of the program **labelled** PROCEDURX. *52* *99*

FIGURE 2.1 The Stack.

From a "logical" user's point of view, the stack is like a bucket; pushing a value on adds to the top of the bucket, popping takes off the top entry in the bucket.

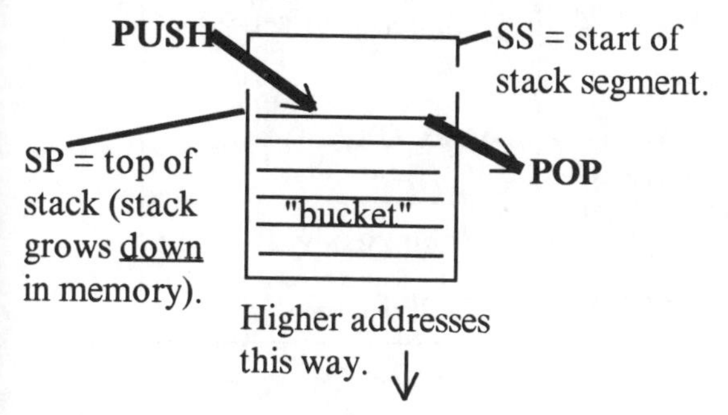

The stack is a temporary storage area, whose actual address we don't need to know. It does have a limitation: When SP=0 the stack is full (in the case of .COM programs, data and code sit at the beginning of the segment, and in theory the stack can grow into them).

If there is nothing in the bucket, SP=FFFEh (or whatever the stack size is -- FFFEh is correct for .COM files). Now put a couple of values in:

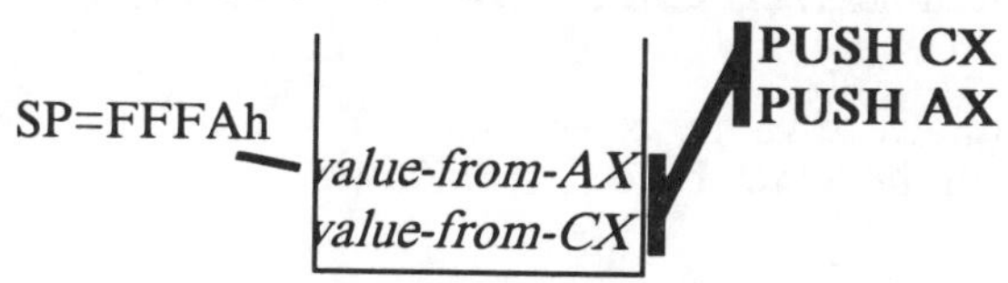

The stack always treats values as 16-bit (word), so each entry occupies two memory locations. Now for POP:

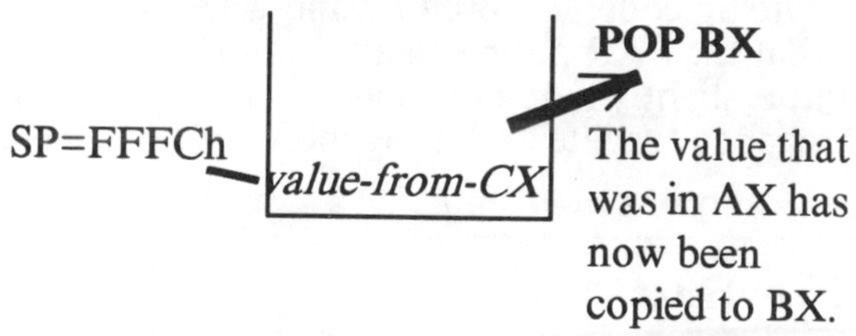

Deviate momentarily---

With DEBUG any instruction that transfers control to another address must contain the actual offset. However, by writing the code in "proper" Assembly language, we do not need to know actual addresses. The second example here shows how a proper Assembler can have a symbolic address-marker, in this case PLACE1.

The third example here is how the code is actually written. The place in the program is "marked" by "PLACE1:".

It is important to note that DEBUG does not understand these symbolic addresses.

```
LOOP 113
   ;absolute offset.

LOOP PLACE1
   ;labelled offset.

 MOV CX,9
PLACE1:
 MOV BX,AX
 LOOP PLACE1
```

40

Now back to "JMP PROCEDURX" -- By default the Assembler would assemble this as a NEAR jump, which means that it would be assembled as an op.code followed by a one-word address containing the value for IP. That is, will only jump within the current code segment (references CS by default, unless **segment override** is specified

35

Note-- always remember that a one-word value, as per '86 CPU standard operation, assembles with the **lower byte first** (in lower address).

57

However we can tell the Assembler to assemble this instruction so that the jump is to be anywhere...

```
JMP  FAR PTR PROCEDURX
```

Which would assemble as the one-byte op.code, followed by one-word IP then one-word CS value. Note that the FAR jump can also jump within the current code segment, but is slightly innefficient as it is a longer instruction, taking a little longer to execute and using more memory.

*****For the purists*****

A technical point here, for the sake of precision, is that "**FAR PTR**" is optional if the symbolic address label is already defined as type "FAR". It is awkward to explain this in detail at this point and it will become clear later.

53

FIGURE 2.2
Involvement of the stack for CALL & RET.

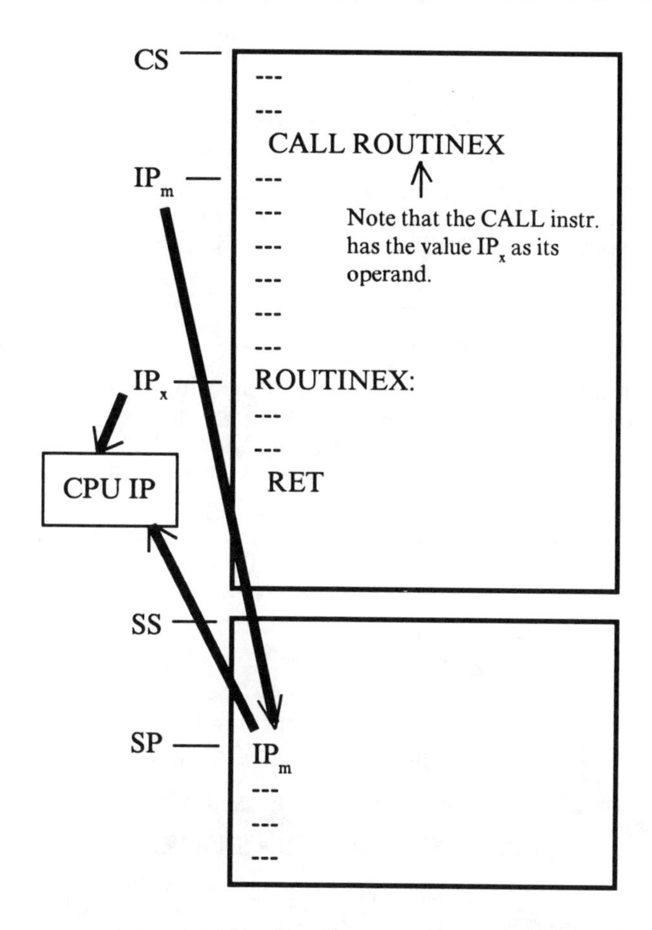

The Sections in the text dealing with the CALL & RET can be clarified by reference to this diagram.
In the case of a NEAR CALL, only the CPU's offset IP is altered -- a FAR CALL will also alter CS.
The CALL pushes IP_m onto the stack, and RET pops it back into the CPU's IP.

SHORT JUMP:

The JMP instruction can be made even smaller by using the Assembler SHORT directive:

```
JMP SHORT CLOSEBY
```

This reduces the instruction down to the one-byte (8-bits) op.code followed by a one-byte two's-complement displacement. This displacement allows jumps to be only +127 to -128 about the current IP position.

*****For the purists*****

"SHORT" is only required if the symbolic address is further down the program, as the Assembler is incapable of looking ahead to see how far it has to jump. If the JuMP is to an earlier point in the program, the Assembler will have already seen where that **label** is so will know whether to assemble a short-jump instruction or not.

99

CONDITIONAL JUMP:

The conditional -Jump instructions test various flags before deciding whether to jump, or not. These instructions are always of the SHORT type. This is very important --- they can only jump 128 locations away from the current code location.

JZ	jump if previous result was 0
JNZ	jump if previous result not 0
JGreater	this means "if the SIGNED* difference is positive"
JAbove	this means "if the UNSIGNED difference is positive"
JLess	this means "if the SIGNED* difference is negative"
JBelow	this means "if the UNSIGNED difference is negative"
JCarry	assembles the same as JB.

TABLE 2.1

The conditional jump instructions are sometimes confusing for the student, but there is no need for confusion. Most CPU instructions affect the flags after they have executed, and the conditional-jump instructions can be used to test the flags and jump accordingly.

Table 2.1 is a summary.

Here is a simple example---

```
add ax,val1
jz  zeroresult ;jumps if previous
               ;result = 0.
               ;(zero-flag set).
```

Another one---

47

44

```
cmp ax,56   ;CoMPare
            ;instruction.
ja  above56 ;jumps if ax > 56
            ;(unsigned
            ;compare).
```

NOTES:

1. * SIGNED CoMPare. The result of the subtraction is treated as a two's complement number. The distinctions between signed and unsigned comarisons, and the CMP instruction are explained **later in more detail**.

2. Variations on the above table are allowed. Examples:

```
JNC  ;jump if Carry flag not set.
JE   ;same as JZ ("E" means "Equal")
JAE  ;unsigned, jump if Above or Equal
JBE  ;unsigned, jump if Below or Equal
```

44

ADDRESSING MODES:

This is not a topic to get worried about -- it's really quite straightforward. Obviously the instructions of your program will be accessing registers and memory, and the mechanisms by which this is done are called the addressing modes.

The best way to show this is by examples:

```
MOV AX,BX
```

The humble MOVe instruction is the equivalent of the LoaD-Acc and STore-Acc instructions of the 6800 CPU, for those who have had exposure to that beastie. It simply moves a value from one place to another, in this case copying the value of BX to AX.

As only registers are involved in the above example, this is called REGISTER ADDRESSING.

The same instruction again, but note that a value is specified this time. This value is NOT an address; it is an immediate value, that is loaded into AX.

```
MOV AX,567
```

This is called IMMEDIATE MODE.

Ah, now this is different. The square brackets signify "the contents of" and it is the contents of address 567 that is loaded into AX.

```
MOV AX,[567]
```

(There is a qualification to the above comment, as the example loads the AX register, which is 16-bit, from a memory location, which is 8-bit. Jump **out** >>>> if interested in following this up).

57

Note too that with an Assembler (not primitive DEBUG though) any address can be replaced by a **label**, so if you had defined address 567 as being represented by label VAL1 (for example), then this would do the same thing:

99

```
MOV AX,VAL1
```

Both of these are called DIRECT ADDRESSING examples.

INDIRECT ADDRESSING is somewhat more abstract. It means that the contents of the operand are used as the address:

36

```
MOV AX,[BX]
```

So the content of BX is the address from which the value is fetched into AX.

That just about covers it, except that indirect addressing does have some options:

```
MOV AX,[BX+5]
MOV AX,[BX+SI+5]
```

The first one adds the contents of BX to 5, and the result is the address, while the second example adds the contents of BX, SI and 5 to form the address. This modified form of indirect addressing is called INDIRECT PLUS DISPLACEMENT if a constant is specified, or INDEXED INDIRECT if two registers are specifed.

SEGMENT REGISTERS:

Another thought -- how do you access data in the Data Segment? This is the place to keep data, so obviously your program must be able to get to it. Simple --- most instructions automatically reference the DS.

For example, the listing shows how VAL1 is defined and referenced:

```
;data segment...
VAL1  DB 0
     ;VAL1 defined here
---
;code sgment....
     MOV AX,VAL1
```

100

In the next lesson you will see more details on how to use the Assembler, so don't worry about that side of things. Suffice to say that you can define a **label** in the data segment, and reference it from the code segment.

99

When the program is assembled, the address of VAL1 will get put into the operand of the MOV instruction -- note however that this is an offset, relative to the DS.

Most important --- when your program is executed, it must have DS set to the beginning of the data area, as the MOV instruction will automatically use DS to compute the physical address:

Remember how this is done--

DS x 16 + VAL1

to get a 20-bit address.

Sometimes, especially with pop-up and **interrupt routines**, the program may be entered with DS not set correctly, so you have to take care of that at the beginning of the program.

139

SEGMENT OVERRIDE:

Although the MOV instruction in the above example automatically referenced the DS register, it is possible to override this. For example you could have data in the code segment, so your program would have this:

```
;code segment...
---
VAL1 DW 0
---
MOV AX,CS:VAL1
---
```

100

NOTE1: that in the case of .COM programs CS = DS = SS, so the question of override doesn't arise normally. With a .EXE program, data could be kept in the code segment, as long as execution jumps around it -- but note also that OS/2 and other operating systems that operate the 286 & 386 CPU's in protected mode, may be very unhappy with data kept in the code segment/s.

NOTE2: Sometimes data is kept in ES (or FS & GS in the 386) so ES override might be useful in this situation. The BP register, although a general-purpose register, by default is treated by the Assembler as an offset into the stack segment SS, thus if you want to use BP to access data in DS or ES, an override is required.

THE MYSTERY OF INDIRECT ADDRESSING

HEAVY GOING HERE! IT'S OKAY TO JUMP THIS SECTION AND COME BACK AS REQUIRED.

Indexed, or Indirect, addressing is something you will have already encountered in the Debug Worksheet, Step 8 -- "mov al,[si+1]" -- now the mystery is to be unveiled. You may prefer to jump this and come back later as required.

Here we have a label "pointer", with a word-size content "place" defined in the data segment.

```
data1 SEGMENT
....
pointer DW place
....
```

Since the Assembler equates all labels to addresses, and "place" is defined further down (see below) as a point in the program, the offset in CS of that point in the program is what will get assembled in the data segment. This is a mechanism for creating a pointer in the data segment.

```
code1 SEGMENT
....
 call [SI + 56]
....
....
 call [SI] . 56
 call [SI] [56]
....
 mov SI , 0
 call [SI] . pointer
....
place:
```

This says: add contents of SI plus 56, then use contents of that address (in the data segment) as the address to jump to (i.e. it is an "**indirect**" mode).

Indexed addressing can have one or two of the SI, BX, DI or BP registers (but not SI+DI or BP+BX; must have combination of "base" + "index" reg.), plus a displacement.

34

The displacement can be 8-bit or 16-bit and is an unsigned number (note that DEBUG has a peculiarity: if you enter a displacement greater than FF00, DEBUG treats it as 2's complement and assembles an 8-bit number -- weird).

Part of the expression can be outside the [ ] and the "." is the same as "+". The instruction "call [SI].56" is the same as the first example. Ditto for next case.

Don't be confused by "call [SI].pointer". Always remember that the Assembler equates labels to addresses, thus the offset of "pointer" (in the data segment) gets assembled as the operand in this instruction. Since this is indexed addressing, execution of this instruction will transfer control to "place:".

There is some inconsistency in the addressing syntax of the Microsoft Assembler, which I won't go into. The Turbo Assembler is somewhat stricter, and sometimes produces an Assembler warning for a syntax that is perfectly acceptable with MASM. The so-called direct-addressing using an actual address is one case: mov AL,[256] -- always use labels if possible. The terms "indirect/direct addressing" for these examples is sometimes misleading -- the **definitions** should help keep some clarity. 34

```
code1 SEGMENT
....
  call place
....
  call pointer
....
```

Just to round-off the discussion, the normal way we would CALL the code at "place:" would be as shown here. In this case the offset of "place" would assemble as the operand and the instruction op-code would assemble as **direct-mode** addressing. 33

And, without wanting to cause total confusion, the second example would assemble the offset "pointer" as the operand, but would assemble the instruction op-code as indirect (& referencing the data segment). Thus the execution would have the same result.

The Assembler decides on the addressing-mode depending upon whether the **label** is in the code or data segment (or some other special significance, such as a segment-name). 52

STRING INSTRUCTIONS

This group of instructions are designed for moving blocks of data from one place in memory to another, and some of them are for searching through and comparing blocks of data. The word "string" does not necessarily imply text, but any block of data.

Jump out here for a quick little alternative **overview** of the string instructions. *56*

Mostly you will use the string instructions responsible for moving data around, such as MOVS, LODS and STOS. Basically, you have the source block in one part of memory, and the destination somewhere else, and you have to set certain registers to point to these source and destination areas before using the string instruction.

The string instructions have an "implied" addressing mode, in that they use certain predefined registers, as shown in Figure 2.3. This is a picture of memory. DS:SI is where the data is got from, and ES:DI is where it's sent.

MOVSB for example would read a single byte from DS:SI and copy it to ES:DI, and would automatically increment both SI and DI, so that the next time the instruction is executed the next byte will be copied.

All the string instructions can be postfixed with a "B" or a "W".

MOVSW would move two bytes of data (one word) and SI & DI would automatically increment by two.

Okay, that's the basic idea. Now go and have a look at the string instructions in detail, as described below. Or if your need at the moment is just to zoom in for a look at one particular instruction:

More on....

STRING OPERATIONS:

String operations make use of SI and DI to point to the source and destination strings respectively, and they are automatically updated each time the string instruction is executed.

DIRECTION FLAG:

There is a Direction-Flag, **DF**, that is cleared by instruction CLD, and set by instruction STD. If DF is clear, the string instruction will automatically increment SI and/or DI to point to the next byte or word, and if DF is set they will be decremented. It is normal to operate on a string starting from the lowest address in memory, so use CLD before a string operation (this is the default for the 80x86 family anyway).

367

REPeat Instruction:

This a prefix, placed on the same line and before a string instruction. It means "check if CX=0, if not perform the following string instruction, decrement CX, then start again". Example:

```
mov    cx,string_length
rep    movsb
```

40

A variation on this is REPNE, which is basically the same, but will also terminate if the zero-flag is set.

LOOP:

NOTE that the LOOP instruction can do much the same as REP. Again, CX is decremented before CX is compared with zero, so movsb will be executed exactly the number of times originally loaded into CX. The loop will terminate with CX=0. There are some **variations** on the basic LOOP instruction.

```
       mov cx,string_length
again: movsb
       loop again
```

363

One warning with LOOP is don't initialise CX to zero before entering the loop, as it will then loop around 65000 times.

When to use LOOP rather than REP? LOOP is not restricted to the string instructions as it is an instruction in its own right, whereas REP is only an instruction prefix designed to work with the string instructions. LOOP can be used wherever a program loop is required, and more than one instruction can go inside the loop -- though note that LOOP can only do a SHORT jump.

MOVSB, MOVSW:

Transfer contents (byte or word) of source-pointer DS:SI to location specified by destination-pointer ES:DI (Hence the name Source-Index and Destination-Index).

CMPSB, CMPSW:

Compares bytes or words pointed to by ES:DI and DS:SI. Sets flags, for use by J-condition instructions.
Example of use with REP;

```
mov  cx,string_length
rep  cmpsb
jnz  difference_found
```

39

This example will compare the two strings until the end of the string (set by value in CX) OR until a non-equal comparison reached (in which case CX will point to the position in the string at which the difference was found, and the zero-flag will be clear).

SCASB, SCASW:

Compare AL or AX with the value pointed to by ES:DI. Note: most often used with REPNE.
Example;

This is a typical use. We want to search the DOS command-tail in the PSP to see if there is a "switch" ("/" followed by a letter).

If the loop terminates without finding a slash, CX will equal zero, so the special conditional-jump

```
;setup DS to beginning of PSP (will be
;for COM files & at start of EXE prog).
;else use ES override....
mov    al,"/"
mov    di,080h ;length of tail in PSP.
mov    cx,[di]  ;(could use override)
mov    di,081h ;command-tail in PSP.
;we will assume that ES is set to the
;start of the PSP-- should be for EXE &
;COM files.
REPNE  SCASB
jcxz   no_slash ;yes, slash was found...
mov    al,[di]  ;could use override.
```

96 35 221 361

FIGURE 2.3
Register usage, string instructions.

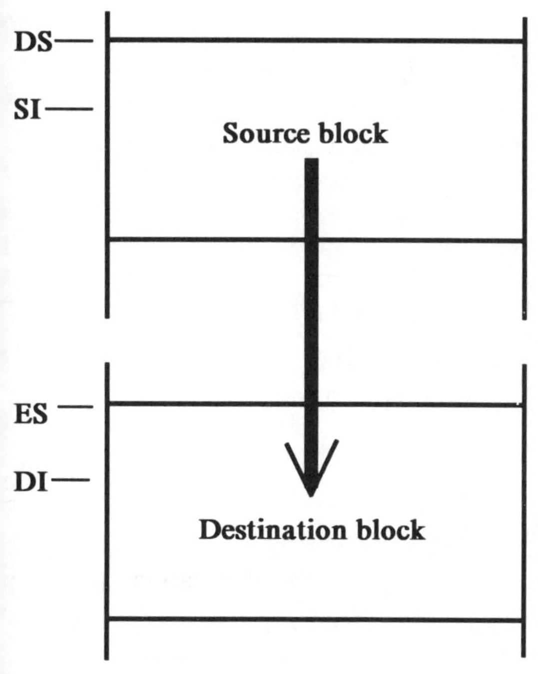

Various operations can be performed on these two blocks, depending upon the string instruction used.
MOVS will move a byte or word of data from the source block to the destination block, and will automatically update SI and DI to point to the next data byte or word to be moved.
LODS operates upon the source block only, getting a byte or word from the source into AL or AX, and updating SI.
STOS is the opposite, working upon the destination block only. The contents of AL or AX is copied to ES:DI and DI is then updated.
CMPS will compare the data in both blocks.
SCAS scans the destination block only, looking for a certain character.

instruction JCXZ, that tests if CX=0, can be used to detect that no slash was in the string.

As the string-instruction automatically increments DI each time, at termination DI will point to the next character past the last one tested. If the slash was found, this next character will be the switch.

LODSB, LODSW:

The value in location pointed to by DS:SI is loaded into AL or AX. SI automatically incremented (+/-1 if LODSB, or +/-2 if LODSW).

STOSB, STOSW:

The value in AL or AX is stored at location pointed to by ES:DI. DI automatically incremented (+/-1 if STOSB, or +/-2 if STOSW).

STOS and LODS are most useful for **video** access, as the format of video-RAM in text-mode requires every odd byte to be an attribute character. Example;

```
;...setup ES:DI....
;...setup DS:SI....
mov cx,string_length
mov ah,attribute
next_char:
lodsb          ;char-->AL
stosw          ;AX-->destination.
loop next_char
```

58 (next_char:)
42 (lodsb)
39 (loop)

THE x86 INSTRUCTION SET

...the saga continues

We have been looking at various aspects of the '86 instruction set, but let's now think about the totality of it, before covering the rest.

Some of "the rest" of the instruction set belong to the '286 and '386 of course, and the Appendices contain a complete summary of the instructions for the x86 family, consisting of the 8088, 8086, 80286, 80386 and 80486.

To clarify understanding we can look at these in groups, as per the above box with items 1 to 6.

So far in this Chapter we have introduced groups 1 - 3; now we will look at groups 4 & 5. Group 6 particularly relates to the more advanced CPU's and is introduced in a later chapter.

ARITHMETIC INSTRUCTIONS

PREREQUISITES:

These include addition, subtraction, multiplication and division. I expect you to have a working knowledge of the principles of binary arithmetic:

* unsigned binary numbers,
* two's-complement binary numbers,
* radix conversion --

  hex <--> binary <--> decimal.

For example, suppose I ask you to express -2 as a 32-bit binary number, and also as a 32-bit hexadecimal number. Can you do it?

If the answer is yes, then you do have a few clues, so read on. Otherwise look back at **An Overview of Numbers**, and consolidate with further study if required.

10

CoMPare: (CMP)

The CMP instruction has already been introduced, but involves arithmetic comparisons, so will be considered again here.

```
CMP AL,127
```

This example instruction subtracts 127 (decimal is the default with an Assembler, unless a "h" is appended to designate hex. DEBUG can only have hex. We will treat 127 as being decimal in this case) from AL, and the result sets appropriate flags.

The CMP instruction can be followed by a **conditional jump**, that jumps or doesn't jump depending upon the flags.

32

Although CMP subtracts the two values, it is only done hypothetically, and the two operands are left unchanged.

CMP doesn't care whether the number is unsigned or two's complement -- it just subtracts them. It is the same for all the addition/subtraction arithmetic instructions -- it is up to the programmer to decide how to treat the operands and the result.

******MOST IMPORTANT POINT******

This point can be clarified -- Since the above example is dealing with 8-bit operands, the range of values depends upon whether we are treating them as 2's compl. or unsigned:

FIGURE 2.4 BCD Arithmetic.

DAA (no operand)
Decimal Adjust for Addition.
Operation: Corrects the result of adding two BCD (packed decimal) values. Works on AL. If the rightmost four bits have a value greater than 9 or the half (auxiliary) carry flag is 1, DAA adds 6 to AL and sets the half-carry flag. If AL contains a value greater than 9Fh or the carry flag is 1, DAA adds 60h to AL and sets carry flag.

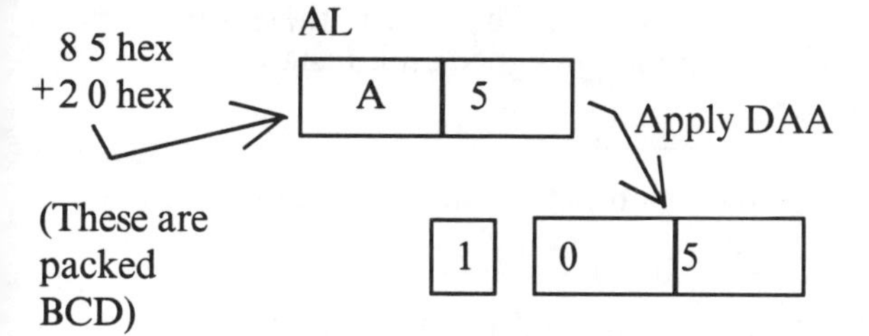

DAS (no operand)
Decimal adjust for subtraction.
The opposite of DAA. After subtracting two values, perform this operation on AL. If the rightmost 4 bits have a value greater than 9 or the half-carry is set, DAS subtracts 6h from AL and sets carry-flag.

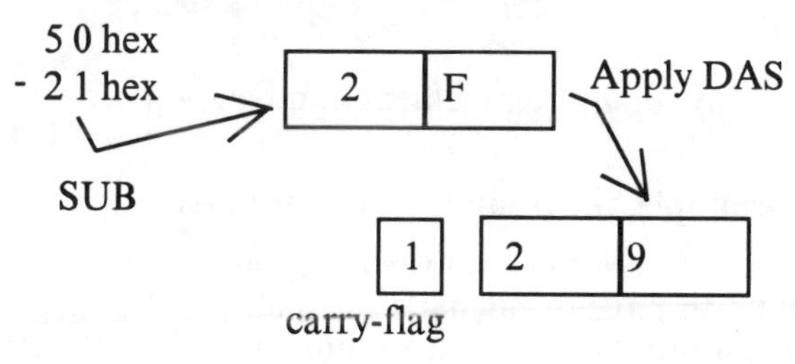

Unsigned: 0 <--> 255
2's compl: -128 <--> +127

So if AL=128, the example CMP instruction will give a hypothetical result of:

128 - 127 --> 1

The result is +1, or in binary 00000001.

Obviously AL is greater than 127, but that is only if you treat the numbers as unsigned. As 2's complement numbers, 128 is actually -128:

Unsigned: 0<------->127,128<----->255
2's comp: 0<------->127,-128<---->-1

So from a 2's-compl point of view, AL is LESS than the operand 127.

That is why there are different **conditional jump** instructions for signed and unsigned numbers. 32

Following the CMP AL,127, we could have any one of the following, depending upon how we want to treat the number:

```
JA   ;jump if AL above 127, unsigned.
JB   ;jump if AL below 127, unsigned.
JG   ;jump if AL greater than 127,
          signed.
JL   ;jump if AL less than 127,
          signed.
```

This can be a point of confusion for novice programmers, so be careful.

It is a good policy to stick with unsigned compares, unless you have particular reason to do otherwise.

NEGate:

This is strictly for 2's complement numbers -- it changes the sign of an operand.

For this example, the result will be -127 in AL.

```
MOV AL,127
NEG AL
```

A useful point to note about the Assembler is that you don't ever have to calculate the binary or hex negative 2's complement number; just put a minus sign in front and the Assembler will do the conversion.

Thus if you wanted to load -127 into AL, just do this:

```
MOV AL,-127
```

INCrement, DECrement:

These two do what their names suggest; add 1 to an operand, or subtract one from it.

```
INC AL      ;adds 1 to AL.
DEC AL      ;subtracts one from AL.
```

Since we have specified an 8-bit operand in these examples, if INC goes beyond 255 (FF hex), then it will simply roll around and start from zero.

Ditto but the opposite for DEC.

ADD, SUBtract:

Recall from the above notes that add/sub arithmetic instructions don't know whether your operands are two's compl or unsigned -- that interpretation is up to you. The size of the operands are important in these calculations, and the instruction determines that from the operands themselves.

SUB works just like **CMP**, setting the same flags (so can be followed by a **conditional jump**), but the subtraction is not hypothetical -- the result of the subtraction is left in AX.

44
32

```
ADD AL,127    ;result into AX.
SUB AL,127    ;result into AX.
```

These instructions can handle numbers bigger than 16 bits. Of course so can the '386, since it has 32-bit registers, but let's for now think that we only have 16-bit registers and we want to add numbers that could possibly have a 32-bit result.

For this example we have two 32-bit values, in BX:AX and DX:CX. The two lower halves are added, leaving the result in AX. The ADD instruction will set the Carry-flag if the unsigned result is greater than the limit (FFFF hex).

```
ADD AX,CX
ADC BX,DX
```

ADC means Add-With-carry, and adds the carry-flag bit plus DX, to BX, with the result in BX.

Thus the total result is in BX:AX.

For subtraction of 32 bit numbers, the principle is the same, and there is an appropriate instruction; SBB (Subtract with Borrow).

For addition and subtraction of BCD numbers, refer to **Figure 2.4**. For a clarification of what BCD is, refer to **An Overview of Numbers**.

45
10

MULtiply,DIVide:

There are two groups of these; MUL and DIV for unsigned numbers, and IMUL and IDIV for signed numbers.

One problem we have with multiply is that two 16-bit operands can produce a result up to 32-bits long. Thus in the case of CPU's with only 16-bit registers, the result may have to reside in two registers.

The MUL instruction uses AL & AX, or AX & DX, by default.

```
MUL BL

MUL  BX
```

The first example makes the assumption that the other operand is in AL, so the result will appear in AX.

The second example makes the assumption that the other operand is in AX, and the result will be in DX:AX.

```
DIV BL

DIV  BX
```

Division has problems of its own. The dividend (the operand to be divided) is in either AX or DX:AX, and the divisor is in any other register or variable (8 or 16-bits).

The first example assumes dividend to be in AX, puts result in AX, in this format:

AH = remainder (left over),
AL = quotient (integer result).

The second example specifies a 16-bit divisor, which assumes that the dividend is in DX:AX, and the result in DX:AX as follows:

DX = remainder,
AX = quotient.

A feature built into the CPU is that if there is an error in the calculation, a certain interrupt is generated, and DOS displays an appropriate error message. In the case of DIV, it is possible for the quotient to be too big for AL or AX -- DOS will abort your program with a "division overflow" message.

This situation has been deliberately left in some code later in the course, for you to discover -- and if you have absorbed this topic, you will immediately recognise the problem and be able to rectify it.

LOGICAL INSTRUCTIONS

These are basically working on individual bits, rather than complete numbers. They relate back to boolean algebra, and as for the arithmetic instructions, I do assume a certain background knowledge. You should have a **basic understanding** of the boolean AND, OR, EXCLUSIVE-OR and NOT functions. *51*

AND:

Performs a logical AND on corresponding bits in two operands, leaving the results in one operand;

```
MOV AL,01001000b
AND AL,00001000b
```

The answer in this case will be 00001000b in AL.

TEST:

TEST is just like AND, but only does the operation hypothetically and doesn't change the operands.

(This is very similar in concept to the relationship between **SUB and CMP**). *44*

The example leaves the result in AL, and sets appropriate flags.

```
TEST AL,00001000b
```

Can be followed by a **conditional jump**: *32*

```
JZ      ;jumps if bit-3 in AL clear.
JNZ     ;jumps if bit-3 in AL set.
```

OR:

Performs a logical-OR operation on two operands;

```
MOV AL,01001000b
OR  AL,00001000b
```

The answer in AL will in this case be 01001000b.

XOR:

Performs a logical-EXCLUSIVE-OR on two operands:

The result in AL = 01000000b

```
MOV AL,01001000b
XOR  AL,00001000b
```

NOT:

Complements all bits in an operand (this is not a 2's complement conversion: see **NEG**).

The result in AL will be 10110111b

```
MOV AL,01001000b
NOT  AL
```

46

SHift-Left,SHift-Right: (SHL, SHR)

SHL and SHR do what they suggest, but it is clearer if their operation is viewed diagrammatically -- refer Figure 2.5. This will shift all the bits in AL one place to the right, moving a 0 into the most significant bit (msb) and the least significant bit (lsb) will fall out to the Carry-flag.

Note that this instruction is sometimes used to test individual bits, since it can be followed by JC (Jump on Carry set) or JNC (Jump on Carry not set).

Note a limit with the 8088/8086 is that the "count" operand can only be value one if in **immediate mode** as per above example. If the shift is to be more than 1 bit, need to first move a count value into CL:

```
MOV CL,3
SHR AL,CL
      ;shifts AL right 3 bits.
```

33

Note that the shift operations can also be on 16-bit registers.

SHL does exactly the opposite of SHR, moving zeros into the lsb and the msb out to the Carry-flag.

Shift-Arithmetic-Right: (SAR)

Works like SHR, except maintains the sign -- most useful for signed numbers. Refer to Figure 2.5.

ROtate-Left,ROtate-Right: (ROL, ROR)

These work similarly to the shift iinstructions, except what falls out is rotated around back in the other end. Refer to Figure 2.5.

Thus the contents are never lost, but circulate around the register.

ROL is the mirror-image of this, sending the msb to the Carry-flag and back around to the lsb.

Rotate-through-Carry-L/R: (RCR, RCL)

RCR and RCL work as per ROR & ROL, except the path of the bits goes through the Carry-flag -- Figure 2.5.

FIGURE 2.5 Shift & Rotate Instructions.

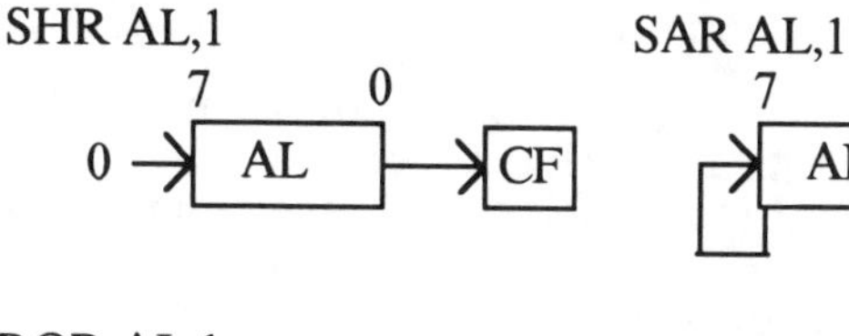

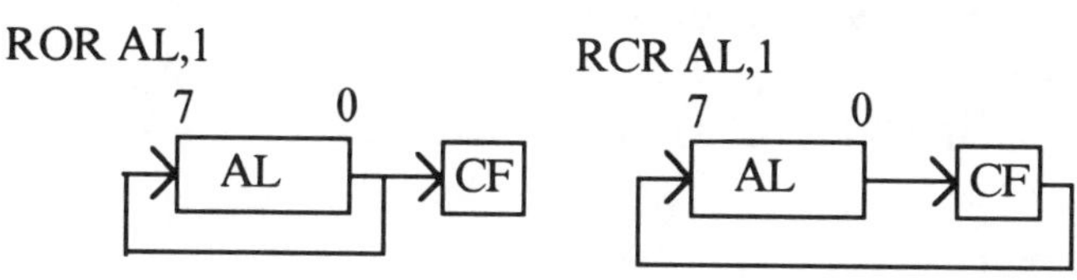

FIGURE 2.6 Boolean Arithmetic

You should be able to understand each of the instructions AND, TEST, XOR, NOT, OR, by examining the examples, however a few basic notes may help.....

AND

When two or more inputs are ANDed together, the output is true (logic-1 usually) if all inputs are true (logic-1), else false.

Tabulating this, for two inputs A & B:

A	B	OUT
0	0	0
0	1	0
1	0	0
1	1	1

OR

When two or more inputs are ORed together, the output is true (1) if any input is true (1). Output is 0 only when all inputs are false (0).

Tabulating:

A	B	OUT
0	0	0
0	1	1
1	0	1
1	1	1

XOR

For two inputs, same as OR except excludes the case of both inputs being logic-1. For any no. of inputs, gives 1 o/p for any <u>odd</u> no. of inputs = 1.

Tabulating for 2 I/p's:

A	B	OUT
0	0	0
0	1	1
1	0	1
1	1	0

THE MYSTERY OF "TYPE"

MAY BE HEAVY GOING HERE! IF YOU WISH, JUMP AROUND THIS SECTION & REFER BACK AS REQUIRED.

"Type" is a loose end that I might as well throw in here -- it is a concept that the Assembler uses and is vital to our proper use of the Assembler. References to type are made throughout the book, so let's get it straight right from the start.

When you get onto the chapter on Assembly programming you may want to refer back here to brushup, or you may feel like browsing ahead for **more information on type**. *99*

Although we are only looking at the instruction set in this chapter, the writing of instructions is tied in with type considerations -- the Assembler performs this type-checking when Assembling the program, and it is a measure of protection against programmer errors. A register/label/literal must belong to at least one of these two groups:

1. SIZE: BYTE, WORD, DOUBLEWORD
2. ADDRESS: SHORT, NEAR, FAR

Any instruction must have operands with the same type, else an Assembler error message will be generated.

SIZE:

Labels are also gone into **later**, but take note of the following: *99*

```
val1  DW  56
....
place2 LABEL FAR
place1:
....
mov  ax,val1
```

100 *99* *99*

"val1" marks a NEAR place in the data, of word-size content 56 (or any numeric value). "DW" means "define a word-size value here". Most importantly, Asm equates val1 to its address. "mov ax,val1" moves the contents of val1 into AX -- the instruction assembles with the address as the operand but with direct-addressing mode. A type-match has occurred here -- val1's content is type WORD, which matches the destination AX.

Refer also to notes on the distinction between **code & data (& segment, etc) labels**. -- "mov ax,place1" assembles with address of "place1" as the operand, but execution loads the actual offset of "place1" into AX, which is an immediate addressing mode. *36*

FAR/NEAR TYPE:

val1's content is of type WORD, and val1 is (normally) of type NEAR. Note that "place1" is of type NEAR (normally -- default depends upon "memory model"). With the exception of certain "**models**", "jmp place1" will be a NEAR jump, as only the offset is involved. So what about FAR, ie to another segment? If place1: was in another segment, I could transfer control to it by using the LABEL directive -- see above -- "place2" marks the same place in the code as "place1", but with the difference that it has type FAR. Thus a jump or CALL instruction to place2 will have an operand consisting of segment and offset. *107*

FAR CALLs and JMPs are used in the **demo TSRs**. I wanted to go to the BIOS ROM, and the address was saved in my program's data area:

```
oldvector2  LABEL FAR
oldvector1  DW  0,0
oldvector3  DD  0
...
jmp  DWORD PTR  oldvector1
jmp  oldvector2
jmp  oldvector3
```

248 *100* *248*

If I had saved the offset followed by segment address as two word-values in "oldvector1", then "DWORD PTR" override is required for FAR transfer -- if left off the jump will be NEAR only.

"DWORD PTR" could be left off if FAR jumping to "oldevector2", which is the same place as "oldvector1". Defining "oldevector3" as "Define Doubleword" also makes type-override unnecessary.

Incidentally, you might think that "FAR PTR" would be approppriate instead of "DWORD PTR" for the JMP to a far-address, but syntactically the Assembler requires the latter, as the operand is data contained in the data segment. If "oldvector1" was defined in the source file as a place-marker in another code segment, then "FAR PTR" would be appropriate. This is the kind of fussy detail you pick up through practice.

PTR Override:

This directive avoids a type-mismatch error message from the Assembler. It temporarily changes the type of the operand. For example: MOV AL, BYTE PTR val1
Temporarily redefines val1 as being of byte-size. At execution-time this instruction will load the first byte of val1 (which in this case will have 56, with 0 in the second byte) into AL.

MINI-SUMMARY OF THE INSTRUCTION SET

This is a kind of mini-reference section, of the '86 instruction set, to complement the **main summary** in the reference section of this book. 360

Although I recommend starting from the **beginning of this chapter** when initially learning the instruction set, this summary is a handy rallying spot for consolidating the learning, as it is heavily hot-linked to the rest of the textbook. 27

Select one of these....

THE SEGMENT REGISTERS:

The **8088** CPU has four segment registers CODE (CS), DATA (DS), STACK (SS), and EXTRA (ES). The **'386** expands upon this theme. 21 196

The **8086 and the 8088** use 20-bit addresses for memory, meaning that they can address up to 1megabyte of memory. But, the registers and the address fields in all the instructions are no more that 16 bits long. So, how to address all of that memory? Their solution is to put together two 16 bit quantities like this: 21

SSSS0
- value in the relevant segment register **SHL** 4. (mult. by 16) 50

AAAA
- apparent address from register or instruction. (16 bit)

-

RRRRR
- real address placed on address bus.

In other words, any time memory is accessed, your program will supply a sixteen bit address. Another sixteen bit address is acquired from a segment register, left shifted four bits (one nibble) and added to it to form the real address. You can control the values in the segment registers and thus access any part of memory you want. But the segment registers are specialized: one for code, one for most data accesses, one for the stack (which we'll mention again) and one "extra" one for additional data accesses.

Some conventions make it especially easy to forget about segment registers. For example, any program of the **.COM** type loads with all of the segment registers containing the same value. This program executes in a single 64K address space. You can go outside this address space if you want but you don't have to. 96

More on segment registers >>>> 16

OTHER REGISTERS:

AX and DX are general purpose registers, with some specialisation for maths and I/O. 18

CX is a general purpose register which is slightly specialized for counting. 39

BX is a general purpose register which is slightly specialized for forming base-displacement addresses. 34

AX-DX can be divided in half, forming AH, AL, BH, BL, CH, CL, DH, DL. *191*

SI and **DI** are 16 bit only. They can be used to form indexed addresses (like BX) and they are also used to point to strings. *38*

SP is hardly ever manipulated. It is there to provide a stack. *29*
Note that **BP** is often used with SP. Use it to access data which has been pushed onto the stack. *257*

More on other registers. *18*
'386 general registers. *191*

INTRO TO INSTRUCTION MNEMONICS:

TWO-OPERAND INSTRUCTIONS:

Ordinary two operand instructions. These instructions perform an operation and leave the result in place of one of the operands. They are

1) **ADD and ADC** *47*
addition, with or without including a carry from a previous addition.

2) **SUB and SBB** *47*
subtraction, with or without including a borrow from a previous subtraction.

3) **CMP** *44*
compare. It is useful to think of this as a subtraction with the answer being thrown away and neither operand actually changed.

4) **AND, OR, XOR** *49*
typical boolean operations

5) **TEST** *49*
like an AND, except the answer is thrown away and neither operand is changed.

6) **MOV** *33*
move data from source to target

7) LDS, LES, **LEA** *101*
some specialized forms of MOV.

ONE-OPERAND INSTRUCTIONS:

Ordinary one operand instructions. These can take any of the operand forms described above. Usually, they perform the operation and leave the result in the stated place:

1) **INC** -- increment contents *47*

2) **DEC** -- decrement contents *47*

3) **NEG** -- twos complement *46*

4) **NOT** -- ones complement *50*

5) **PUSH** -- value goes on stack (operand location itself unchanged). *29*

6) **POP** -- value taken from stack, replaces current value. *29*

IMPLICIT REGISTER INSTRUCTIONS:

These instructions do not follow the general operand rules but require the use of certain registers. The important ones are

1) The **multiply and divide** instructions *48*

2) The "adjust" instructions which help in performing arithmetic on ASCII or packed decimal data

3) The **shift and rotate** instructions. *50* These have a restriction on the second operand: it must either be the **immediate** value 1 or the contents of the CL register. *33*

4) **IN and OUT** which send or receive data from one of the hardware ports. *134*

5) CBW and CWD -- convert byte to word or word to doubleword by sign extension

FLOW OF EXECUTION INSTRUCTIONS:

They are---

1) **CALL, RET** -- call and return *31*

2) **INT, IRET** -- interrupt and return-from-interrupt. *62*

3) **JMP** -- jump or "branch" *28*

4) **LOOP, LOOPNZ, LOOPZ** special (and useful) instructions which implement a counted loop. *39*

5) various **conditional jump** instructions *32*

STRING INSTRUCTIONS:

See also....
STRING-HANDLING INSTR's *38*

String instructions. These implement a limited storage-to-storage instruction subset and are quite powerful. All of them have the property that

1) The source of data is described by the combination **DS and SI**. *38*

2) The destination of data is described by the combination **ES and DI**. *38*

3) As part of the operation, the SI and/or DI register(s) is(are) incremented or decremented so the operation can be repeated.

They include

1) **CMPSB/CMPSW** comp. byte/word *40*

2) **LODSB/LODSW** load byte/word into AL or AX *42*

3) **STOSB/STOSW** store byte or word from AL or AX. *42*

4) **MOVSB/MOVSW** move byte/word *40*

5) **SCASB/SCASW** compare byte/word with contents of AL or AX. *40*

6) **REP/REPE/REPNE** a prefix which can be combined with any of the above instructions to make them execute repeatedly across a string of data whose length is held in CX. *39*

FLAG INSTRUCTIONS:

Flag instructions:
CLI, STI, *139*
CLD, STD, *39*
CLC, STC. *361*
These can set or clear the interrupt (enabled), direction (for string operations) or carry flag.

DEFAULT SEGMENT REGISTERS & SEGMENT OVERRIDE:

Finally, in order to use the assembler effectively, you need to know the default rules for which segment registers are used to complete addresses in which situations.

a. **CODE SEGMENT REG. (CS)**: *54*
CS is used to complete an address which is the target of a **NEAR** DIRECT jump. *28*
On a NEAR **INDIRECT** jump, DS is used to fetch the address from memory but then CS is used to complete the address thus fetched. *34*
On **FAR** jumps, of course, CS is itself altered. The instruction counter is always implicitly pointing in the code segment. *28*

b. **STACK SEGMENT REG. (SS)**: *27*
SS is used to complete an address if BP is used in its formation. Otherwise, DS is always used to complete a data address.

c. **STRING INSTRUCTIONS**:
On the string instructions, the target is always formed from **ES and DI**. The source is normally formed from **DS and SI**. If there is a segment prefix, it overrides the source not the target. *38* *38*

WORKSHEET: ADDRESSING MODES

This Worksheet uses DEBUG (covered in **Worksheet-(DEBUG)**) to examine some instructions and the various addressing modes. *22*

This worksheet uses only two instructions:
MOV and *34*
INT *61*
Have a close look at them before continuing.

1.

The letters are DEBUG commands, so type what you see below exactly as shown-- (DEBUG Reference Section >>>>>) *22*

```
-E 1000 AA 55 11 22 44 66 77 88
-D 1000 1007
-A 100
MOV AX,33         ;comments aren't typed
MOV BX,AX         ;in.
MOV CX,[1000]     ;what addr. mode?       33
INT 3                                     341
-U 100 109                                24
-R                                        22
-G=100                                    24
```

DON'T just type this in parrot-fashion. Understand what you're doing on each line.
Note that the "-" is the DEBUG command prompt, and you don't have to type that.

G=100 obviously runs the program, but a warning here. Don't leave out the "=" otherwise your computer will crash!

Having run the program, examine the registers and be sure that you know what the program has done.
Note that **"INT 3"** just stops the program at that point and returns control to DEBUG --- INT 3 is absolutely essential at the end of every DEBUG program. *341*
What addressing modes are the instructions using?

Stop and think before continuing--- the contents of address 1000 has been loaded into CX, but note that MOV references the **Data Segment**, so the source address is actually DS:1000. *35*

How can you use DEBUG to examine registers to verify that the above program worked?

Review segment regs from Chapter 1. *16*
Notes on segmentation and **effective addresses** *54*

Don't go on yet. There is another problem with address 1000 --- every memory location is one-byte (8 bits), but the instruction asked that register CX be loaded --- but CX is 16 bits.

Be very clear on this --- the '86 family of CPU's use byte-addressing. The address bus itself can be 20-bits, 24-bits, 32-bits, or whatever, but the CONTENTS of an address is only 8-bits. So what this instruction does is---

```
CL <--- contents of 1000
CH <--- contents of 1001
```

The instruction does this automatically.
Note that---
MOV CL,**[1000]** *33*
would move only the contents of 1000.

2.

```
-R
-A 100
MOV BX,1000
MOV DX,[BX]          34
INT 3                341
-U 100
-R
-G=100
```

Again, run and examine the registers before and after. Explain what each instruction does, and give the addressing mode used in each case.

3.

```
-A 100
MOV DH,[BX+3]        34
MOV AX,[BX+3]
INT 3
-U 100
-R
-G=100
```

Examine the registers before and after.
Also what are the addressing modes used?

4.

```
-E 2000 11 22 33 44 55 66 77 88
-D 2000 2007
-A 100
MOV BX,2000
MOV SI,0
MOV AL,[BX+SI+3]                34
MOV AH,[BX+SI+2]
MOV DX,[BX+SI+2]
INT 3
-U 100 10F
-R
-G=100
```

Analyse this.

5.

INITIALISATION OF SEGMENT REG'S:
One thing you will have noticed is that DEBUG initialises all the segment rgisters to the same value. This makes it easy for us to learn, since there's only the one segment to worry about. But we can easily change them.
A limitation of the 8088 is that a segment register cannot be loaded in the **immediate mode**, so it must be done in two steps--- *33*

Reference on segment initialisation *18*

```
-A 100
MOV AX,4000
MOV DS,AX
MOV AX,B800
MOV ES,AX
MOV AX,3000
MOV SS,AX
MOV SP,1000
INT 3
-U 100
-R
-G=100
-R
```

WORKSHEET: STRING INSTRUCTIONS

1.

You experimented with an example program in **Step-8** of Worksheet -(DEBUG), while learning to use DEBUG --- well now you're in a position to understand how that program works. Here it is again. Go through it with DEBUG's Trace command, and verify that each instruction works as you expected. *25*

Firstly, these hex values must be put into the **data segment DS**, at offset 200 hex--- *35*

06 42 55 40 50 45 52

Next, the program is to be assembled into the **code segment CS** at offset 100. Don't type in the comments. *54*

```
MOV CX,0        ;clear counter register.
MOV AX,B800     ;display RAM address.
MOV ES,AX       ;  /
MOV DI,06B0     ;  /
MOV SI,200      ;source offset.
MOV CL,[SI]     ;get number of bytes      34
MOV AH,F8       ;setup attribute byte.
CLD             ;clear direction flag.    39
MOV AL,[SI+1]   ;retrieve next char.
INC SI          ;incr source pointer.     47
STOSW           ;                         42
LOOP 113        ;                         39
INT 3                                     341
```

Next, unassemble the program and make sure it's correct.

This example causes a message to be displayed on the screen.
Note that the B800 moved into ES is required to correctly address a Colour Graphics Adaptor (**CGA**). If your computer has a **monochrome adaptor**, use B000. *78* *77*

Note that STOSW sends two bytes to the display RAM. One byte is the character, while the other is the attribute for the character, that is it determines how the

ıaracter will look on the screen
linking, reverse-video, colour, etc).
ıese requirements are set by the
splay-adaptor board, and are gone into
more detail in **Chapter Three**. 61

ou will notice that the above program
es **indirect** addressing 34
xample: MOV AL,[SI+1]).
our task now is to rewrite the program
make use of the string instructions
ıch as **LODSB**) in place of the indirect 42
ddressing, for fetching the message
om the data area.

ow, instead of a message at CS:200,
ere will be a BCD 16-bit value.
ılues are stored with least
gnificant digits at the lowest address
pposite to the 6800 family), so a
ord-size value will have the lowest
gits at address 200 and the highest
gits at 201 ---

DDRESS:	200	201
NTENT:	7......3.....0	7......3.....0
	digit-1 digit-0	digit-3 digit-2

ur program is to read the BCD value,
nvert each digit to ASCII, and display

e basic structure of the previous
ogram can be used, with some changes.
viously each byte of data is two BCD
gits, and these must be separated and
nverted to ASCII. This conversion is
ıply a matter of adding 30h to the
git ---

GIT:	**0**	1	2	3	4	5	6	7	8	9
CII:	**30**	31	32	33	34	35	36	37	38	39

perform the separation of the two
gits, you may need to examine the
ift and ROtate instructions, and 50
ssibly the logical instructions such
AND, OR and XOR. For example; 49

```
AND AL,0Fh   ;masks off the most
             ; signif. digit.                 49

AND AX,0Fh   ;masks off all but the lsd.

MOV CL,4     ;this will rotate AL right
ROR AL,CL    ;by four bits. lsb's fold
             ; back into msb.                 51

MOV CL,4     ;can also rotate a 16-bit
ROR AX,CL    ; register.
                                              51
```

These examples are not intended to show
an actual solution to the problem,
simply to illustrate how these
instructions work.
The rest is up to you.

****** SOLUTIONS ******
OVER-PAGE, BUT DON'T LOOK!

SOLUTIONS:

I'm reluctant to provide complete solutions here, as the temptation will be to just copy what I've done, without understanding. These solutions are a little bit incomplete.

2.

```
-E 200 0C "Hullo world"
   mov cx,0
   mov cl,[200]
   mov ax,B800
   mov es,ax
   mov si,201
   mov di,06B0
   mov ah,F0
next_char:
   lodsb
   stosw
   loop next_char
```

3.

```
   mov cl,4
   mov dl,cl
   mov ah,F0
   mov bx,[200]
next_digit:
   rol bx,cl
   mov al,bl
   and al,0F
   add al,30
   stosw        ;must setup ES:DI
   dec dl
   jnz next_digit
```

3

BIOS & DOS SERVICES

Now we are going to learn the mysteries of interrupts, and the BIOS & DOS services, that are invoked via a software interrupt. It is recommended that you work through in the order listed alongside.

You'll have to just pop out to another chapter for a few moments to have a look at what the CPU does when an interrupt occurs. I suggest you have a bit of a look at this as it'll help when you come back to this chapter and go onto looking at the interrupt table.

The rest of the headings here are just what's in this chapter. After looking through this theory, put it into practice at the end of the chapter by doing the worksheet, that uses the BIOS & DOS services for keyboard and screen I/O.

INTERRUPT VECTOR TABLE

For the 8086 and 8088 (and the '286 & '386 in real-mode and maybe also when in protected-mode) the table resides at physical address 00000 up to 003FFh.

Each entry is four bytes of memory, and contains a "**far**" address of a BIOS or DOS service routine (or a user-installed interrupt service routine). *28*

INT n

This is the instruction to invoke a software interrupt, where n is a pointer into entry number n in the table. The entry contains the address of the called routine. Figure 3.1 shows the structure of an interrupt table entry.

A hardware interrupt works in the same way --- it requires an interrupt **controller chip**, which allows a number of interrupt wires to come from external devices (such as the keyboard). The IBM-PC has one of these chips, and each external interrupt wire has a corresponding entry in the Interrupt Table. This is taken care of by the hardware --- there are eight external interrupts into the interrupt-chip, and these are dedicated to the table entries n = 08 to 0Fh. *137*

The 8259 Interrupt controller chip has eight I/O devices connected to it:

DEVICE	n	
Timer	8	*167*
keyboard	9	*69*
colour graphics	A	*75*
2nd serial	B	*160*
serial	C	*160*
hard disk	D	*215*
floppy disk	E	*215*
printer	F	*153*

The question may well arise in your mind: how does an interrupt from, say, the keyboard, cause the CPU to look in entry number 8 in the table? The answer is that the 8259 can be wired-up so that after sending an interrupt signal to the CPU it communicates the number 8 to the CPU over the data bus. The interrupts coming into the 8259 are numbered 0 - 7 but the 8259 translates them all to some other range, in this case 8 - F.

For now let's stay with software interrupts, and start with the most fundamental of all, the BIOS services......

FIGURE 3.1 Interrupt Table

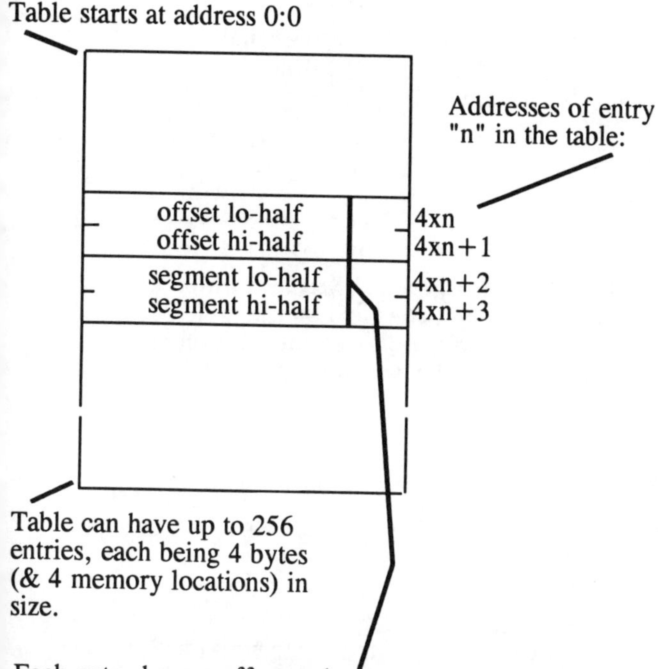

Each entry has an offset and a segment value to make up the complete FAR address. The offset is at the lower two addresses, lo-half at lower address. The segment (paragraph) address is in the next two bytes, again with lo-half at lower address.
The terminology we use to refer to a FAR address in this form is paragraph:offset.
Note that it computes to a 20-bit address, though each element is 16 bits.

A hardware interrupt, or a software interrupt, for example:

INT 10h

will access entry 10h in the table. That is, the current IP (Instruction Pointer), CS (Code Segment) and flag registers will be pushed onto the stack, and IP loaded with the offset from the table, and CS loaded with the segment-value from the table.
Hence the CPU will commence execution at the interrupt routine.
All interrupt routines must terminate with an IRET instruction, which has the effect of popping the original IP, CS and flags back off the stack, into the CPU -- hence the CPU picks up from where it was before the interrupt.

INTRO TO BIOS SERVICES

These were originally built entirely into ROM, thus available at power-on and at all times. DOS functions on the other hand are loaded into RAM memory from the **boot-disk**. 4

BIOS provides the Basic Input/Output services, called from an application program by means of the INT instruction, of the format: **INT n** 64

Where n is an integer number.

BIOS allows a program to access the keyboard, screen, printer, serial port, and disk drives. DOS functions, also called by the INT instruction, provide similar services, generally at a higher level of sophistication than the BIOS services. There is considerable overlap of functionality.

INTRO TO DOS FUNCTIONS

Interrupts **20h** through **27h** are used to communicate with DOS. Mostly, you will use interrupt 21h, the DOS function manager. 349

You request the individual services of interrupt 21h by means of a function code in the AH register. For example, by putting a nine in the AH register and issuing interrupt 21H you tell DOS to print a message on the console screen.

THE FIRST DOS FUNCTIONS

Most of the functions originally offered in DOS 1.0 were direct descendents of CP/M functions:

AH	DESCRIPTION	
09	print a message on screen.	350
0A	get a console input line.	351
0F	open a file.	351
10	close a file.	351
11	find 1st file matching a pattern	351
12	find next file matching pattern	351
13	erase a file	351
16	create a file	352
17	rename a file	352
1A	set disk transfer address	352

FIGURE 3.2
Video BIOS ROM.
The original video BIOS services are located on the motherboard, in the BIOS ROM -- refer to Figures 1.1/1.6. In the case of EGA & VGA, extensions to the BIOS video handling are contained in a ROM physically mounted on the display adaptor card. This card also has the video-RAM, which may be from 4K to 1M depending upon the type of adaptor.

VIDEO RAM.
Typically 16K for MDA and 256K for VGA. Mapped as per Figures 1.3/4.1/4.4+.

Just for the record, and thinking ahead to Chapter 4, the DB-15 VGA pinout is given here.

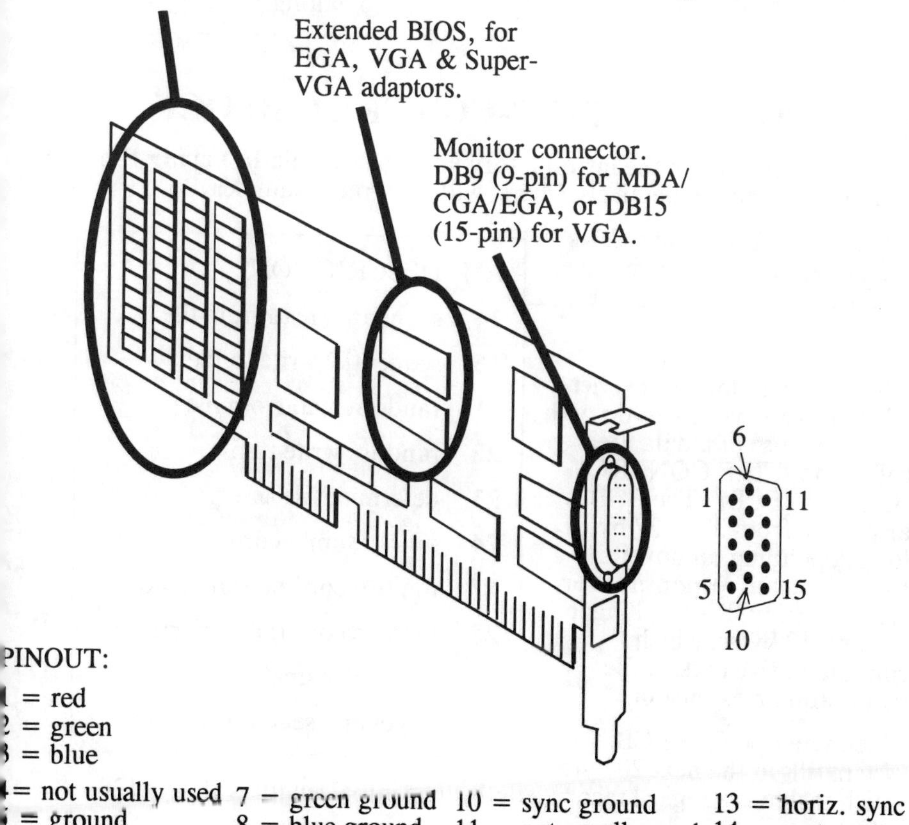

PINOUT:

1 = red
2 = green
3 = blue

4 = not usually used	7 = green ground	10 = sync ground	13 = horiz. sync
5 = ground	8 = blue ground	11 = not usually used	14 = vert. sync
6 = red ground	9 = key (no pin)	12 = not usually used	15 = not used.

DOS FUNCTIONS SIMILAR TO BIOS SERVICES

The next set provide no function above what you can get with BIOS calls or more specialized DOS calls. However, they are preferable to BIOS calls for portability reasons:

AH	DESCRIPTION	
00	terminate execution	*350*
01	read keyboard character	*350*
02	write screen character	*350*
03	read COM port character	*350*
04	write COM port character	*350*
05	print a character	*350*
06	read keyboard or write screen with no editing.	*350*

FILE I/O USING FILE-CONTROL-BLOCK

Note that apart from the introductory notes below, **file I/O using the FCB** is discussed in detail elsewhere, with program examples. *221*

DOS file I/O using the FCB is the earlier, and more primitive, method:

AH	DESCRIPTION	
14	sequential read from file	*351*
15	sequential write to file	*352*
21	random read from file	*352*
22	random write to file	*353*
23	determine file size	*353*
24	set random record	*353*
27	multi-record random read.	*353*
28	multi-record random write.	*353*
29	parse filename	*353*
2A-2D	get and set date and time	*353*

All of the calls mentioned here which have anything to do with files make use of a data area called the "FILE CONTROL BLOCK" (FCB). The FCB is anywhere from 33 to 37 bytes long depending on how it is used. You are responsible for creating an FCB and filling in the first 12 bytes, which contain a drive code, a file name, and an extension.

When you open the FCB, the system fills in the next 20 bytes, which includes a logical record length. The initial length is always 128 bytes.

The system also provides other useful information such as the file size. To perform actual I/O to a file, you eventually need to fill in byte 33 or possibly bytes 34-37 of the **FCB**. Here you supply information about the record you are interested in reading or writing. *221*

FILE I/O USING HANDLES

Note that apart from the introductory notes here, file I/O using **file-handles** is discussed fully, with code examples, elsewhere. 225

Beginning with DOS 2.0, there is a whole new system of calls for managing files which don't require that you build an **FCB** at all. They have these characteristics: 66

1. To open, create, delete, or rename a file, you need only a **character string** representing its name. 225

2. The open and create calls return a 16 bit value which is simply placed in the BX register on subsequent calls to refer to the file (this is called the "**handle**"). 225

3. There is not a separate call required to specify the data buffer.

4. Any number of bytes can be transferred on a **single call**; no data area must be manipulated to do this.

BIOS & DOS SCREEN I/O

Accessing the screen through the BIOS and DOS services makes our programs more portable, though slower, than direct video RAM access.

DOS VIDEO FUNCTIONS:

INT 21h invokes the DOS functions, and the value in AH selects the particular function. Note the references below to "standard output" --- this defaults to the screen, but can be redirected --- refer to the notes on Standard Input & Standard Output, >>>>> if you want to know more, or give it a miss if you don't.

Here are some useful ones:

AH	DESCRIPTION
2	Send a character to the standard output device. DL=char.
9	Send a string of chars to the standard output. Requires: DS:DX points to string. Note: string must be terminated by dollar sign ($).

350

350
224

BIOS VIDEO SERVICES:

INT 10h is the key interrupt service for BIOS video access. ("h" signifies hex).

342

Here are some of the functions of this service:

AH	DESCRIPTION
0	Sets the video mode. Requires: AL=mode. Note: the **allowable mode** depends on what adaptor is plugged in.
1	Set size of cursor, or turn it off. Requires: CH=start-line, CL=end-line. Note: line 0=top text, 7=bottom (**CGA**). bit-5 set = no cursor.
2	Set cursor position. Requires: DH=row (0-24), DL=col(0-79), BH=video page.
3	Read cursor position. Requires: BH=video page. Returns: DH=row, DL=col, CX=cursor size. Note: an undocumented feature of some BIOS's is that they also change AL.
8	Read char & attr current curs. position. Requires: BH=video page. Returns: AL=character, AH=attrib.
9	Write char & attr at curs. position. Requires: BH= page, CX=repeat-count, AL=char to display, BL=attribute. Note: in graphics modes BL=colour.
A	Write char, leave attr as-is. Requires: reg's as for function-9. Note: although functions 9 & A write a char to the screen, they do not move the cursor position.
B	Set palette for graphics or border for text modes. Requires: BH=0 ;border (text mode). BL=colour. BH=1 ;palette (graphics mode) BL=palette code (0 or 1).
C	Display 1 pixel (graphics mode only). Requires: DX=row, CX=column,AL=colour of dot.
E	Display char and move cursor. Requires: AL=char,BH=page, BL=foreground colour in graphics mode. Note: as well as moving cursor to next position, also handles carriage-return char (0Dh), beep (07h) and scrolls screen if required.
F	Current video mode. Returns: AL=mode, AH=number of columns of text in current mode,BH=page number.

77

78

BIOS & DOS KEYBOARD I/O

As with the screen, we have the choice of going directly to the hardware, or via the BIOS & DOS services. In the vast majority of cases the services are quite satisfactory.

If you really want to jump ahead into the nitty-gritty of the keyboard interface, then feel free to do so >>>>>>> The rest of us continue below...

137

BIOS KEYBOARD SERVICES:

INT 16h is the culprit here, with AH selecting a function.

345

AH	DESCRIPTION
0	Read next char in keyboard buffer, if no key ready, wait for one. Returns: AL=ASCII char, AH=scancode.
1	See if a char in buffer (but don't get it out). Returns: zero-flag set if no key, else clear and AL=ASCII char, AH=scancode. Note: unlike function-0, doesn't wait if no char. If there is a char, tells us what it is, but leaves it there, so must use function-0 to get it out of buffer.
2	Fetch keyboard status. Returns: AL=bit codes. bit 7=insert state. 6=CapsLock key on. 5=NumLock key on. 4=ScrollLock key on. 3=ALT key held down. 2=CTRL key held down. 1=left-SHIFT key held down. 0=right-SHIFT key held down.

64

Just a quick little note or two on the hardware. You press a key, a signal goes to the **8259 Interrupt Controller** chip, which generates an interrupt to the CPU. CPU responds by finding out from the 8259 which hardware device caused the interrupt, then looking in the interrupt-vector-table for the address of the keyboard-service-routine, then going there.

Sounds a bit long-winded, but it's all automatic and not something we need to worry about --- though we do need to understand what happens if we want to write very clever programs and TSR's.

Those people who opted to **jump out** will have seen all that hardware detail.

137

One final very useful detail, concerning the keyboard-service-routine. Actually, it's **interrupt-9** in the interrupt-vector-table. What it does is

341

read the char from the keyboard, do a few housekeeping chores, including checking to see if you're holding down the ALT, SHIFT or CTRL keys, then converts the char to the ASCII code and puts it into a buffer.

When the characters are read from the keyboard they aren't in ASCII --- they are what is called the "**scancode**". Note that the BIOS services return both codes. *137*

This buffer is a FIFO (First In First Out) queue, in which the characters wait until the program currently running in the computer decides to read them. The BIOS and DOS services get their characters from this buffer.

DOS KEYBOARD FUNCTIONS:

Again, it's **INT 21h**, with AH selecting the appropriate function.

Refer later for notes on **standard input**.

Before we take leave of keyboard I/O, another little thought to ponder---

AH	DESCRIPTION
1	Wait for a character from the standard input, and echo to screen. Returns: AL=ASCII char.
7	Almost identical to function-1, but char not echoed.
8	Identical to function-1, but char not echoed.

350

350

224

350

EXTENDED CHARACTERS:

You have seen the ASCII table. Most of the so-called non-printing chars do actually print --- if you use the BIOS services to send any ASCII value from 0 to 255 to the screen, it will appear. There are all sorts of strange characters.

Of course on your keyboard you only have the usual characters, so how do you enter ASCII-code 193 (decimal)? Simple:

ENTERING ASCII-193 (decimal):

Hold down the ALT key and type 193 on the numeric keypad. ASCII-193 looks like this: ┴

The 8-bit ASCII code has proved to be a problem however, as IBM wanted to add more codes. For example they brought out a keyboard with function-keys F1 to F10, but since all 255 ASCII codes were already assigned, they had a problem.

Solution; have two bytes for these "extended" characters. If your program reads the keyboard buffer and discovers the ASCII code is zero, that means it is an extended character, and the code for that character is to be found in AH (refer above). With DOS functions, that return only a single byte in AL, if it is zero, then the DOS function must be called again to read the second character.

To find a complete list of **keycodes**, look in the appendices. *368*

The **IBM ASCII character set** is also in the appendices. *370*

MS-WINDOWS ASCII CODES:

370

Later on in the book we get onto Microsoft Windows, the graphical user interface for DOS, and there we encounter some problems with the character set. Windows has a choice of many fonts, and only one of these supports the conventional US 8-bit character set -- the TERMINAL font. Furthermore, only some applications support the terminal font, and some incorrectly support it.

If your Windows application does offer the option of Terminal font, you can enter the full 256 characters by holding down the ALT key, as previously described, but the decimal code must be preceeded by a <zero>.

OTHERS

There are numerous other services offered by the BIOS and DOS, apart from the basic ones mentioned earlier in this chapter. What follows is a list, with hotlinks:

WORKSHEET: CONSOLE I/O

This Worksheet is designed to make you think. Your task is simple---

1.

Write a program, using **DEBUG**, to read any character from the keyboard and display it. *21*
Use this program to see what the ASCII characters between 128 and 255 look like on the screen.
Also use this program to find out the scancodes of the following extended characters (keep a record of these).

<F1> to <F10>
cursor keys
<home>
<end>
<insert>
<del>

ANSWER (look as last resort) >>>> *74*

2.

Write a program, using BIOS keyboard services, to detect when <ALT> is held down and <z> simultaneously pressed.
When detected, use DOS **function-9** to put a message on screen "ALT-z pressed". *350*

HINTS
The Reference Chapters contain a **complete listing of all keycodes.** *368*
Find out the 16-bit code that **INT-16h** will return in AX, for <ALT-Z> pressed. *345*
A possible algorithm for your program could be something like this --

BEGIN
READ KEYBOARD
IS IT <ALT-Z>?
UNTIL
DISPLAY MESSAGE
END

3.

Ditto as above, but the screen message is to be **output directly**, NOT using BIOS or DOS services. *58*

SOLUTIONS :

1.

Table of keycodes 368
Table of IBM ASCII codes 370

```
100   MOV AX,0  ;read keyboard.
103   INT 16        ;keyboard-->AX          345
          ;AH=scancode,AL=ascii.
105   CMP AL,20   ;blank char to end.   44
107   JE 113                              32
109   MOV AH,0E  ;display char inAL.
10B   MOV BH,0    ;page number.
10D   MOV BL,07   ;foreground colour
10F   INT 10                              342
111   JMP 100                             28
113   INT 3                               341
```

If you use the **trace** command, you will be able to examine AX after each INT 16h. WARNING--- don't trace through BIOS INTerrupt routines--- the easiest way around this problem is to "**G**"o: 25 24

```
G=100 103   ;This will start execution at
        ;100, and stop at 103.
```

If you are using the "T"race command, and you come to an INT instruction:

```
10D MOV BL,07
10F INT 10   <---Trace is here (IP=10F)
111 JMP 100
```

```
G 111          ;this is what you need.
;Do NOT put an equals sign.
```

For extended characters, no need to change the previous program; just execute the first couple of instructions;
-G = 100 105

2.

```
-E 200 "ALT-Z pressed$"
-A 100
100   mov ah,0
      int 16            345
      cmp ax,2C00
      jne 100
      mov dx,200
      mov ah,9
      int 21            350
      int 3
```

3.

Here is a possible solution, written in Assembly language:

```
;data....
message   DB "ALT-Z pressed"                      100
  ....
;code....
   mov    ax,B800h  ;for colour card              78
   mov    es,ax
   mov    si,OFFSET message                       100
   mov    di,640   ;video RAM offset              77
   mov    ah,0F0h     ;attribute                  77
   mov    cx,13       ;character count            39
nextchar:
   lodsb              ;load char                  42
   stosw              ;store char&attr            42
   loop   nextchar                                39
```

If entering this in DEBUG, with the code at say offset 100h and data at say 200h, use the "E" command to enter the data and the "A" command to assemble the code. Remember that DEBUG won't accept labels, so instead of "OFFSET message" you need to put the actual address of the data, which is 200h. Also, instead of "loop nextchar" you would need to put the actual address after loop. Also, DEBUG won't accept the leading 0 in "mov ah,0F0h", so leave it off, as too the trailing "h", since DEBUG works in hex by default.

4

DIRECT SCREEN I/O

The previous chapter introduced screen I/O from the point of view of going via the BIOS & DOS services. This does not require as much knowledge of the hardware compared with that required if we are to program the video interface directly.

Our programs can send data directly to the screen circuitry, bypassing BIOS/DOS services entirely.

This chapter goes into depth on this aspect, as well as expanding on the BIOS & DOS services.

INTRODUCTION

The **memory map** back in Chapter One shows that RAM chips at a certain location in the memory map are connected to the screen. What actually happens is that anything you send to this "video RAM" is read by the screen-driver circuitry and put onto the screen. 9

You have a choice how to do your screen output--- either send characters or graphics directly to this RAM, or use the BIOS & DOS video services. The former is what we will look at here. Direct writing to the video RAM gives us very precise control of what we will see on the screen, and allows much faster redrawing of the screen, but may cause compatibility problems when you try to run your program on different "IBM compatibles".

OVERVIEW OF THE STANDARDS:

There is a profusion of video standards, however we can focus on the main thrust. The earliest monochrome adaptors were called **MDA**, and these days the MDA is still selling well, due to its good resolution (720x350 pixels), though a basic modern adaptor card will have more features -- my own card on one of my home machines is a combination MDA/Hercules/CGA. 77

CGA (Colour Graphics Adaptor) is your basic colour adaptor, with low resolution text modes and graphics modes. The 320x200 resolution is somewhat of a strain on the eyes for viewing text, so higher resolution standards were developed. 78

EGA (Enhanced Graphics Adaptor) is roughly upwards compatible with CGA, but allows resolution up to 640x350 and 16 colours. 80

VGA (Video Graphics Array) is chronologically the latest. The basic VGA standard is roughly upwards compatible with MDA, CGA and EGA, and has resolution up to 640x480 and 16 colours (or shades of grey) -- rather, the basic VGA is 640x480 and 16 colours, but the skies the limit, depending on how much memory and number of "bit planes" your display adaptor has -- this is discussed below. 80

DISPLAY ADAPTOR BOARD:

This is a board plugged into one of the **expansion slots** of the PC, that contains the video RAM and driver circuitry. The driver circuitry contains a special chip that reads the data from the RAM and puts it onto the screen.

140

This chip is capable of driving the screen in one of two different major classes of modes:

- TEXT MODES
- GRAPHICS MODES

TEXT MODES:

ASCII characters stored in the video RAM are continuously read by the CRT- controller chip, which converts them to dots on the screen.

There are a number of text-modes, depending on what kind of display-adaptor you have (MDA, CGA, EGA, VGA, etc).

GRAPHICS MODES:

The information contained in the video RAM must be different in these modes.

Unlike text-mode which requires ASCII characters, graphics-mode requires information for turning pixels on & off and their colour. A pixel is an individual dot on the screen, and in the simplest graphics mode, each bit in the video RAM corresponds to one pixel on the screen. Thus if you set a particular bit =1, the corresponding pixel on the screen will come on.

Let's have a look at some of these modes in more detail---

IBM MONOCHROME DISPLAY ADAPTOR:

This is the simplest display adaptor, generally only found on very cheap PC's.

The video RAM on this board looks like Figure 4.1.

The data must be stored in the RAM in the format shown in Figure 4.2.

The lower-address byte (even addresses) is the **ASCII** character.

370

The MDA supports only 80x25 display, that is, 80 columns and 25 lines. This is referred to by DOS as "mode 7".

So, at every odd address of the video RAM you've got to put an attribute byte --- this determines how the preceding ASCII char will look on the screen. For the mono adaptor the options are limited --- refer to figure 4.3.

Of course there is no colour, but there would be if a CGA, EGA, or VGA with colour monitor was connected. In such a case the foreground colour would select the colour of the character itself, while background is the colour around the character.

For the MDA adaptor, these are the allowable settings of foreground and background and the effect of each:

	background	foreground
no char displayed	000	000
white box	111	111
normal video	000	111
underlined	000	001
reverse video	111	000

TABLE 4.1

IBM COLOUR GRAPHICS ADAPTOR:

We will concentrate here on the CGA adaptor, as it is supported by a lot of software, and also EGA and VGA, although being higher-resolution displays, also are downward-compatible with CGA.

The video RAM on the CGA board occupies a different address range to the MDA, and this poses a problem if you are going to write code that must run on all types of computers. Fortunately there is a BIOS service that tells us the type of board, and another that returns the current mode. Refer to Figure 4.4 for a picture.

When the adaptor is being used in text-mode,only 80x25x2 = 4K bytes of this RAM are required (x2 since each character also has an attribute byte, as for MDA).

Since there is 16K of video RAM (more on other types of adaptors), the text-mode can be organised as "pages" in the RAM, each page holding a different screen image, and the screen can be switched between them. Usually however we stick with page 0.

FIGURE 4.1 MDA Video RAM

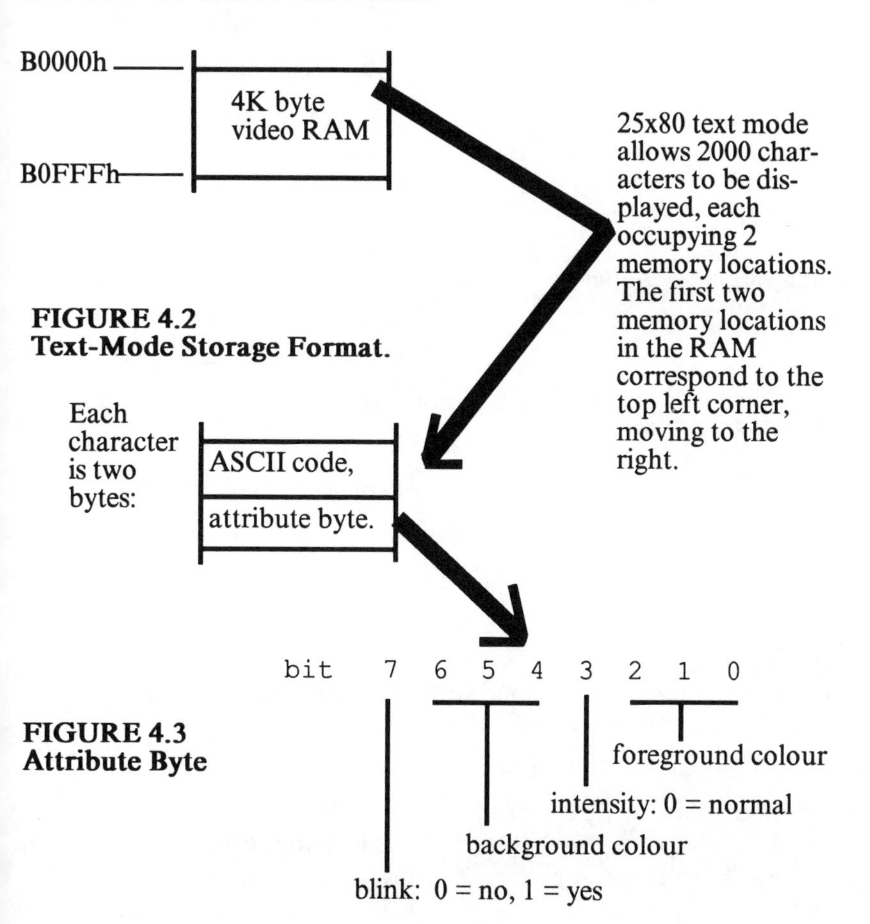

NOTE that CGA text-mode has the same storage format -- the only difference is that the CGA video buffer is at a different segment address. With MDA, the above attribute cannot of course represent colours -- refer to text, Table 4.1. With CGA graphics mode, you do need to be a little careful, as the foreground colour can only be four possibilities -- see Table 4.6 -- but there is a choice of two palettes. Therefore when using the BIOS services to specify an attribute for text (when the screen is in 320x200 graphics mode) do not specify any value above 3 in bits 0 - 2 of the attribute byte. The background for CGA can be chosen from Table 4.7.

There are various text modes:

MODE	DESCRIPTION
0	40x25 monochrome.
1	40x25 colour.
2	80x25 "
3	80x25 colour.

TABLE 4.2

When the adaptor is being used in the graphics modes, these are the options---

MODE	DESCRIPTION
4	320x200 pixels, colour.
5	320x200 pixels, monochrome.
6	640x200 " monochrome.

TABLE 4.3

In 320x200 colour graphics mode, the video RAM is organised as per Figure 4.5.

-- So, 2 bits per pixel, which means that the first 2 bits of the video RAM (at B8000) correspond to the top left hand pixel on the screen, and the last two locations in the video RAM correspond with the bottom right corner of the screen... but there is one complication.....

The video RAM is broken into two equal partitions, from---

B8000 to B9F40 and
BA000 to BBF40.

The first partition holds the pixels for the even scan-lines (0,2,4,...198), while the second partition hold the pixels for the odd scan-lines (1,3,5,...199).

CGA, EGA & VGA PROGRAMMING

FIGURE 4.4 CGA Video RAM

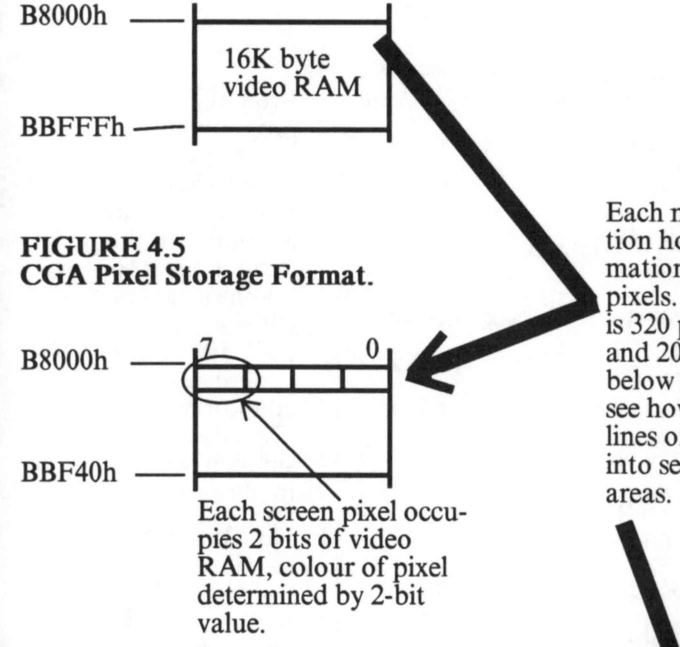

FIGURE 4.5
CGA Pixel Storage Format.

Each memory location holds the information for four pixels. CGA 200x320 is 320 pixels across and 200 down. See below Figure 4.6 to see how the alternate lines of pixels are split into separate RAM areas.

FIGURE 4.6 CGA Split Buffers.

B8000h – B9F3Fh	even scan-lines
BA000h – BBF3Fh	odd scan-lines

SETTING MODES:

M	TYPE	TEXT	RESOLUT	COL	MDA	CGA	EGA	VGA
0	text	25x40	320x200	16		x	x	x
1	text	25x40	320x200	16		x	x	x
2	text	25x80	640x200	16		x	x	x
3	text	25x80	640x200	16		x	x	x
4	grap	25x40	320x200	4		x	x	x
5	grap	25x40	320x200	4		x	x	x
6	grap	25x80	640x200	mono		x	x	x
7	text	25x80	720x350	mono	x		x	x
13	grap	25x40	320x200	16			x	x
14	grap	25x80	640x200	16			x	x
15	grap	25x80	640x350	mono			x	x
16	grap	25x80	640x350	16			x	x
17	grap	30x80	640x480	mono				x
18	grap	30x80	640x480	16				x
19	grap	25x40	320x200	256				x

"M" here means "Mode" (decimal values).

"Text" column refers to rows x columns.

"grap" means "graphics mode".

TABLE 4.4

From the programm[illegible] point of view, we want to know how to switch an adaptor into the various text and graphics modes. BIOS **INT-10h**/subfunction-0 sets the adaptor mode. The table summarises the modes. *342*

Note that the so-called "Super-VGA" is not a standard and so not included in this table. I have however included some details on the Super-VGA modes a little **later on.** *90*

DISPLAYING TEXT IN GRAPHICS MODE:

A point you will notice from the table is that a row/column specification is given even when the display is in graphics mode. Direct video access to the RAM is awkward for displaying text, as you can't just MOVe an ASCII character to an even-address in video RAM -- the format of storage in the video RAM is not as ASCII characters followed by attribute bytes.

HOWEVER, if you write to the screen via the BIOS **INT-10h** services, the BIOS routine will translate the ASCIIcharacter into the correct bit-pattern, and store that bit pattern at the cursor position in the video RAM. Thus you can display text quite easily when the display is in one of the graphics modes. *342*

INT-10h's subfunction for moving the cursor to a particular row & column works equally well in graphics mode, as does the subfunction for setting the attribute when writing a character -- refer back to the **MDA notes** for info on the attribute byte -- though in this case the foreground and background colours are actual colours -- see the "irgb" colour table below -- Table 4.7. *77*

Summarising the attribute byte again:

BIT	MEANING	
7	blink	
6	r	background
5	g	(refer table below)
4	b	
3	intensity	
2	r	foreground
1	g	(refer table below)
0	b	

TABLE 4.5

INT-10h, subfunction-9 writes individual chars with an attribute that you specify, and subfunctions A & F use the default attribute. More info on setting colours is below. *342*

CGA GRAPHICS:

When any of the graphics adaptors are in text mode, the physical address of the video RAM is B8000h. When CGA is operating in graphics mode, all even scan-lines are stored in video RAM at B8000h to B9F3Fh, and all odd scan lines start at BA000h, to BBF3Fh. Figure 4.6 shows this.

As illustrated in Figure 4.5, each byte of the RAM uses two bits per pixel. This is further clarified here:

EACH MEMORY LOCATION:

BIT:	7 6	5 4	3 2	1 0
CONTENT:	-1-	-2-	-3-	-4-

This shows how the pixel information is stored in 320x200 graphics modes 4 & 5. At address B800:0000, the 8-bit memory content is structured as above. Bits 7 & 6 hold the colour information for the very top left hand dot on the screen (-1-), while the next two bits hold the colour info for the next dot on the same row (-2-), and so on.

This is scan-line 0 on the display, and it is important to note that the next scan-line, number 1, is stored in video RAM at BA00:0000.

Since there are only two bits per screen pixel, there can only be 4 colours:

BITS	PALETTE-0	PALETTE-1
00	background	background.
01	green	cyan
10	red	magenta
11	yellow	white

TABLE 4.6

Note that these colours are affected by the background colour -- yellow for example may in some circumstances look more like brown. The colours look true for a black background only.

So if you set both bits to zero, you won't see the dot, as it will be the same colour as the background.

One of the BIOS **INT-10h** subfunctions allows you to select which palette you want to use, and the background colour (subfunction 0Bh). You can also set the palette and background by going directly to the hardware: the "Colour Select" register on the CGA adaptor card:

The possible 16 colours can be selected from Table 4.7.

NOTE: Port 3D9 is different on VGA cards.

PORT-ADDRESS 3D9h:

BIT:	7	6	5	4	3	2	1	0
CONTENT:	x	x	p	q	i	r	g	b

Where p=palette 0 or 1.
q=intense colours, if graphics,
i-bit background, if text mode.
i=intensity bit.
i-bit border, if text mode,
i-bit background, if 320x200 gr,
i-bit foreground, if 640x200 gr.
rgb=red, green, blue primaries.
border, if text mode,
background, if 320x200,
foreground, if 640x200.

FIGURE 4.7

342

FIGURE 4.8 CGA Graphics Screen Coordinates

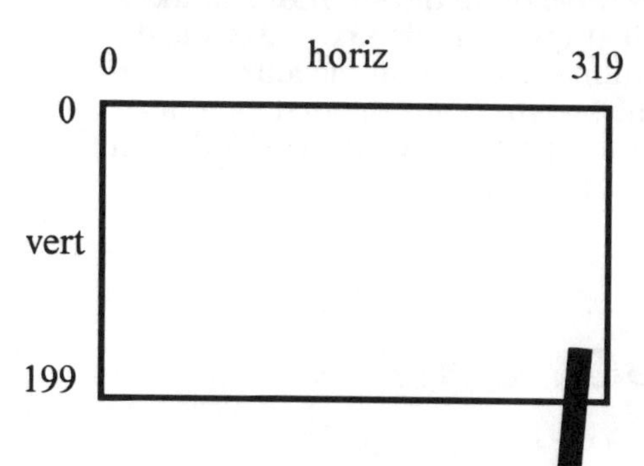

FIGURE 4.9
Algorithm to Find Address in RAM.

Vert. = odd or even?
if even (scan lines 0,2,4...)
then RAM segment B800h.
if odd (scan lines 1,3,5...)
then RAM segment BA00h.

/2, discard remainder.

multiply by 80.

= offset_scanline.
(this gives the RAM offset for the start of the required scan line).

To place the dot somewhere on the selected scan line:

horiz/4
gives a quotient & remainder.

RAM_offset = quotient + offset_scanline.

EXAMPLE CALCULATION:

If a dot (pixel) is to be in the centre of the screen, it would have horix = 160 & vert = 100 (relative to the top left corner).
vert = even, so segment is B800h.
(vert/2) * 80 = 4000
= offset of start of required line.
horiz/4 = 40
Total RAM offset = 4000 + 40 = 4040.
Thus the total address for the pixel is B800h:4040d.
That memory location controls 4 pixels, and since there was no remainder after horix/4, the appropriate bits are 6 & 7 (remainder = 1; bits 4 & 5, for remainder = 2; bits 2 & 3, and for remainder = 3; bits 0 & 1)

Notice from the earlier summary table of all the adaptor standards, that CGA can also be in 640x200 graphics mode. However the dots cannot have any colour information -- each bit in the video RAM corresponds with one pixel on the screen. Thus the first memory location, at B800:0000, holds the information for the first 8 dots at the top left corner of the screen -- that is, a bit is either on or off.

HOW TO PUT A DOT ON THE SCREEN:

With BIOS **INT-10h** it is very simple, as we need only supply the required vertical & horizontal coordinates and specify the "WRITE_DOT" subfunction.

There is no need to know anything about how the pixels are physically stored in video RAM.

Drawing dots using INT-10h is however very slow, so we may opt for direct access, in which case we do need to know how pixels are stored.

Let's take the case of CGA 320x200 colour -- have a look at Figure 4.8 for a picture of screen row and column coordinates.

Remember 2-bits per pixel, thus 4 pixels per byte, so one horizontal row (scanline) requires 320/4 = 80 bytes of video RAM.

Recall also that odd & even scan lines are stored in separate RAM, so if we want to draw a single dot, we must first ask if the vertical displacement is odd or even -- this develops into the algorithm of Figure 4.9.

i r g b	COLOUR
0 0 0 0	black
0 0 0 1	blue
0 0 1 1	cyan
0 1 0 0	red
0 1 0 1	magenta
0 1 1 0	brown
0 1 1 1	light grey
1 0 0 0	dark grey
1 0 0 1	light blue
1 0 1 0	light green
1 0 1 1	light cyan
1 1 0 0	light red
1 1 0 1	light magenta
1 1 1 0	yellow
1 1 1 1	white.

TABLE 4.7

Colour table -- refer to Table 4.5, Table 4.6, Figure 4.7.

342

Still refering to Figure 4.9, having calculated the RAM offset, we then need to know which two bits in that location:

remainder	bits
0	6 & 7
1	4 & 5
2	2 & 3
3	0 & 1

So, by applying this algorithm, we can calculate the RAM_offset for any pixel, then send the colour info to those two bits in the video-RAM.

EGA/VGA GRAPHICS:

You will notice from the **summary table** that these adaptors more or less support the CGA modes, including the physical mapping of the video graphics RAM. *82*

Other specifically EGA and VGA modes however have their own RAM layout for representing the pixels. Mode 19 (decimal) is VGA only, and is particularly good when you want lower resolution but lots of colour. It is 320x200 and 256 colours.

To achieve this choice of colour per pixel requires 8 bits (1 byte) of memory, so the RAM looks like this:

ADDRESS	CONTENT
A0000h	pixel colour, top l.h.corner.
A0001h	pixel colour,next right.
A0002h	pixel colour,3rd from corner.
--etc--	

There is no split memory for odd & even scan lines, as in CGA. The address range A0000h to A013Fh is the 320 pixels of the first scan-line, then A0140h is the start of the second scan-line, and so on.

The other specifically EGA & VGA graphics modes store the pixel information in a very different way, using a technique called "bit planes".

BIT PLANES:

Refer to Figure 4.10. The RAM is hardwired into "planes", all planes being at the same address range A0000h to A95FFh*. Consider the very first location in each plane -- bit-7 of each is the colour code for the top l.h. corner pixel, while bit-6 is the next pixel, and so on.

Thus the first memory location is the pixel info for the first 8 pixels, the second memory location controls the next 8 pixels to the right, and so on.

If each plane is wired to the same address how do we write data to each plane individually? Hardware on the adaptor card can be used to "turn-off" all but the plane/s we want to access.

Think about bit-7 at location A0000h. It controls the very first pixel on the top corner of the screen, and since I've shown 4 planes in the diagram of Figure 4.10, that's 4 bit-7's, so we have a 4-bit colour code for each pixel, allowing 2^4 = 16 possible colours.

Now a most important point -- simply by adding another plane, we double the number of possible colours.

* A VGA adaptor in mode 18, which is 640x480, with 4 planes, allows 16 colours. Each plane is:

480x640/8 = 38400 bytes
So 4 planes requires--
38400x4 = 153600 bytes

Many basic VGA adaptors are supplied with a minimal quantity of RAM, but with spare sockets for expansion, and some also allow larger bit-planes (as well as more of them), for higher resolutions -- new standards are 800x600 and 1024x768.

Calculate this last one, if it has 256 colours (8 bit-planes) --
1024x768x8/8 = 786K bytes

ACCESSING THE BIT PLANES:

Raising the question asked earlier -- how do we access each plane individually?

There is register on the adaptor card called the "Map Mask Register", each bit of which corresponds to a particular plane:

BIT:	7	6	5	4	3	2	1	0
PLANE:	7	6	5	4	3	2	1	0

Thus to access plane-0, we set bit-0 in the Map Mask Register.

Since a memory access is an entire byte, but we may only want to change a single bit in one memory location, another register makes our job easier -- the "Bit Mask Register".

For example if we were to set bit-7 of this register, then when we do a MOVe instruction to a location on the currently selected plane, only bit-7 at the addressed location would be affected.

The adaptor card economises on port addresses by putting some registers at the same address, which is an extra complication for us. Certain control registers are used to resolve this conflict-- The "Sequencer Address register" is used to select the Map Mask Register, and the "Graphics 1 & 2 Address Register" is used to select the Bit Mask Register.

As the complexity is going beyond what is expected of an introductory program, I advise those students interested in programming the EGA & VGA adaptors in graphics modes, to refer to a specialist book. Excellent references are given here:

Note also the Advanced Graphics Worksheet at the end of this chapter.

USEFUL REFERENCES:

"EGA/VGA: A Programmer's Reference Guide", B.D.Kliewer, McGraw-Hill, USA 1988.

"Advanced Programmer's Guide to the EGA/VGA", G.S.Sutty & S.Blair, Brady Books, USA 1988.

FIGURE 4.10 Bit Planes.

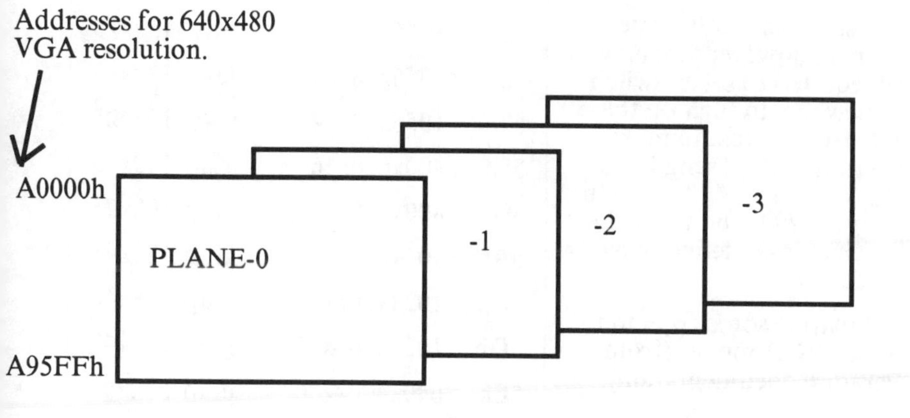

SUPER-VGA PROGRAMMING:

I haven't included the so-called Super-VGA in Table 4.4, as it is not a standard as such.

Super-VGA includes 800x600 and 1024x768 pixels, but unfortunately as a defacto standard it leaves much to be desired, with individual chip makers going their own ways.

The most undesirable consequence of this is that to drive application software in these higher resolutions and/or colours requires special drivers to be supplied by the manufacturer of the board.

The most consistent standard appears to to be the 800x600x16-colours. 800x600x16 employs the bit-planes, four of them, each being 64K. To place a pixel on the screen, use the formula: ((vert. * 800) + horiz.) / 8

This formula gets you down to one 8-bit memory location, but of course a pixel = 1 bit.

The extended-BIOS of adaptors based upon the Paradise chipset define mode 58h as being for 800x600x16, which is a graphics mode, capable of displaying text of 100 cols x 75 rows, and with a video RAM starting address of A0000h.

This mode can be selected by the INT 10h/subfunction-0, as per normal, however you may be required to set a "switch" somewhere to turn-on these extensions. Just to make life tough, the Tseng Labs chipset defines 800x600 x16 as mode 29h, and the Video Seven chipset defines it as mode 62h.

Tabulating some common Super-VGA modes (from Paradise documentation):

MODE	RES,COL.	TYPE	TEXT
54h	1056x387x16	text	132x43
55h	1056x400x16	text	132x25
56h	1056x387x4	text	132x43
57h	1056x400x4	text	132x25
58h	800x600x16	grap	100x75
59h	800x600x2	grap	100x75
5Ah	1024x768x2	grap	128x48
5Bh	1024x768x4	grap	128x48
5Dh	1024x768x16	grap	128x48
5Eh	640x400x256	grap	80x25
5Fh	640x480x256	grap	80x30

TABLE 4.8

WORKSHEET: VIDEO GRAPHICS PROGRAMMING

Whether your computer has a CGA, EGA or VGA adaptor, you can switch it into the basic CGA modes. This worksheet will require you to switch the screen into mode five, and then use direct writing to the video RAM to draw a vertical line on the screen. Do NOT use the BIOS services, except to change the mode.

There you are, short and sweet -- I don't mind what length, or what colour -- just any line longer than a few centimetres -- but your program must be polite enough to wait for a keypress after drawing the line and then change the screen back to standard 80x25 text mode prior to exiting back to DOS.

Hints: examine the section on programming **CGA graphics**, particularly Figure 4.9. *83*
The previous chapter introduced the BIOS & DOS video services and you may wish to refer back there for details on **how to change the mode**. *68*

(SOLUTION ON NEXT PAGE, BUT DON'T LOOK)

SOLUTION TO VIDEO GRAPHICS WORKSHEET

Figure 4.9 is the key to solving this problem. A dot in the centre of the screen, at coordinates horiz=160 and vert=100, relative to the top left corner, computes as segment B800h, (vert/2) * 80 = 4000 decimal, being the starting address (offset) of the required line. Horiz/4 = 40, being the offset into that line. So the total address for that pixel is B800h:4040d

Now, if we wanted to put another dot immediately below it, it would have the same offset, but we would use segment BA00h, giving a total address of BA00h:4040d.

Then, to put yet another dot below that one, we're back onto an even scanline. Since each line of dots on the screen is 320 and 4 dots per memory location, the RAM requirement for each line is 80d. Therefore the address is B800h:4120.

A possible program:

```
    mov     di,4040         ;offset of top pixel.
    mov     cx,6            ;a total of 12 pixels will be written.
    mov     al,11000000b    ;turn on 1 pixel out of the four (yellow/brown or white).   83
nextpixel:
    mov     ax,B800h        ;even scanlines.                                            84
    mov     es,ax
    mov     es:[di],al      ;write the even line to ES:DI                               34
    mov     ax,BA00h
    mov     es,ax
    mov     es:[di],al      ;write the odd line to ES:DI                                34
    add     di,80
    loop    nextpixel                                                                   39
```

NOTE that if using DEBUG, cannot have labels & values must be in hex.

WORKSHEET: ADVANCED GRAPHICS

> **WARNING:**
>
> This Worksheet is for advanced students. It requires a knowledge of the Microsoft or equivalent Assembler & the development cycle. The next chapter will need to be digested first -- then come back here.

The Video Graphics Programming Worksheet on the previous page is kindergarten stuff -- now for something heavy. The program PCX2SCRN, available on the Companion Disk, reads a graphics image from a file on disk, and displays it on the screen.

Graphics images can be created by "paint" and "draw" programs and can be saved in various formats. Images can be of two varieties: bit-map or vector. Of the former, a very common format, supported by PC-Paintbrush and Windows-Paint, is .PCX.

This program reads a file called TEMP.PCX, that you will have to create by a paint program, and displays it on an EGA or VGA monitor. The intention here is partly to show how a bit-map .PCX image is stored, and partly to show how to program the video-RAM mode-16 bit-planes directly -- not through the BIOS, for reasons of speed.

I simply took an existing .BMP graphics file supplied with MS-Windows as one of the background patterns -- the chess one is nice --, read it into Windows-Paint and saved it in .PCX format.

The program for use with this Worksheet is located on the Companion Disk, as PCX2SCRN.ASM, and is not listed in this book, due to its somewhat more specialised nature. The assembly process is straight-forward --

MASM PCX2SCRN;

LINK /t PCX2SCRN;

Then to execute from the DOS prompt --

PCX2SCRN <enter>

Note that the executable file is in .COM format and requires **EXE2BIN** after LINK: however Borland's **TLINK** and Microsoft's latest LINK (supplied with C v6.0), only need the "/t" switch after LINK to generate a .COM file.

103
113

PCX2SCRN.COM will read the bit-map file TEMP.PCX (which must be in the current directory) and display it on the screen. Your mission, should you decide to accept it, is to modify the program so that only half of the image displays, on the top half of the screen. The .PCX image format stores each bit-plane separately, and your second task is to display only one of the bit-planes -- so only a single colour will appear.

To do all of this you will need to know the format for .PCX storage, and also how to access the RAM bit-planes. The program on disk is liberally commented, and will be your major source of information, however I have made some helpful notes on the next page.

NOTE that although this is a stand-alone program, it can quite easily be converted to a procedure that you call from within an application, and of course you can specify any filename you wish, either within the program or from the DOS command-tail.

PCX FILES:

The exact format depends on the video-mode. The file always starts with a header that identifies what type of video-mode the image is intended for. My program is only for mode-16, which is 640x350x16, supported by EGA and VGA monitors. You might like to look at the program listing while reading this. Byte-3 of the header identifies the type of data compression used to store the data -- nearly always this =1, meaning "run-length-encoding", which is a simple technique in which a string of zeroes in the data is replaced by a unique code followed by the number of zeroes.

The video-RAM for mode-16 is organised as four bit-planes, each representing red, green, blue, and intense, and each plane is stored separately in the PCX file. Thus all we need to do in our program, is switch the video-RAM to plane-0, read that portion of the data file, to the video-RAM, then switch the RAM to plane-1 and read the next block of data. All very well, except for the run-length encoding, which has added some complexity to my source code -- however you should be able to follow it from the comments.

You will find it useful to remember that one bit in the video-RAM equals one pixel, so the first byte in the RAM will be the first eight pixels at the top left corner, so since there are 640 pixels horizontally, the first row will require 640/8 = 80 bytes of RAM. So the second row of pixels will start at offset 80 (decimal) in the video-RAM, and so on. Since the number of rows on the screen is 350, the number of bytes required for the bit-plane is 350x80 -- you will be able to locate these figures in the source code.

5

TH[illegible] ASSEMBLER

There are two main parts to this chapter; introduction to using the Assembler and secondly how to develop and debug programs. There is also a corresponding worksheet. The first part develops an overall picture of how to use the Assembler, using an example program.

Content of this chapter...

The process of writing a compiled or assembled program is standardised.

People familiar with any kind of programming will recognise this basic structure, even though in many cases it is disguised within an integrated development environment.

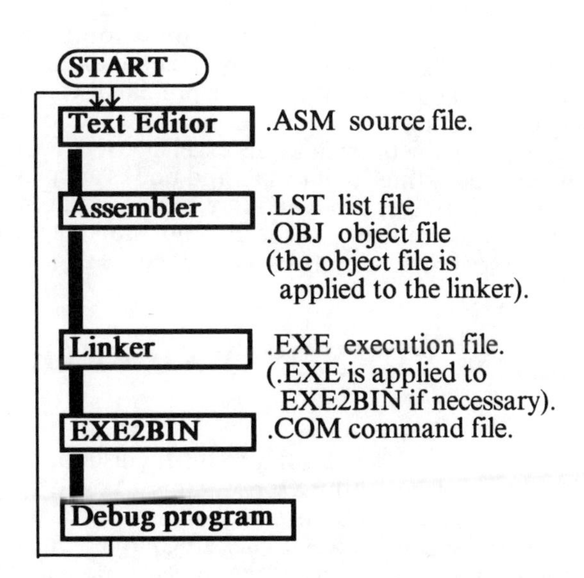

FIGURE 5.1 Classical Dvelopment Cycle.

ASSEMBLER INTRODUCTION

STANDARDS:

Note that Assemblers for the 80x86 family vary considerably with regard to syntax, directives, etc, and these notes refer to the Microsoft Assembler, popularly referred to as MASM. Other products such as the Turbo Assembler (TASM) and A86 are for most purposes equivalent to MASM. Furthermore these notes mainly refer to versions of MASM pre-5.0, ie do not include information on the simplified segmentation directives introduced with that version, since they are non-standard, ie out of line with the broad standards adopted by most Assemblers.

Well... let let me qualify this. TASM for example is MASM-compatible but also has some improvements -- for complete compatibility TASM allows a command-line switch that causes TASM to fully emulate all of MASM's little quirks.

I do discuss various simplified directives as introduced with version 5.0, but the main thrust of the book is not to use them. This is after all a textbook, and it is absolutely essential to understand the pre-5.0 directives and pseudo-ops. The pre-5.0 directives are always generated by compilers when command-line-switched to produce Asm output. All unassemblers, such as the excellent SOURCER, are the same. Plus most code listings in journals and books are pre-5.0. Finally the pre-5.0 directives give you more control and fundamental appreciation of "what is going on". This does not stop the student from graduating to the simplified directives later, of course.

.COM VERSUS .EXE PROGRAMS:

At this point, it is necessary to distinguish the difference between COM programs and EXE programs. As you already know, DOS supports two kinds of executable files. .EXE programs contain more than one segment. Refer back to Chapter One for a **memory map** showing how the segment registers are initialised when a .EXE program is loaded from disk.

18

A .COM program, in contrast, always contains just one segment, and loads from disk with all four segment registers containing the same value. A .COM program, thus, executes in a simplified environment, a 64K address space. You can go outside this address space simply by temporarily changing one segment register, but you don't have to, and that is the thing which makes .COM programs easy to work with.

Both types are important. Most programs that you write will be in the .EXE format, indeed OS/2 insists on it. However special cases require the .COM format -- TSR's such as resident "pop-up" programs, background resident programs, and device drivers. Since it is essential to know about the .COM format, and since it is easier to work with, at least when learning, we start this chapter with a .COM example program.

Reflect back.... you've been using **DEBUG** and creating little programs -- these were in .COM format! The essential requirement is that the code & data should start from at least an offset 100h from the beginning of the segment, and all segment registers had to be the same value. This is what you were doing all along.

Using the Assembler will require you to do a lot more housekeeping -- all those directives and pseudo-ops. Read on to find out about them....

STEPS TO LEARNING THE ASSEMBLER:

WRITING A SIMPLE .COM PROGRAM

For our first attempt let's write a program which says "HULLO WORLD".

Unlike DEBUG, you use a text editor to enter the program, then run it through the assembly process, however for now we'll consider just what constitutes a .COM "source file". This simple program to display "HULLO WORLD" on the screen is a skeleton that will form the basis of any further .COM programs you write.

```
comseg segment                                        101
;Set up COMSEG code & data section.
   assume cs:comseg,ds:comseg                         102
;Tell assembler conditions at entry.
   org 100h                                           102
;program begins with 100H byte prefix
main proc far                                         102
   jmp start
;data area..........
msg db "Hullo World $"                                100
;code area....
start:
;........................
   call displaymsg                                    31
;........................
   mov ah,4Ch      ;DOS exit function,                357
   mov al,0        ; back to DOS
   int 21h         ; command-line.
main endp                                             102
;...................
displaymsg proc near                                  99
   mov dx,offset msg ;message-->DX.                   100
   mov ah,9         ;DOS function-09.                 350
   int 21h         ;  /
   ret                                                31
displaymsg endp
;...................
;...more procedures could go in here...
;...................
comseg ends                                           101
end main ;execution entry point.                      101
```

PROGRAM STRUCTURE:

The assembler uses the general form:

name opcode operands

Comments must be preceded by a semicolon.

As with any assembler, the core of the opcode set

consists of opcodes which generate machine instructions but there are also instructions to the assembler itself, sometimes called pseudo-ops, or Assembler Directives. In the example, these lines generate machine code ---

JMP, MOV, MOV, INT, RET

The Directives are ---

DB, SEGMENT, ASSUME, ORG, ENDS, ENDP, PROC and END.

The following contiguous text, over the next few pages, goes into more detail on the program structure, however if you want to momentarily jump ahead and get the overall picture, refer to page 102.

The format is we discuss the individual elements of this program, then go on to putting it together. The chapter then progresses onto .EXE programs.

What follows is a description of the example program's structure. The headings are here for you to jump to them, or you can continue reading the whole lot:

LABELS:

A label is a convenience, identifying a particular point in your source code. Usually it is of the form:

label:

and is a symbolic-address followed by a colon. Note that it should start on column-one.

In certain cases, such as labeling some data in the data segment, the **label does not have a colon** --- this is the Assembler's syntax requirement. *52*

Of course when the source code is run through the Assembler, producing machine-code (object code), the labels are replaced with actual addresses.

SHORT, NEAR, FAR DIRECTIVES:

Earlier in this database it was mentioned that a JuMP or CALL can have SHORT, NEAR, or FAR addressing. Each type will assemble as a different op.code, and obviously the Assembler must be able to determine what kind is required. If your memory of this is failing, jump back:

NEAR	*28*
FAR	*28*
SHORT	*32*

Obviously it would be no good if the Assembler assembled a JuMP as a NEAR jump if you wanted to go to another segment. The Assembler defaults to NEAR, so to tell it otherwise we have to include "Assembler-Directives", or "pseudo-operations", that tell the Assembler what we want.

DB, DW, DD:

DB means "Define Byte", and is used by the Assembler to signify that what follows is not code, but single-byte data, to be placed straight into memory:

```
label DB ...data...
```

52

"Type" is very important with the Microsoft Assembler, which is a mechanism to avoid programmer errors.

Other define-data directives are DW (Define Word) and DD (Define Doubleword), which serve the same purpose as DB except they inform the Assembler that the data is a particular size, that is byte (8-bit), word (16-bit), or doubleword (32-bit).

The reason this is important is that if a "type" mismatch occurs, for example:

```
;data area....
VAL1 DW 67
;code area...
MOV AL,VAL1
```

This would trigger an assembly error, as you are trying to load data defined as 16-bit into an 8-bit register. Note that it is completely irrelevant that the value in VAL1 is less than 8-bits in this example.

OFFSET:

```
mov dx,offset msg
mov dx,msg
```

99

the first instruction puts the ADDRESS of **label** MSG in register DX, the second instruction puts the CONTENTS of storage at label MSG in register DX.

If MSG is the **label of a word of storage**, then the second instruction will be understood as a desire to fetch that data into DX. If MSG is a *52* label, then "OFFSET MSG" means "the integer number which represents MSG's offset from the start of the segment."

"Offset" is a pseudo-op that modifies the operation-code of the move instruction, so that at execution-time, MOV will treat the operand as an immediate value. At assembly-time MSG is equated to whatever its offset in memory is, so that offset is the actual operand assembled into the instruction.

Note that there is another instruction that will do exactly the same thing, though it has a slightly slower execution-time: LEA dx,msg

"LEA" means Load Effective Address, meaning the offset of MSG.

Another little note, for the sake of completeness, is that OFFSET has a companion: SEG, that means "load the segment-address of the label". Let's leave that one for now.

More on "Type" *52*
About "Type override" *52*
LEA *362*

RADIX:

The assembler's default radix is decimal. To represent numbers in other forms of notation such as hex or binary, use a trailing letter --- 21h is hexadecimal 21, 00010000b is eight bit binary. An important point with hex is that if the number starts with an alphabetic letter, always precede it with a zero digit, so that the Assembler doesn't think the number is a label. Note also that it is possible to switch the default radix.

SEGMENT ... ENDS DIRECTIVES:

SEGMENT tells the assembler you are starting a section of code or data.

The ENDS statement tells the assembler you are finished with the section of code or data.

END:

END goes at the end of every source file. When you are assembling a subroutine, it terminates with "END <enter>", but when assembling the main routine of a program you terminate it with "END label", where 'label' is the place where execution is to begin. Look back at the example program.

ASSUME DIRECTIVE:

Another pseudo-op illustrated in the program is ASSUME. The assembler uses ASSUME information to decide on the default segment register from which data accesses will be made -- this is encoded into the instr. op. codes.

In this case, we can inform the assembler that both the CS and DS registers will address the segment called COMSEG at execution time. Note that COMSEG is an arbitrary name I gave to the common segment.

PROGRAM SEGMENT PREFIX:

ORG tells the assembler to move its Location Pointer to some particular address. In this case, we have asked the assembler to start assembling code hex 100 bytes from the start of the section called COMSEG instead of at the very beginning. This simply reflects the way .COM programs are loaded. When a .COM program is loaded from disk, DOS sets up all four segment registers to address the same 64K of storage. The first 100 hex bytes of that storage contains what is called the Program Segment Prefix (PSP).

Your .COM program physically begins after this. Execution begins with the first physical byte of your program; that is why the JMP instruction is there.

EXAMINING THE OVERALL STRUCTURE OF THE EXAMPLE .COM PROGRAM

Have a gander at the source code of the example program...>>>>>

```
comseg segment
  ...
comseg ends
```

98

You can see that one overall segment was defined, starting with "comseg segment" and ending with "comseg ends".

The segment contains two PROCedures, or subroutines, and notice that the lower one is terminated by a **RET** instruction, and the top one terminated by a DOS **function-4Ch** call, which returns control to the DOS command-line. The top procedure is the "main" one, entered

31
357

when execution starts, and it can in turn call others (which can in turn call others).

If it so happened that this program was itself called by another program, then it is most likely that we would have to put a RET at the end of the main PROCedure instead of the function-call.

Notice the directives required for the PROCedure. It starts with PROC and ends with ENDP, preceded by a label, and with a FAR/NEAR declaration.

name PROC *far/near*

...

name ENDP

FAR or NEAR after PROC is optional, as are certain other qualifiers, and if left off the default is to NEAR.

NEAR procedures are those called within the current segment, while **FAR** procedures are those called from another program in a different segment. The outer procedure will nearly always have to be defined as FAR.

99
99

The name of the procedure can be whatever you wish. The name is a label that can be used for addressing purposes.

ASSEMBLING THE EXAMPLE PROGRAM

1. The source file should be created by an **editor**, with the name HULLO.ASM (actually the name is arbitrary but the extension .ASM is conventional and useful). You can use your favourite word processor for this purpose, but save it as an ASCII-only file.

2. The next step is to run it through the **Assembler**.

after creating your program "source file" using a text editor and saving it as <u>ASCII only</u>, with .ASM extension, you are then ready to assemble....

MASM HULLO;

don't forget the semicolon

then link....

LINK HULLO;

108

again, remember the ";"

only do this next step if the program is .COM....

EXE2BIN HULLO.EXE HULLO.COM

DEL HULLO.EXE

in fact, recent LINK programs have a /t switch that eliminates this step.

110

Invoke the Assembler as shown in the box, but don't type the extension -- MASM and TASM both assume .ASM.

HULLO.ASM is an arbitrary name for the file -- you could have called it FRED.ASM if the fancy took you.

The ";" on the end prevents MASM from asking questions, but leave it off if you want the option of producing .LST output. TASM works the same with or without the ";" and requires a command-line switch to generate .LST output.

3. If you issue DIR at this point, you will discover that you have acquired HULLO.OBJ (the object code resulting from the assembly) and optionally HULLO.LST (a listing file).

4. The next step is to run the file HULLO.OBJ through the **LINK** program, which will convert it into HULLO.EXE.

111

If you had written your program as .EXE in the first place, you would stop at this point. However if it is .COM-format, as is our case, EXE2BIN is required. Borland's TLINK version 2.0 will accept "/t" immediately after the program name, to automatically generate .COM output instead of .EXE, so EXE2BIN isn't needed. The latest releases of Microsoft's LINK also accept this switch, but I have had trouble with it, so in Microsoft's case stick with EXE2BIN.

Note that IBM no longer include EXE2BIN with DOS, but Microsoft and all compatibles do. You must use the correct EXE2BIN for your version of DOS.

Without the /t switch, if the program is in .COM-format, the linker will give an error message that no stack segment was defined --- simply ignore this as it isn't required for the .COM format.

5. EXE2BIN is the final step for a .COM program. It produces the actual program you will execute. Note that you have to type in HULLO.COM, as EXE2BIN uses the default extension .BIN instead of .COM for its output file. At this point, you might want to erase HULLO.EXE.

6. To run the program... at the DOS comand-line just type "HULLO <enter>"

WRITING .EXE PROGRAMS

Skeleton .EXE program here.
Note that it continues on the next page:

When a .EXE program is loaded from disk, the values in the segment registers are all different, unlike a .COM program in which they are all the same. There is no need to be intimidated about this --- a little more care is needed when writing a program, but the advantage is that programs can have separate data and code segments as big as 64K each.

A note about this. If you write applications in Assembly language it is extremely unlikely that you will ever develop a program as large as 64K, due to the efficiency/compactness of Assembly. However if the Asm program is a module to be linked with other

```
stack1 segment stack 'stack'                       101
       db 64 dup(0)                                100
              ;dup means DUPlicate.                100
stack1 ends                                        101
;................................
data1  segment
var1   db  41h,43h                                 100
var2   db  "A"
var3   dw  100 dup(0)                             100
data1  ends
;................................
code1  segment
 assume      cs:code1                              102
main1 proc far                                     102
       ;FAR tells the Assembler RET
       ;will be out of this segment
       ;ie, back to DOS.
 mov ax,data1           ;since DS initially
 mov ds,ax              ;points to the PSP,
 assume ds:data1        ;have to change it.
```

modules, the latter perhaps written in a high-level language, you may be constrained to EXE format. OS/2 requires it for all programs.

Okay, now down to work....

Have a look back via this hotlink to see how a .EXE program **loads from disk**.

Initially, DOS makes DS and ES the same value, pointing to the Program Segment Prefix (**PSP**). Also IP should be zero, since it is pointing to the start of the code segment, CS.

When writing your program, always remember that the segment registers have different values.

Any memory reference will automatically access the data segment ---

```
;data segment ...
 vall   DW  0
;code segment ...
 mov ax,vall
```

```
; ....... continues from previous page
        ....
....    ;this is your program.                     18
...     ;it can have PROC call's here
....    ;if you wish.
....
 mov ah,4Ch          ;DOS exit                     357
                     ;function
 mov al,0            ; back to DOS
 int 21h             ; command-line.

main1 endp                                         102
;............................
;...proc's here if required...
;............................
code1 ends
 end main1                                         101
;..................................................
```

Of course **segment override** can be used. 101

Sometimes you may wish to define some data inside the code segment:

Though note that a CPU operating in protected mode may object to a write to a code segment. The example could of course equally apply to ES (and FS & GS).

```
;code segment...
....
jmp code_continues
err_msg db "fatal crash$"                          100
code_continues:
mov si,offset CS:err_msg                           100
....
```

THE SIMPLIFIED SEGMENT DIRECTIVES

```
    DOSSEG
    .MODEL  SMALL
    .STACK  200h
    .DATA
val1    db    0
val2    db    1
    ...
    .CODE
start   proc   far
    mov    bx,@Data
    mov    ds,bx
    ...
    ...
    mov ax,4C00h
    int  21h
start   endp
    ...
          ;could have procs here
    ...
    END   start
```

These apply to MASM 5.0+ and TASM 1.0+. The example program listed here shows how they are used.

Defining the stack is simple enough -- in this example it is 200h bytes in size.

Also the data segment is quite clear. Notice that there's no terminating ENDS. Notice also that the code at the beginning of the code segment is slightly different -- you might like to refer back to the EXE skeleton and compare -- now we must use a special pre-defined symbol: "@Data", since we don't actually name the data segment as before.

DOSSEG is optional and is helpful for the Assembler when your Asm program is to be linked to high-level language modules.

.MODEL specifies the segment-structure of the program. It is followed by one of these: TINY, SMALL, MEDIUM, COMPACT, LARGE or HUGE.

TINY specifies a .COM-format program. SMALL, which would suit us for small .EXE programs, specifies that there is just one data segment and one code segment. MEDIUM model is for larger programs that require more than one code segment but still only one data segment, COMPACT is the reverse. LARGE specifies both data and code will be more than one segment, while HUGE specifies that segments are not limited to 64K in size.

.MODEL makes sure that the Assembler segment names correspond to those used by high-level languages, and that procedure calls/rets default to NEAR or FAR to suit the high-level language -- all ensuring smooth linking.

THE SOFTWARE DEVELOPMENT CYCLE

Here we are going to consider how to setup an efficient development cycle, and also what to do if the program you have written doesn't work.

SETTING UP THE SYSTEM:

For a start, how have you set up your system? If working on a hard disk, you will require a directory in which to keep your program under development, or maybe you have it on a floppy.

The Assembler, debugger and text-editor need not be in the same directory or on the same drive, but they must be in the path -- this will enable you to execute them from your working directory.

The **AUTOEXEC.BAT** file contains DOS's search path:

```
PATH C:\;C:\DOS;C:\GALAXY;C:\TASM
```

7

This example tells DOS to look in the root directory, then in \DOS, then \GALAXY, then \TASM, where \GALAXY contains the GALAXY.EXE wordprocessor and \TASM contains the Turbo Assembler, Debugger and utilities.

Some arcane wordprocessors require you to be in the same directory as the wordprocessor to run it -- give these a big miss. An alternative is a pop-up text-editor such as Sidekick.

There is a difference between a wordprocessor and a text-editor -- the former usually has various "document" modes, in which the text-file is saved with control-characters embedded into it, for such things as formatting and character-attributes. With Wordstar for example, make sure you open in "nondocument" mode.

Your Assembler expects source code as straight text, without control-codes.

If you are using a PC that is setup in a manner not described as above, you may have to do directory-hopping to use the various programs. This is most time-wasting. Some systems may be set up with **batch** files, that do things you may not like.

21

Consider an alternative --

MAKING A BOOTABLE FLOPPY:

this is what many Assembly language developers recommend anyway, to minimise the risk of stuffing up the system -- put everything onto a floppy disk. Make a **bootable** floppy:

```
FORMAT A:/S
COPY C:\COMMAND.COM A:
```

4

This will format a floppy and place the system files onto it. If it is a high density drive (say a 1.44M 3.5inch) and you want to format a medium density floppy (say 720K) you will need to specify a switch on the command-line -- this varies with the version of DOS.

I'm not saying you have to make up a bootable floppy for development -- it's just a practice that some developers recommend. Apart from choosing the configuration, you will also need the actual software:

TEXT EDITOR:

Then get your hands on a nice text-editor -- there is even a very nice one that you can use that is completely free -- public domain -- though note the on-disk documentation states that it is free for individual use only. It is Wordstar compatible and is called VDE (Video Display Editor) -- available as PC-SIG number 1273. Since VDE is only about 30K, lots of room is left on your floppy.

I am quite fond of GALAXY, which is shareware, though rather large, at 150K -- use version 2.4x, not 3.x. The former version is now distributed as GALAXY-LITE, through most shareware channels.

Borland products are always top-notch, and their TURBO editor is no exception. It is not much bigger than VDE and is optimised for the programming environment.

ASSEMBLER/DEBUGGER:

The system you are putting together will require an Assembler and a debugger. The Companion Disk contains A86 and D86 (PC-SIG #1111). The Author of these shareware products has allowed them to be supplied with the Companion Disk, for individual use to do the various exercises in this book. Any further work will require the product to be registered with the Author. I have supplied documentation for these on the Companion Disk, though you can get the latest version & a printed manual upon registration with the Author. A86 & D86 Assembler and debugger, are also extremely compact and excellent for putting onto a floppy.

If you go for the Microsoft products, you will require MASM and CODEVIEW. Borland's equivalent are TASM and TD.

PUTTING IT TOGETHER:

Let's further develop the theme that you have opted to make up your own **bootable floppy** -- with text-editor on, use the latter to create an **AUTOEXEC.BAT** file, in which you can create your own path -- note that you do not have to put the A:\ drive in the path, since that is your working drive & path, and DOS always looks in the current directory first before using the path to look for the file. *4* *7*

It is only necessary to specify those items in the path, that are located on the hard drive. Make sure the path includes the directory where LINK and EXE2BIN are located, if they aren't on the floppy.

If your machine is a genuine IBM, it may not have EXE2BIN, so "acquire" it from somewhere, but be sure that it is for the same version of DOS.

Having setup your floppy, **boot up on it** (CTRL-ALT-DEL) and there you are, ready to go! *4*

Incidentally, if you can avoid using the hard disk at all, you will just about eliminate the risk of catching a virus! Also it will minimise the risk of injuring the hard drive -- TSR's in particular can cause unexpected effects.

AN EFFICIENT ENVIRONMENT:

Firstly have a think about what you do to assemble a program -- to take it from a .ASM source file to a final **.EXE** or **.COM** executable file.

In the case of MASM you would go through a process like this:

```
MASM SOURCE;
LINK SOURCE;
EXE2BIN SOURCE.EXE SOURCE.COM
DEL  SOURCE.EXE
```

105

Where SOURCE.ASM is the source file created on a text editor -- this can of course be any name, but must have .ASM extension.

The last two lines are only required if the program is in .COM format.

Now isn't this an incredibly long-winded process to have to go through each time? Some newer Assemblers, such as Microsoft's Quick-Assembler offer an integrated environment that automates this process, but serious programmers tend to shy away from such environments, as they like the flexibility of separate Assembler, debugger and text-editor, each of which can be much more powerful than an integrated system.

Incidentally, we are assuming here that your PATH is setup correctly so that DOS can find these programs from wherever you happen to be working -- look back over the last couple of pages if unsure about this.

The above sequence of DOS commands need NOT be typed in every time you reassemble your program -- take the time now to make up a **batch** file to automate the process:

```
ASM2COM.BAT
MASM %1;
LINK %1;
EXE2BIN %1.EXE %1.COM
DEL  %1.EXE
```

7

I have gone into detail on **batch files for TASM** a little later on.

113

Use your newly-acquired VDE (or whatever) to create this. ASM2COM.BAT is the name I've given it, so to run it all you have to do from the the DOS-prompt is:

```
C:> ASM2COM  SOURCE
```

A useful little thought at this point: After using the editor to create your program, you then exit to DOS, then you run this batch file, then you try the program to see if it works, then if it doesn't you load the debugger. Then back to the editor. Whew! Integrated environments minimise the drudgery of this cycle, but even in a non-integrated system, there are further improvements that you can make, apart from the batch file. For example, most editors allow you to shell out to DOS with a single keystroke, run the batch file, etc, then jump back in with a single keystroke or at most by typing "exit".

Having assembled the program, try it, and if it doesn't work, it's time to debug.

For debugging you have a number of choices, but let's postpone that part for now, and consider the assembly requirements for A86/D86 and Turbo Assembler/Debugger.

For A86, it is hardly worth using a batch file, since there is no need to use LINK or EXE2BIN -- A86 recognises the source format and will produce a .COM file directly:

```
C:> A86 SOURCE.ASM
```

Note that the extension must be specified.

However if the file is .EXE format you may prefer to setup a batch file:

```
A86 %1.ASM %1.OBJ
LINK %1;
```

The following notes describe how to get going with the Turbo Assembler. A little later on, the debugging process is described in more detail -- a vital topic, as much of your time will be involved in finding out why your program doesn't work!

USING TURBO ASSEMBLER:

The Turbo Assembler is called TASM.EXE and the Debugger is called TD.EXE. (TD.OVL should not be left behind when making up a working disk/directory, as it is part of TD -- this note applies to pre-version-2.0, as TD has now been made into one large EXE file).

TD is one of the finest debuggers around, very easy to use for such power, and with the most useful bonus of using the **virtual-8086** mode of the 80386 CPU. If a '386 machine is used for 8086 development, TD gives you tremendous protection against crashes, as well as improved tracing.

There are many command-line switches that can be used with TASM and TD, but the example here should get you by. Your source-file in this example is called SOURCE.ASM:

```
TASM /ZI SOURCE
TLINK /V SOURCE
```

The first line will produce SOURCE.OBJ.

/ZI causes the output file to have debugging information for use by TD.

The second line converts SOURCE.OBJ to SOURCE.EXE.

/V causes the output file to contain a symbol table for use by TD.

Assuming our program is EXE format, that's as far as we go. Of course the first time round, your program won't work, so off to the debugger...

```
TD -DS -SC SOURCE [arguments]
```

This starts the debugger.
TD will expect SOURCE.EXE and SOURCE.ASM to be in the current directory or path.

-DS sets optimum screen-swapping for TSR's.

-L tells TD to operate in assembler-mode.

-SC tells TD to ignore case.

Note that from within TD you can configure the defaults so that it will not be necessary to specify switches on the command-line.

BATCH FILES: *21*

You can of course put all of the above into batch files. Incidentally, .COM files are a problem with TD, and we need to do things slightly differently. The batch files here & below show the particular case for producing and debugging a .COM file:

ASM2COM.BAT

```
tasm /zi %1
tlink /v %1
tdstrip -s %1    see note
del %1.exe       see note
tlink /t %1      see note
```

The batch file here is only for TASM pre-2.0. With version 2.0, TDSTRIP has been expanded to produce the .COM file directly, so the extra steps aren't required. TDSTRIP.EXE is a utility supplied with Turbo Assembler, that removes the symbol table from SOURCE.EXE. Refering to pre-2.0, I ran TLINK again, with the /t switch, that produced SOURCE.COM.

The reason for this roundabout way is that .COM programs cannot hold the symbol table required by TD.
TDSTRIP places the symbol table in a new file SOURCE.TDS --- TD will automatically look for this.

```
ASM2COM.BAT

tasm /zi %1
tlink /v %1
tdstrip -s -c %1
```

The new ASM2COM.BAT shown on this page is for TASM version 2.0+. The "-c" switch performs the .COM trick.

ASM2COM.BAT uses the %1 replaceable parameter, so you invoke the batch file from the DOS command-line by:

```
C:> ASM2COM SOURCE
```

Now we lead innexorably on to debugging. Chances are it won't work, and at this stage there are various options -- read the next few pages to find out all about these options, but for now, since we're looking at batch files for use with TASM, let's round it off and see how to load the Turbo Debugger (TD) with a batch file:

```
BUG.BAT

td -ds -sc %1 command-tail-argument
```

BUG.BAT is invoked by:

```
BUG SOURCE
```

If SOURCE is .COM type, TD will look for SOURCE.TDS for the symbols. The rest of the stuff shown on that line in BUG.BAT is just the argument required for your program -- of course your program may not need any arguments.

Set up batch files like the above if you want to avoid endless tedium.

VIRTUAL-8086

208

To operate TD with the '386 in virtual-8086 mode, a device driver must be specified in the **CONFIG.SYS** file:

```
DEVICE=\TASM\TDH386.SYS
              ...note different name for v2.0+
TD386 -e128 SOURCE command-tail-arg.
```

5

The 2nd line shows how to run the debugger once DOS has loaded.

TD386 is a special program that is run instead of TD. Your machine must have extended memory for TD to load into. -e128 specifies how many K's to set aside for anything other than TD.

On the same line you can place the name of the program to be debugged, plus a command-tail or argument if required.

Of course if the above was to be made into a batch file, "SOURCE", being our hypothetical program-name, would be replaced with a replaceable-parameter, "%1".

MINIMUM FILES NEEDED:

I found it just possible to make a 720K **bootable** diskette with a text-editor, TASM, TD & utilites on it, if you need to do such a thing. 360K is out of the question, but not if you use A86 & D86 instead. Actually, even if you have a hard disk it is still a good idea to boot up and work from floppies when doing Assembly development work -- I have already laboured that point enough.

As a minimum you will need ---

TASM.EXE

TD.EXE

TD.OVL -- *pre-2.0 only.*

TLINK.EXE

Also, don't forget a text-editor,

and perhaps:

TDSTRIP.EXE

And if working on a '386 ---

TDH386.SYS

TD386.EXE

DEBUGGING

The above notes on the Turbo Assembler also described how to invoke the Turbo Debugger. A debugger is what we can use to find the fault in a program, but here we have a number of choices:

1. One option is to observe what the program does when it is executed, then go back to the source file and examine it. Go through

it carefully, use the text editor to make the correction, then reassemble. Not such a bad method, but some bugs are more elusive!

2. DEBUG

22

Another option is to use DEBUG. DEBUG can load a program from the command line:

```
DEBUG SOURCE.COM [arguments]
```

Or SOURCE.EXE, as the case may be.

"arguments" are the optional command-tail parameters that your program may require. DEBUG will come up with the familiar "-" prompt, and in the case of a .COM format program, typing "U 100" will unassemble the program.

However this unassembly will be without symbols -- to trace through is thus awkward for largish programs, so it is recommended that you obtain a printout of the source file beforehand -- better yet obtain a printout of the .LST file.

With MASM, leave the ";" off the end of the command-line, and MASM will ask you what files to generate -- one option will be a .LST file, which contains the binary (machine) code alongside the source listing. A .LST file is most helpful for using DEBUG, due to DEBUG's lack of symbols.

Or, placing commas like this will produce a .LST file:

```
MASM SOURCE,,,;
```

Using the Trace command with DEBUG can be a problem, as DEBUG will trace into every procedure and interrupt routine -- to execute an INT instruction in one go requires a "Go" command, but for that you need to know the address immediately after the INT instruction -- the .LST file will show you that, or use the "Unassemble" command to find out:

In this case, if you have "T"raced to address 120, then type "G 122" to execute the INT without tracing into it.

```
120  INT 16
122  MOV AX,0
```

DEBUG is a valid tool for debugging, but also is primitive. Turbo Debugger for example does not have the above problem of tracing into an INT or procedure (though you can if you wish). Powerful debuggers also show the original source code and allow you to trace through that, so a printout is not required. DEBUG has a problem with program output -- no screen switching is employed, so program output to the screen superimposes on top of DEBUG's display!

And if you switch to graphics mode, DEBUG's display may become unusable.

Despite all of these problems, if you have been using DEBUG and are familiar with it, you may find it sufficient for this course. It is better to have a tool that you can use than a more powerful one that you can't.

3. D86

Medium-level debuggers, such as D86, are more flexible than DEBUG, and quite easy to use. D86 must be used in conjunction with A86, as the latter automatically produces a .SYM file, which is the symbol information to enable D86 to unassemble the executable file with symbols for addresses and variables.

You invoke D86 by:

```
D86 SOURCE [arguments]
```

Where "arguments" are the optional command-tail parameters that your program may require.

Once inside D86, typing <alt-F10> brings up context-sensitive help. The screen displays the unassembled program, flags, registers, help, and a memory-dump area.

The help section shows you that <F1> is for single-steps (tracing) and <F2> will "Go" through a procedure or INT in one step.

A fascinating aspect of D86 is that you can execute any '86 instruction in real-time. Where the cursor is on-screen, type any instruction, such as "MOV AX,0", and D86 will execute it immediately. This is a convenient method of changing parameters during tracing, and you don't have to know any strange commands, just the normal instruction set.

To display variables and dump areas of memory, to view while tracing, type any number from 1 - 6, then enter what you want to view:

```
B1,VAR1
W2,VAR1
T10,ARRAY
```

These are three examples, to be typed after the single-digit number. The first example means to display a single byte of memory, called VAR1. The second example means to display two words of memory, starting at VAR1. The third example displays ten text (ASCII) bytes of memory, starting from ARRAY -- ie displays ASCII characters.

Type "Q" to quit.

Quite easy to use. If you register you get a very large printed manual for A86 & D86, plus useful utilities. D86 is still rather limited however

-- you don't see the original source file during debugging, only an unassembled executable file with symbols placed in it. Also, as with DEBUG, there is a clash with program output to the screen, and D86 is just about impossible to use in graphics mode.

My conclusion: easy to use, very compact (only about 16K -- A86 is under 30K), an excellent tool for the student.

4. CODEVIEW & TURBO-DEBUGGER

Professional debuggers. Probably the two most popular are Microsoft's CODEVIEW (CV.EXE) and Borland's Turbo Debugger (TD.EXE).

Of the two -- sorry Microsoft -- the Turbo product is far easier to use. However that is only one aspect of it -- CV will also work with OS/2 and MS-Windows, while TD version 1.0 is restricted to DOS, with 2.0 functional with Windows also, but at the time of writing not OS/2.

These products do take awhile to learn, and perhaps the student may wish to give them a miss. It depends on your particular setup -- if you had TD on-hand, I would recommend to go for it, as the investment in time to learn to use TD will pay off later in decreased debugging time. Here is how to get going with TD:

USING TURBO-DEBUGGER

The above notes on Using Turbo Assembler describe that switches must be used for the

GENERAL NOTES ON USING TD:

ALT-char to pop-up a heading on the menu-bar.

ALT-V (iew) to open up new windows.

"Watches" window can display any variables you specify.

"Variables" window displays variables related to current execution.

<F6> moves you between windows.

<ScrollLock> to move/resize windows --

(use [shift]arrow-keys, then <enter>).

<F4> executes code from current arrow-head to highlighted instruction.

<F7> executes next instruction.

<F8> executes next instruction, but won't trace into procedures or INT's.

<F9> run program at full speed.

CTRL-BREAK stops execution (maybe).

ALT-F5 switchs to your program's scrn o/p

assembler and linker to include symbol information in the executable file (or as a separate file in the case of .COM programs), for use by TD.

Actually, the Microsoft assembler (MASM) and linker can also produce an executable file that TD can use, but the symbol information must first be converted to a form that TD understands -- Borland supply a utility for that purpose.

TD is very sophisticated, but here are a few notes to get you going. Refer back to the notes on **loading TD**. If you specified the -L command-line option when loading TD, it will come up with a "CPU Window", which has detailed info on the CPU. Alternatively, if you did not use the "-L" switch (which isn't in the BUG.BAT file example), the "View" menu can be used to bring it up. This window consists of a number of "panes":

113

NOTES ON THE CPU-WINDOW:

<TAB> to move between panes.

The panes show memory-dump, regs, flags, and stack.

ALT-F10 brings up a local menu for the current pane.

<F1> will give context-sensitive help, but requires the file TDHELP.TDH.

The code-pane looks slightly confusing, as it is mixed original-source and dissassembled code --- use "Mixed" in local-menu to modify this if req'd.

"View Source" in local menu is useful as it pops up a window of the original uncluttered source -- can also trace through it.

The arrow-head in the code-pane shows the current location of CS:IP.

"New CS:IP" from local-menu shifts the arrow-head to the currently highlighted instruction (not executing anything).

A general note on TD is that you may find the CPU-Window overwhelming at first. In that case don't use the -L switch, or if the CPU-Window is present when starting TD (by the -L switch or the defaults settings), it can be closed by pressing <F3>. For most purposes you may find the source file far more useful to trace through.

If by any chance the source-file window is not open, and the CPU-Window is, pop-up the CPU-Window Unassemble-Listing Pane's Local-Menu (<ALT-F10>), and select View-Source.

While viewing the Source-File, <alt-F10> can be used to pop-up a useful Local Menu, and don't forget that <F6> moves you between open windows.

One awkward aspect of the Source-File-window is that you can't jump to a place in the file without executing to it -- the local-menu in the CPU-window is required for that.

Version 2.0 of TD is wonderful -- you can backtrace, and there is special support for debugging TSRs. It also supports a mouse, which v1.0 didn't.

USING CODEVIEW:

If you use CODEVIEW, Microsoft's debugger, to debug an executable file, the program will show as an unassembled listing, without symbols, unless you assemble and link with certain switches to cause the symbol information to be included in the executable file.

A couple of important notes about this-- after debugging the file, reassemble and link without the switches, as the executable file is larger than necessary with the symbol information in it. Another vital point-- pertinent to version 5.0 and earlier only -- CODEVIEW cannot show source code or symbol information of .COM files. There is no way around this, and you are forced to trace through pure unassembled code showing absolute addresses -- to do this effectively will require a printout of the .LST file.

Note that the Turbo Debugger can trace source code and show symbols of .COM files. Microsoft have recently fixed this problem.

Here are the required switches:

```
MASM /ZI SOURCE , , , ;
LINK /CO SOURCE;
```

Note the commas -- these are optional, and tell MASM to produce .OBJ, .LST and .CRF output files.

To run CODEVIEW:

```
CV /S SOURCE[.COM] [arguments]
```

The source file does not require the .EXE extension specified, but the extension must be specified if the file is .COM type.

"arguments" are anything that your program expects on the command-tail.

"/S" optimises screen swapping.

Once inside CODEVIEW, you will probably become confused, so beforehand invest some time to learn how to use it. The user interface is typical of Microsoft -- part pull-down menus and part command-line -- a half-done job, much like Windows before they finally got it right with version 3.

Supplied with the CODEVIEW package is a tutorial disk -- this cannot be run from the hard disk, so if you can legally obtain a copy of it on floppy disk, do so, and run it from drive A:.

As a note on the side, you may be interested how the demo is achieved. It is an automated slideshow of what CODEVIEW does and how it works, that makes use of DOS's redirection symbols "<" and ">" to redirect keyboard input from the keyboard to a disk file.

ADVANCED DEBUGGING

HARDWARE DEBUGGERS:

Although debuggers are nice tools, still there will be occasions when you will be pulling your hair out. Some bugs are so elusive, and there are circumstances when the debugger can't trace, or can't detect the exact place of failure.

If your program is going off into never-never land, and the debugger is hung-up or otherwise hopeless, you may wonder just what the computer is doing, just where is it in memory, as it stares dumbly back at you -- if only you could press a magic button at that point, and the computer would be interrupted, even though completely crashed, and tell you exactly what it is doing and how it got to that point. Or maybe there is an intermittent fault, that won't happen when you want it to -- jump on the switch when it does happen, and you've captured the recent history leading up to the bug.

There is such a magic device -- it is called a "hardware debugger", and consists of a plug-in board (usually). This board has its own CPU and memory, so is always working, regardless of what the computer is doing. The hardware debugger quietly logs everything the PC is doing -- it may have up to 512K of RAM, to keep a complete history of what your PC has been up to.

At the point where your program crashes and you have been tearing your hair out, just push the magic button -- this consists of a cable from the hardware debugger, with a button on the end. Suddenly your computer will spring to life, as the debugger takes over, and on-screen you will see a debugging program much like TD or CV.

Using this program you will be able to view the complete history as recorded in the hardware debugger's RAM.

One of the most popular hardware debuggers is the Periscope.

DEBUGGING TSR's:

When you get onto the lesson on resident programs (TSR's) you will find it useful to refer back here. Ditto for device drivers. The following notes refer to TD version 1.0 specifically, and the principles apply to general debuggers. TD version 2.0 has special support for TSRs and isn't discussed here.

A resident program is a real problem for a conventional software debugger. A TSR consists of two portions -- an install and a runtime portion, but after loading the TSR with the debugger and executing or tracing the program, the debugger will only go through the install portion.

The install portion of a TSR typically will alter an interrupt vector, say the keyboard-handler, INT 16h, to point to the runtime portion, so whenever DOS or an application program calls INT 16h, control will go to the TSR runtime portion instead of to the BIOS routine.

It is possible to use the debugger to examine this vector -- the interrupt table is at the very start of memory -- INT 16h for example is a 4-byte entry at 0:58h.

Knowing where the runtime portion is located in memory, it is possible to change the debugger's CS:IP setting to that, but tracing from there may still be a problem, for a number of reasons:

The keyboard buffer does not have the correct character in it for "popping up" the TSR. The debugger itself may object, telling you that the program has terminated (since you have just executed the install portion).

A way around this latter problem is not to execute the install portion, but to siimply set CS:IP to the runtime portion and start tracing.

Still you will have the first problem mentioned above, and besides, you are not working in a true environment, since the install portion has not been executed.

This last method however can be used in many cases to locate faults, and is worth trying first. Note that the runtime portion will most likely first read the keyboard buffer to see if the correct "hot-key" has been pressed -- since there is nothing in the buffer, and you have no way of putting anything in while tracing (at least nothing straightforward with TD), you may have to jump over that portion of code without executing it (which again is awkward with TD -- will need to do it from the CPU-Window, Local-Menu, Set CS:IP).

here is a technique that I have tried with TD version 1.0, not
ocumented anywhere, that enables you to trace a TSR in its exact
perating environment. The principles should be applicable to other
ebuggers. Here goes:

. Load the TSR, from the DOS prompt: Example --

ROWSE \PROGS\FILE1.HTX

his could be any TSR, and the argument shown is that pertaining to
he particular TSR.

. Load Turbo Debugger, in protected-mode optimally, with any
rogram as a dummy: Example --

D386 -E128 -L -SC \GALAXY\GALAXY

he dummy program could be a wordprocessor, but be sure to include
he full path, even if the program is in DOS's path.

. The -L switch causes the CPU-Window to appear. <F5> will zoom
his to fill the screen, if it doesn't already. Use <TAB> to go to the
emory-dump pane, and then <ALT-F10> for Local-Menu, then
oTo 0:58h. Write down what this vector is -- remember that it will
e offset (IP) first, followed by segment (CS), and each of these will
ave the low-byte first.

. <TAB> to the Unassembly-Listing pane, pop-up Local-Menu with
ALT-F10>, GoTo the vector (example 1B06h:04E2h), and examine
hat code. Note that there are no symbols, so a source or .LST
rintout will be very helpful. If the runtime portion is entered from
NT 16h, most likely the code will start by calling the old INT-16h
nterrupt routine (in BIOS ROM) to test if a character is waiting in the
eyboard buffer. Move the cursor to beyond this, to just after the
orrect hot-key has been detected and the character has been unloaded
rom the buffer -- then press <F2> to set a breakpoint. DON'T set the
reakpoint earlier, as you won't be able to get out of the debugger to
un the program.

. Press <F9> to run the dummy program. The dummy program
hould appear, and you can start it up as normal. From within the
ummy, you can pop-up the TSR, and immediately control will revert
 the debugger, and you can then trace through the TSR.

SETTING UP A PROFESSIONAL ENVIRONMENT

Once we start to get into larger jobs, perhaps involving assembling, compiling and linking many modules, or a team effort, the system must be setup somewhat more rigorously than with a simple batch file. Many modern compilers are usually installed with various libraries and programs in different directories, so immediately we have the problem of sorting this out; the various compiler/s and linker/s must be able to find the various libraries etc. Also, the repetitive operations of the development cycle are awkward to handle with a simple batch file as the size of the job grows; instead we turn to the MAKE file. The MAKE file gives us some enormous advantages and can highly automate the cycle.

SETTING UP THE PATHS:

You should be familiar with DOS's PATH command, that specifies where DOS will look for a file if it can't find it in the current directory. Modern compilers, assemblers and linkers go a step beyond this, by using what is known as "environment variables" to specify paths. A compiler may access modules in a directory called INCLUDE, and a linker may access library modules in a directory called LIB. Often the main compiler, linker and utilities are in a directory called BIN. These names are typical, but the directories do not necessarily have these names.

The program that you are developing may be in an entirely different directory, and this will be the current directory that you will set DOS to while you are working on the program.

Below I have listed typical CONFIG.SYS and AUTOEXEC.BAT files. Notice the PATH command; it shows the way to the C compiler, linker, assembler, etc, in directory BIN, and also to a wordprocessor in directory WORD5. This is fine, but when you run the compiler, called CL (for example), say in the case of a C source file called SOURCE.C:

```
C:\CWORK\> CL SOURCE
```

The compiler may need to access INCLUDE modules that are specified in SOURCE.C. By default it looks first in the current directory, CWORK, and if not found will look at the environment variable INCLUDE for the path.

You specify environment variables using DOS's SET command; see the AUTOEXEC.BAT file below. Incidentally, to find out all the environment settings of your computer, just type SET <enter> on the DOS command-line.

Note that although C is being used as the example here, simply because the computer I'm now using is set up for C, the theory applies to any compiler or assembler.

After compiling and/or assembling, you will have one or more .OBJ files, and the next step is linking. One or more .OBJ modules can be linked together to produce a .EXE file, but note that LINK may need to link some library modules. By default LINK looks first in the current directory, then at the path specified by LIB.

See the example AUTOEXEC.BAT file:

Type "SET <enter>" to verify environment variables.

AUTOEXEC.BAT:

```
C:\DOS\share
PATH C:\C600\BIN;C:\WINDOWS;C:\;C:\DOS;C:\WORD5
C:\C600\BIN\mouse.com
PROMPT $P$G
numlock off
break on
verify on
set TEMP=C:\WINDOWS\TEMP
SET LIB=C:\C600\LIB
SET INCLUDE=C:\C600\INCLUDE
SET HELPFILES=C:\C600\HELP\*.HLP
SET INIT=C:\C600\INIT
```

To increase environment space, use "SHELL" in CONFIG.SYS.

DOS 3.3 defaults to 160 bytes of environment space, and the "/e:512" increases it to 512 bytes. The "SET" entries I made all added to the environment, exceeding the 160 bytes, which caused an "Out of environment space" message from DOS at boot-up.

CONFIG.SYS:

```
shell=command.com c:\ /e:512 /p
files= 30
BUFFERS=20
country=061
device=C:\C600\BIN\himem.sys
device=C:\C600\BIN\smartdrv.sys 768 256
```

MAKE FILES:

326

Setting up paths is only half the story. A MAKE file automates the development cycle, like a batch file but more powerful.

DOS comes with a program called MAKE.EXE, but most compilers & assemblers come with their own. Microsoft C version 6.00 has one called NMAKE. A vital note at this point -- your computer is likely to have two, even more MAKE.EXE's, in different directories -- it may be a disaster if the wrong one executes. To take care of this, make sure the PATH command specifies the search pattern in the required order -- searching starts from the left.

A MAKE file is a text file that you create using a text editor, just as for batch files. The MAKE file is executed by MAKE.EXE as shown here, where NMAKE.EXE is Microsoft's program and WINSOFT.MAK is my creation. It could be any name, and the extension is optional.

```
C:> NMAKE  WINSOFT.MAK
```

A broad generalisation is that a MAKE file has three parts. The first defines the macros. For the example below, wherever $(ASMFLAGS) is encountered, it gets replaced by what is to the right of the equals sign. Note that the name WINSOFT could also be a macro, so that the filename would only have to be typed in once.

```
#MAKE FILE STRUCTURE:
#macro...
ASMFLAGS = /DLMODEL=0 /DTC=0
 ......
#inference rule...
.asm.obj :
 MASM $(ASMFLAGS) $*;
  .....
#execution, based on inference rules...
WINSOFT.OBJ  :  WINSOFT.ASM
#no command follows above line.
  .....
#execution, without inference rules...
WINSOFT.EXE : WINSOFT.OBJ
 LINK /t WINSOFT.OBJ,WINSOFT,nul,LLIBCE.LIB;
#note a command follows target:dependencies line.
  .....
```

The second part is the inference rules. These define the operations to be performed, without actually doing them.

The first line specifies that we want our .ASM modules to be assembled to .OBJ modules, and the second line tells how to do it. "$*" is the MAKE file's terminology for referring to the .ASM file we are going to assemble -- we don't specify the actual filename yet, since it is possible that we may be assembling many

.ASM files. You could have inference rules for any other operations, such as compiling .C to .OBJ.

Finally we have the actual part of the MAKE file that executes. The format is;

```
target : dependencies
    [command]       #optional
```

Notice with WINSOFT.OBJ that no command-line follows. This causes LINK to use the previous inference rule. This is real convenient if we have lots of .ASM files to assemble -- for example if we had another file called DUMMY.ASM, we just add this line:

```
DUMMY.OBJ : DUMMY.ASM
```

Note that the target commences on column one, while the command-line, if present, commences with an indent.

The LINK operation does not make use of an inference rule, since the second [command] line is included -- inference rules are of use when multiple files are to be treated the same way, such as assembling many .ASM files to .OBJ files.

Now a most important point; the "dependencies" are the files that determine whether the "target" file is to be produced -- MAKE.EXE makes a note of the time & dates of all files it works upon, and will not perform any operation if the dependencies are unchanged from before. In other words, if you had to compile several modules, and you changed just one, MAKE will only recompile that one -- this is an enormous speedup in the development cycle, compared with using batch files.

A SIMPLE MAKE FILE:

The exercises in this book only need a simple MAKE file, should you want to experiment. To execute:

```
C:> MAKE makefilename.ext
```

I've put a macro in -- change this line to whatever filename you're currently working on. The second line is required by NMAKE only. No inference rules are used here, since we are not dealing with multiple modules. Of course you can put switches after MASM and LINK as required.

```
MYFILE = source
FINAL : $(MYFILE).exe #reqd by NMAKE
$(MYFILE).obj : $(MYFILE).asm
  masm $(MYFILE);
$(MYFILE).exe : $(MYFILE).obj
  link $(MYFILE);
```

WORKSHEET: ASSEMBLER

1.

Nothing difficult here; just put what you have learnt in this chapter into practice. Go through the complete exercise of writing a program, assembling, linking, and running it...

Example program source code *98*

Assembling the program *103*

2.

One thing about Assembly is its "basicness" --- no floating point numbers for example. For various number conversions you will need appropriate routines, of which there are plenty around. Example -- that of displaying or printing a binary number as its decimal equivalent, or more precisely as **ASCII** *370* decimal digits.
ASCII is what the screen and printer understand, so a binary number must be converted to **BCD** *59* digits, then each digit must be converted to ASCII.
Okay, here's my little routine---

```
;.....................................................
;data...
asciitbl db 10 dup(0)                          100
;..................................
bin2dec proc near                              99
;requires no. in DX:AX. returns 8-digit
;asciiz string in ASCIITBL...
 mov di,offset asciitbl                        100
 mov bx,di                                     47
 add di,8                                      53
 mov byte ptr [di],0                           47
 dec di
ssss:
 mov cx,10      ;divisor for conversion.
 div cx         ;quo-->AX, rem-->DX.           48
 add dl,30h     ;conv. to ascii.               47
sssss:
 mov [di],dl                                   34
 dec di                                        47
 mov dx,0 ;high bytes now 0 *assumption
 cmp ax,0                                      44
 jne ssss                                      32
 mov dl," "
 cmp bx,di      ;start of ASCIITBL             44
 jbe sssss                                     32
 ret                                           31
bin2dec endp                                   102
;.....................................................
```

Your job is to put this routine inside all the correct ASM directives for making a .COM program, and assemble & run it -- this routine is only a procedure, not a complete program. The program should start by putting a binary value into DX:AX then call BIN2DEC -- the simplest way to do this is with a couple of MOV instructions.. You could use DEBUG or some other debugger to have a look at its execution.

THINK
Are you sure you know what the above routine is doing? Do you know the difference between straight-binary numbers and BCD (Binary Coded Decimal)? If not 100% clear about this, go off and find out!

WARNING
The 32-bit binary value in DX:AX should not be above a certain value, else the program will abort.
This has been done deliberately, for some programming exercises later on.
To play safe you might like to start testing your program by putting zero into DX. If your program loads DX:AX with 245 decimal (for example), a run of the executable program should display "245" on the screen, confirming that it works.
Have a think about why there is a limit on the maximum value for DX:AX.

3.

The above program will be more useful if you can **display** the result. *58*
Write an additional module for the program, to display the ASCII-bcd value.

6

PC HARDWARE

Here's a quick view of the main hardware topics in this book:

Before proceeding with this Chapter, have you covered the background? Earlier chapters introduce various concepts that are built upon now, so it is worthwhile itemising these here -- ask yourself whether you have comprehended each of the following:

In Chapter One we had a vague overall look at the architecture of the CPU and the PC. If you need to refresh your memory on any of that, pop back.

In Chapters Three & Four we got onto console I/O. Again, go back for a look-see if necessary:

This brings us up-to-date. Now for this Chapter. Look at these in the order given:

VLSI CHIP-SETS

144

Throuhout this course you will find discussion on various interfaces and chips, and in some cases specific chip type-numbers are mentioned. Some chips specifically referred to are on the original IBM-PC, which is no longer made. This is not such a problem however, as later PC's always attempted to maintain compatibility with earlier machines. The actual chips used have changed with the models, generally becoming more integrated as technology advanced, but upward compatibility was maintained.

Thus what you will find is that some individual chips mentioned in this course, such as the 8253 Programmable Timer, and the 8255 programmable Peripheral Interface, still exist in recent models, but in an integrated form -- that is, more functions combined onto the one chip.

Many of these early chips are what we would call MSI -- Medium Scale Integration, graduating to LSI -- Large Scale Integration. Now we have VLSI -- Very Large Scale Integration.

The notes to follow, particularly on the ISA, EISA and MCA architectures, make reference to some of these more recent VLSI chips.

Should you require more detailed information than is provided here, the original and most precise documentation is of course Intel's own manuals:

Intel Peripherals manual, #296467
Intel Microprocessors manual, #230843

CPU (SYSTEM) BUS

It is essential at this point in the course to clarify the distinction between memory and I/O. It most helpful to have a mental picture of the hardware differences.

You saw back in **Chapter One** that the CPU has three major buses:

Address bus,
Data bus,
Control bus.

9

Now we must look at the control bus in more detail --- refer to Figure 6.1.

FIGURE 6.1
CPU bus, showing some of the control signals.

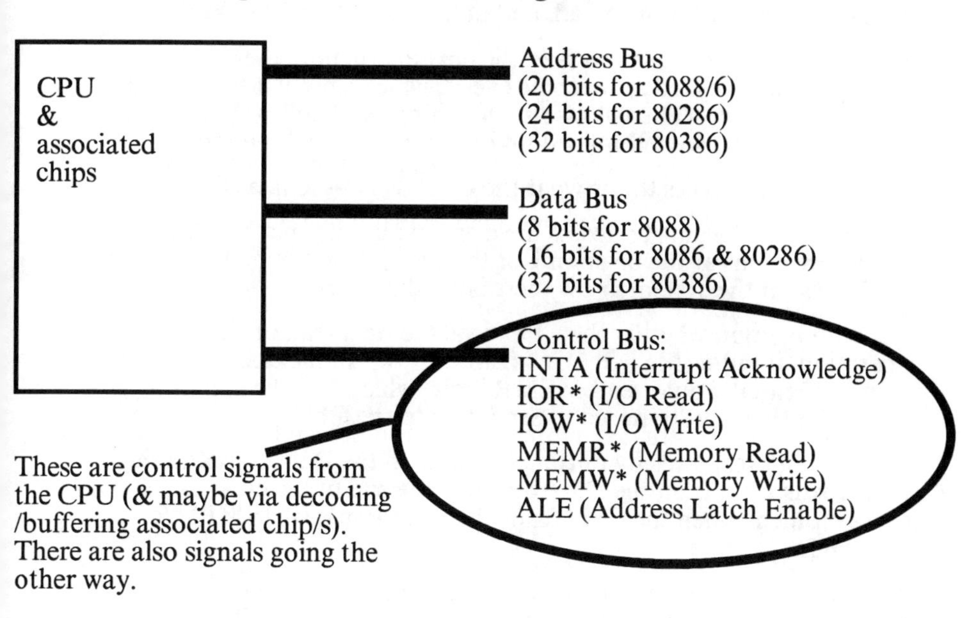

FIGURE 6.2
Generalised CPU machine cycle.

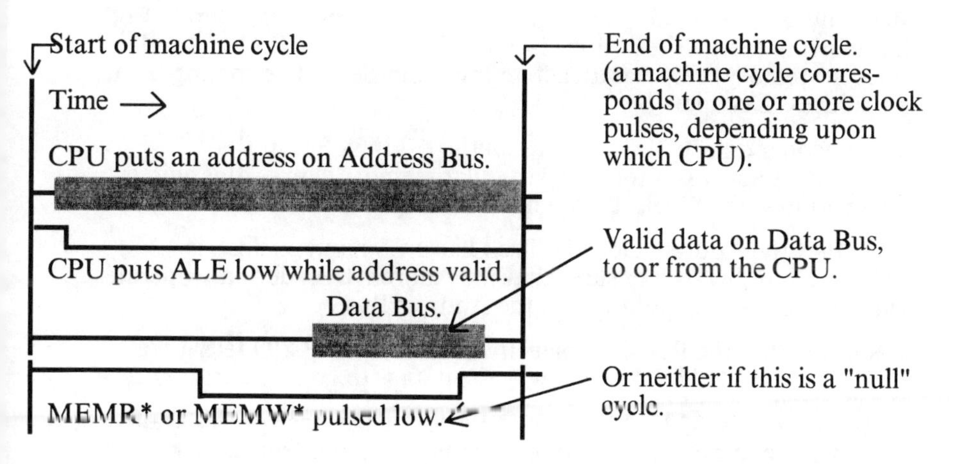

Perhaps you're a software person, and you really don't dig this kind of stuff--- fear not, it's not so bad, and in fact quite helpful to know.

For a memory access, say to read the next instruction, the CPU goes through what is called a "machine cycle", which simply means it reads or writes memory. There is also such a thing as a "null cycle", in which the CPU is doing something within itself for that clock-period.

For a memory-access this is what the CPU does --- look at Figure 6.2.

When the CPU wants to access the memory, it puts an address onto the Address Bus at the beginning of the cycle, then it puts ALE low to let the rest of the system know there is a valid address.

Depending upon whether the CPU wants to do a read or write operation, it pulses MEMR* or MEMW* low. In the case of memory-read it would send MEMR* low, which tells the memory chips that they are supposed to send data to the CPU.

The memory responds by putting the data on the Data-Bus, and the CPU reads what is on the Data Bus near the end of the cycle --- the exact moment when the CPU reads the Data Bus is when MEMR* goes high.

There is still a loose end to the above description. How does the memory determine which data to put on the Data Bus? The CPU is sending out an address, so is asking for the data at a particular memory location. This is what the circuitry looks like at the memory end --- refer to Figure 6.3.

Basically, a memory chip has a data-bus, an address-bus, Chip-Select input/s, and read/write control input/s. This example RAM (Random Access Memory) chip has an active-low Chip-Select line coming from an Address Decoder.

This decoder detects the presence on the Address Bus of the appropriate addresses for this particular memory chip --- this chip is being addressed, it "selects" the memory chip.

Note that the Address Decoder itself has a CS input --- ALE is connected to this --- it ensures that the Address Decoder only operates when there is a valid address on the Address Bus.

Assuming that the RAM is correctly addressed, the CPU tells it via MEMR* and MEMW* which way the data is to go.

Notice that only A17 - A19 go to the Address Decoder --- this is an example circuit only, and specific circuits may differ from this, but generally it is only necessary for some of the address lines to go to the decoder. This is because the memory chip resides at a range of addresses --- the lower-order address bits go directly to the chip, to select a particular memory byte.

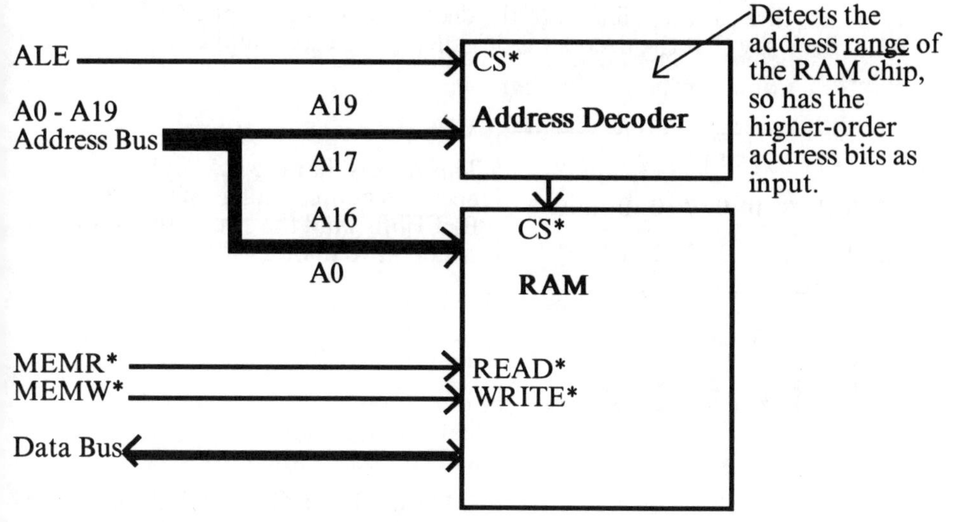

FIGURE 6.3
Interface, CPU to memory.

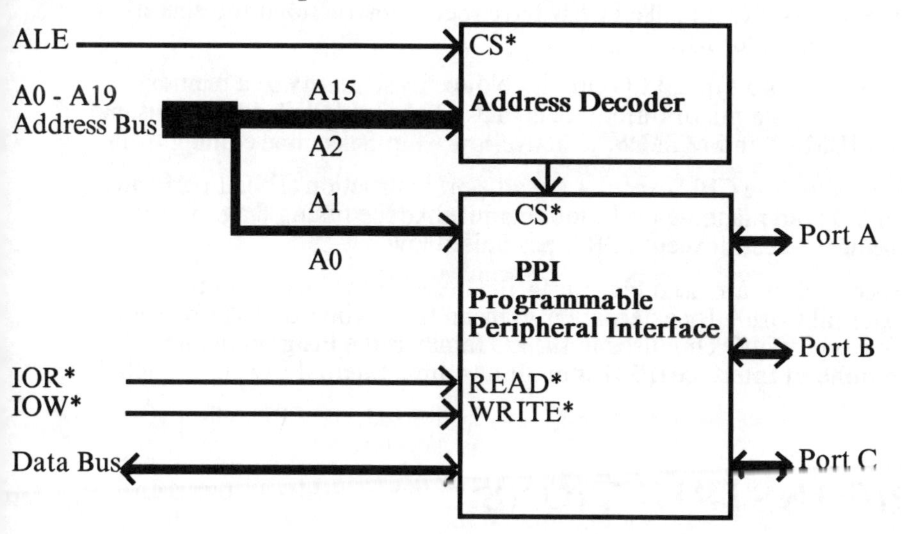

FIGURE 6.4
Interface, CPU to I/O port.

Get the idea? --- the higher address lines select the chip, while the lower lines select a particular location on that chip.

There are three address lines into the decoder in this example, A17 - A19. Let's say that the decoder is designed to detect an input of 101 binary---

19	18	17	16	15	14	13	12	11	...	0
1	0	1	0	0	0	0	0	0	...	0
1	0	1	1	1	1	1	1	1	...	1

This means that the RAM chip occupies address range A0000h to BFFFFh. And the size of the RAM would have to be 2^17 = 128K bytes.

I/O PORTS

If you peek back at the diagram of the **Control Bus** for the CPU, you will see that there are a couple of lines called IOR* and IOW*. These are for reading and writing I/O ports. Unlike some CPU's, such as the 6800 family, that do not distinguish between memory and I/O operations, the Intel '86 family have special instructions and special control lines for I/O.

130

Figure 6.4 is a typical I/O circuit. Notice its similarity to a memory interface --- a major difference is that IOR* and IOW* go to it, instead of MEMR* and MEMW*.

Whenever the CPU executes a read-port instruction (IN), it performs an I/O read machine-cycle, looking just like the timing diagram for memory access, except IOR* gets pulsed low.

Special chips are used for interfacing between the buses and the external world. By external I also mean the keyboard, disk drive, etc. One type of I/O chip used in the PC family is the Programmable Peripheral Interface (PPI) chip. It has three external I/O ports, each 8 bits.

I/O INSTRUCTIONS:

Although the address bus is used to select I/O ports, only A0 to A15 are used, so the address range is only 64K. With the I/O instructions, data is always via the AX register. The I/O port address must be

FIGURE 6.5
Keyboard Interface.

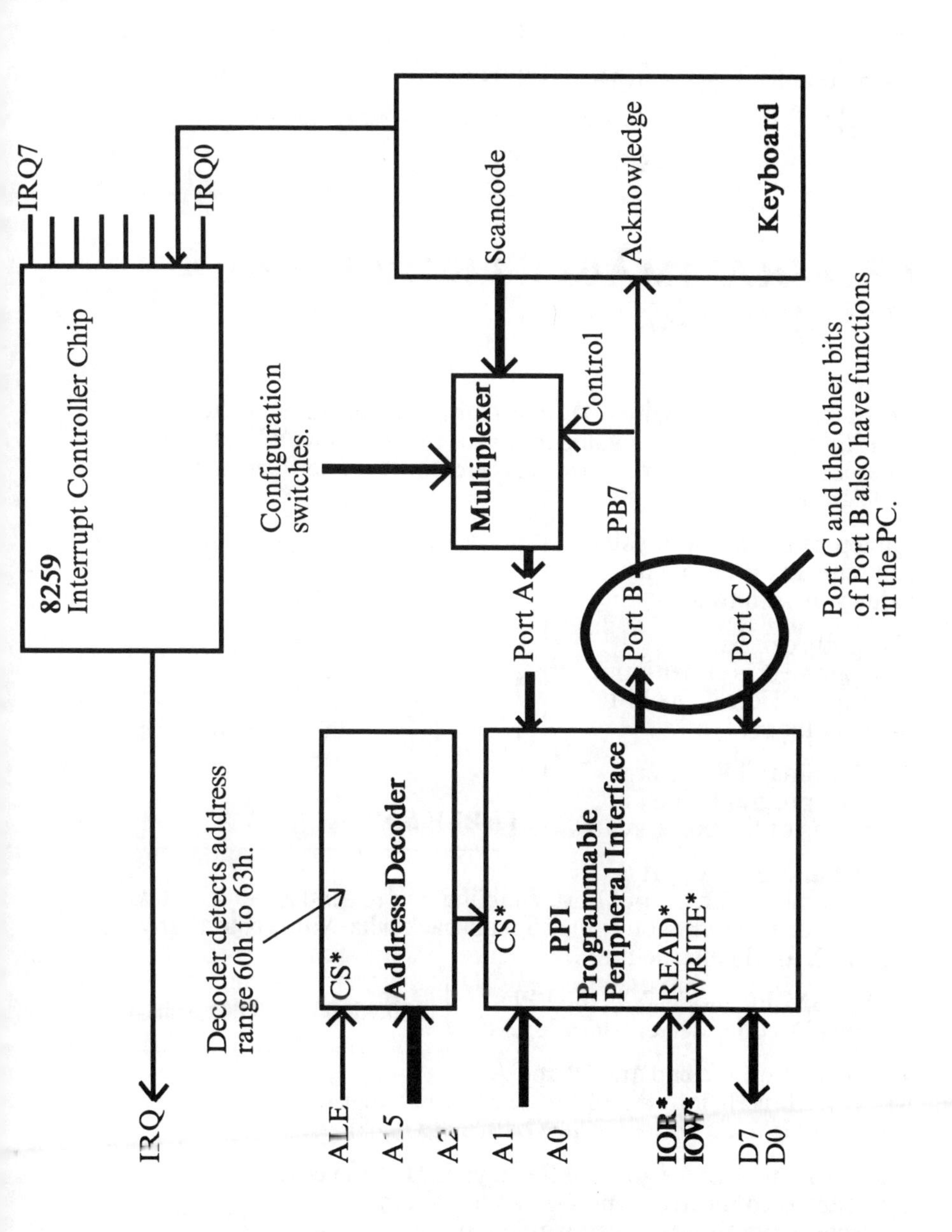

placed in DX before executing the I/O instruction if the address is over 256.

Examples:

```
IN AL,2Fh      ;A byte from port-address 2Fh loaded into AL.
IN AX,2Fh      ;Input a word from 2Fh to AX.
OUT 5,AL       ;Contents of AL written to port 5.
MOV DX,3FCh    ;Read a word from port
IN AX,DX       ;3FCh.
```

PROGRAMMABLE PERIPHERAL INTERFACE:

(With reference to Figure 6.4). Those three ports are each latched. That is, when you send a value to one of them, by an OUT instruction, it comes out of that port and stays there until you perform another OUT to that port.

Each port is 8 bits and you can send any 8-bit binary value you wish to it.

The ports can be programmed as either input or output. Here is the PPI's memory map:

A1	A0	REGISTER
0	0	Port A
0	1	Port B
1	0	Port C
1	1	Command Register.

TABLE 6.1

The Command Register is used for programming the directions of the ports.

Note that even if a port is programmed as an output port, enabling you to send a value to it with an OUT instruction, you can also read-back what you wrote at any time with an IN instruction.

In the IBM-PC model-XT, the PPI's Address Decoder detects the address:

0000 0000 0110 00xx binary.

The two x's on the end are A0 and A1, which go directly into the PPI to select which register. In hex, this corresponds to an address range of 0060 to 0063h.

Remember this, as we go onto the keyboard in the next section --- the keyboard is connected to port-A, so to read the character from the keyboard would require:

```
IN AL,60h
```

You see, we can bypass BIOS and DOS entirely, and talk directly to the hardware!

KEYBOARD HOUSEKEEPING

This section talks a little bit about interrupts in general, since interrupts are tied in with how the keyboard interfaces to the computer.

The topic of resident (TSR) programs is also related to keyboard handling -- this comes later, in Chapter Eight.

Select one of these:

HARDWARE DESCRIPTION:

(Refer to circuit of Figure 6.5). The keyboard scancode is routed via a multiplexer (MUX) to the Port-A on the **PPI** chip, when PB7=0. (If PB7=1, the configuration switches are routed to Port-A). The address of Port-A is 60h, and Port-B is 61h. The keyboard also generates an interrupt to the 8259 Interrupt Controller chip, causing INT09.

136

SCANCODES:

Each key generates a unique scancode and the keyboard outputs the scancode when the key is pressed and again when it is released (and of course generates an interrupt each time). The difference is determined by PA7=0 when pressed, and PA7=1 when released.

Note that it is the job of the BIOS routine **INT09** to convert the keyboard scancode to **ASCII**, and place it in the input buffer. *342* *370*

A small detail --- the keyboard interrupt goes into the IRQ1 input of the Interrupt Controller chip, hence to the CPU's interrupt input, IRQ.

Question--- how does the CPU know that a keyboard interrupt is "INT 9" (ie to look at the ninth entry of the interrupt table for the address of the keyboard-handler routine)?

Answer--- The CPU and the Interrupt Controller communicate automatically over the data-bus, and take care of this detail. INT-8 to INT-F correspond to IRQ0 to IRQ7.

KEYBOARD HOUSEKEEPING:

Normally a program accesses the keyboard via BIOS & DOS interrupts, which read ASCII characters from the buffer, but we can access the keyboard hardware directly. The program INT9.COM does this--- it is a TSR, so look at it a bit later, when we get onto that topic.

The code here shows the direct hardware response to a key-press;

Pulsing PB7 momentarily high is an acknowledge to the keyboard that the scancode has been read.

If you look into the INT-9 routine, contained in the BIOS ROM, you would see the code listed here somewhere within the routine.

```
in   al,60h    ;read scancode from PA.   134
push ax        ;save it.                 27
in   al,61h    ;read PB.
or   al,80h    ;set PB7=1                49
out  61h,al    ;    /                    134
and  al,7Fh    ;clear PB7.               49
out  61h,al    ;    /
pop  ax                                  27
```

INTERRUPT PROGRAMMING RULES

CPU INTERRUPT STEPS:

This is how the CPU responds to an interrupt:

1	CPU doing "whatever".
2	Interrupt occurs (hardware or software).
3	CPU clears **interrupt-enable flag** (ie disables interrupts).
4	Pushes current CS, IP, Flags onto **stack**.
5	CPU determines type-code and looks up Interrupt Address Table; loads CS:IP.
6	Commences execution at new CS:IP.

367

27

Note that the other registers are NOT altered, and if the interrupt routine changes them it must also restore them before exiting.

INTERRUPT ROUTINE HOUSEKEEPING:

Now let's look at the code skeleton of an interrupt routine....

Save all registers that will be changed within the routine, and restore before returning. However, CS, IP & Flags are already saved by the CPU when int. occurred so no problem with these.

Note a potential problem; if instructions in the int. routine implicitly reference their own stack or data segments, then DS or SS will need to be set to the correct value, as they will have whatever values they had before the int. occurred (which would be the calling program's data & stack area -- okay if the int. routine wants access to that area).

A typical format for an int. routine is:

```
int1:
....push all reg's used in routine....
push  cs     ;set ds=cs (if required).      27
pop   ds     ;    /
...
sti   ;OPTIONAL. Enables interrupts.        139
...
mov   al,20h ;end of interrupt to 8259.     64
out   20h,al ;    /                         134
....pop all reg's pushed at beginning..
iret                                        27
```

IRET will pop the original flags, CS and IP off the stack. (so do be careful to exit the routine with stack in the same state as when the routine was entered).

Note that STI can be anywhere in the routine -- it depends on whether we want another interrupt to occur during this one. (at the end of the routine IRET will pop the Flags, which will enable interrupts, so STI is optional).

Note that DS will be as it was before the interrupt -- an unknown quantity -- hence to access data defined in the same segment as CS, put DS=CS. Or set DS to wherever the data is located.

PC EXPANSION BUSES

INTRODUCTION

You have been through the lesson describing the CPU bus, which is the highway between the CPU and all other memory and I/O chips.

It consists of three components: address bus, data bus and control/status lines.

If you look under the lid of a PC, one thing most obvious is the plug-in cards. These are typically the following:

* **Display adaptor card** (usually with a parallel printer port as well), *77*
* **Multi-I/O card** (typically with two serial ports), *156*
* **Disk adaptor card** (usually drives up to 2 floppy-drives and 2 hard disks). *218*

Some PC's will have part of this on the motherboard rather than as plug-in cards.

Also are other boards available, such as a modem, for communications over the telephone line, or a Fax card.

The socket into which these boards plug is basically an extention of the CPU bus, with address, data and control lines, but usually it is in a somewhat modified form.

These notes focus on the IBM-family of PC's, commencing with the XT model, AT model, and PS/2. Each of these has a different expansion bus:

XT	ISA,8-bit (Industry Standard Architecture)
AT	ISA,16-bit (" " ")
PS/2	MCA,8/16/32-bit (Micro Channel Architec)

Most PS/2's and PS/2-compatibles use the MCA bus, while most PC-compatibles use the ISA bus. Note that IBM do make some PS/2 machines with the 16-bit ISA bus, not because they want to, but due to demand.

Just about every new plug-in board that hits the market is for the 16-bit ISA bus these days -- most manufacturers have the attitude of aiming for the biggest market first, and maybe bring out an MCA version later. The pages of ads in popular journals are nearly all for 8 and 16 bit ISA cards. This is where the market is.

Some recent top-end PC-compatibles have an extended version of ISA, called EISA (Extended Industry Standard Architecture) -- which has a 32-bit data bus. There are boards for this architecture, but a limited range at the moment -- however EISA has one important feature going for it, that gives it an incredible edge over MCA:

It is interesting to note that an 8-bit ISA card can be plugged into a 16-bit ISA bus or an EISA bus, and will still work. Also a 16-bit ISA card will work in an EISA bus.

MCA cards on the other hand will only work in an MCA bus.

Don't underestimate this -- all those hundreds of millions of dollars invested in plug-in cards need not be thrown away when upgrading to an EISA system. In some cases there's not much point in keeping the old ISA card, as in the case of a hard-disk interface board -- unless you want to live with a small slow drive on a blazingly fast 386 or 486 system. Ditto with an 8-bit display card -- it will slow down screen updates.

There is a good reason for keeping an 8-bit MDA card, and multi-I/O, modem, plus a host of others, when upgrading.

ISA

Early PC's use an **8088 CPU**, which, despite advertisements, is only an 8-bit CPU, since that figure is based on the size of the data bus. Hence the ISA bus also has only an 8-bit data bus.

Some PC-compatibles have an 8086 CPU, which internally is identical to an 8088, but has an external 16-bit data bus. As far as I am aware, these machines still have only an 8-bit ISA bus.

The advent of the AT-model, with 80286 CPU having a 16-bit data bus, saw the introduction of the ISA bus with a 16-bit data bus.

So that 8-bit cards would still work, the older connector was retained, but a second connector was placed next to it, that the 16-bit cards would use -- refer to Figure 6.6.

8-BIT ISA SIGNALS:

130

a0-a19	20-bit address bus.
d0-d7	8-bit data bus.
ale	Address Latch Enable.
1rq2-7	Interrupt Request lines, go to interrupt handler chip.
drq1-2	
dack1*-3	DMA request and ack
iochrdy	tells CPU make wait states
ior*	
iow*	i/o read/write control.
smemr*	
smemw*	Mem. read/write control.
osc	14.31818Mhz clock pulses.
clock	Bus clock signal (4.77Mhz on original PC's).
aen,tc	Used by DMA controller.
iochchk*	tells CPU parity / error.
resetdrv	signals PC being reset.

FIGURE 6.6
ISA expansion bus.

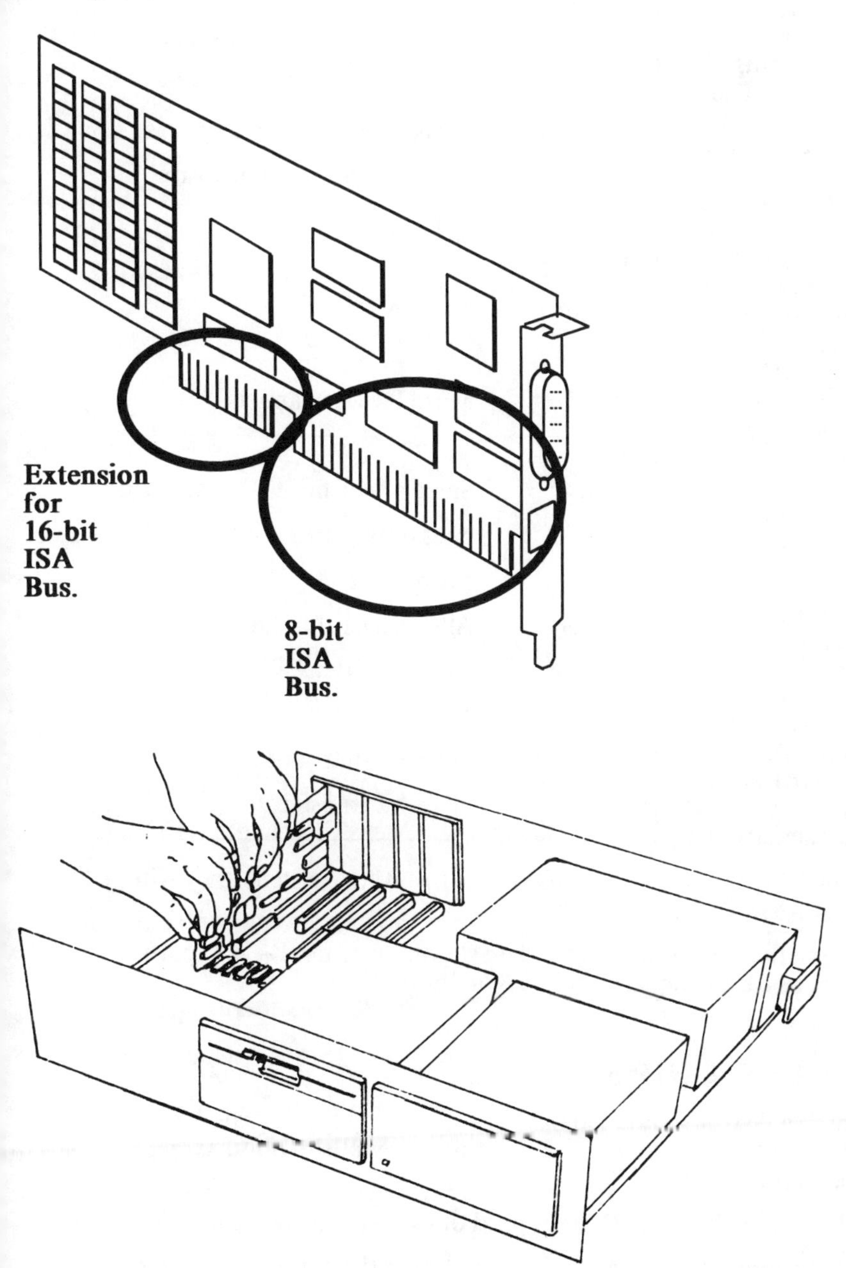

This figure (6.6) shows how the two connectors are physically arranged -- end-to-end. The top one is the 8-bit ISA connector, while the bottom one is the extension to allow 16-bit cards to plug in. Each connector has two rows of metal pads on each side -- the card is a printed circuit with gold-plated "fingers" on both sides of the card, so that when the card is inserted into the connector the fingers meet the pads.

Of the 8-bit ISA signals, most of these signals have a direction to the cards, but some go back to the PC motherboard, such as the irq and io-ch-rdy signals.

16-BIT ISA SIGNALS:

d8-15	Extends data bus to 16 bits.
sbhe*	System Bus High Enable, tells cards when data on data bus.
irq10-15	The AT has extra hardware interrupt lines.
drq0	
dack0*	
drq5-7	
dack5-7*	More DMA channels.
memr*	
memw*	Same as smemr/w --those earlier ones only active if within 1M address range.
master	Allows a card to take over control of the AT.
memcs16*	
i/ocs16*	Tells PC that card is capable of 16-bit transfers.

Although 8-bit cards will work okay in a 16-bit ISA system, they will not run quite so fast as 16-bit cards.

This is something to be aware of when shopping around -- a display adaptor card for example, could be 8 or 16-bit.

82230/1 VLSI CHIP SET:

Modern '286, '386SX and '386 based PC's use highly integrated chip-sets, combining many of the functions previously found as separate chips.

The 82335, 82230 and 82231 are typical of this -- refer to Figure 6.7.

Some of the individual chips mentioned during the course, such as the 8259 (interrupt controller) are contained within this chipset. This

FIGURE 6.7
ISA VLSI Chip-Set.

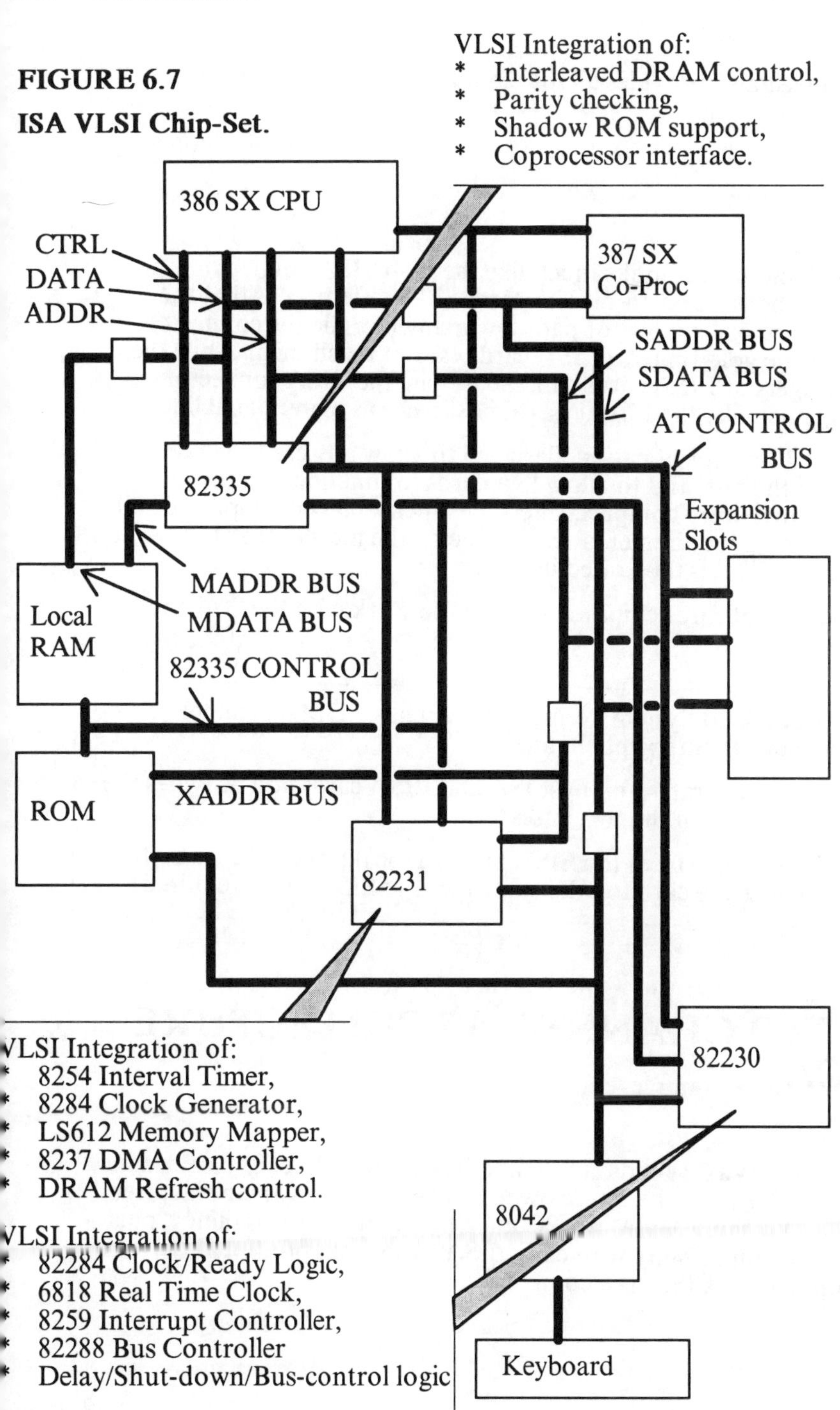

VLSI chipset also provides all the circuitry to drive the ISA bus.

EISA

The EISA connector looks much like the 16-bit ISA connector, and will accept both 8 and 16-bit ISA cards. The difference is that the EISA connector has rows of pads lower down inside the connector, such that the gold fingers of ISA cards cannot reach them, while the longer fingers of EISA cards can. So despite the EISA connector looking much like the ISA, it has almost twice as many signal lines.

EISA is a 32-bit specification, designed to allow any card to take control of the bus, and to allow ISA cards to function. As the specification is very complex, Intel developed a chip set to provide all the interfacing requirements, thus reducing the motherboard chip-count. This is illustrated in Figure 6.8.

The basic set of three chips are designed to work with the '386 and '486:

1. The Integrated System Peripheral (ISP) has 7 DMA channels, 5 timers, and 16 interrupt channels.
2. The EBC arbitrates amongst ISA and EISA cards and provides the interface between the two buses.
3. The BMIC interfaces the EISA bus to a local bus on the card. It also enables the card to take control of the EISA bus if required.

MICRO CHANNEL ARCHITECTURE (MCA)

MCA also has a 32-bit data bus, and has a similar level of performance to EISA. It is an architecture owned by IBM, and any manufacturer wishing to include MCA in a PC must licence it. It is this factor, plus MCA's incompatibility with earlier ISA cards, that prompted development of EISA as a competitor.

FIGURE 6.8

EISA VLSI Chip-set.

All chips trademark Intel.

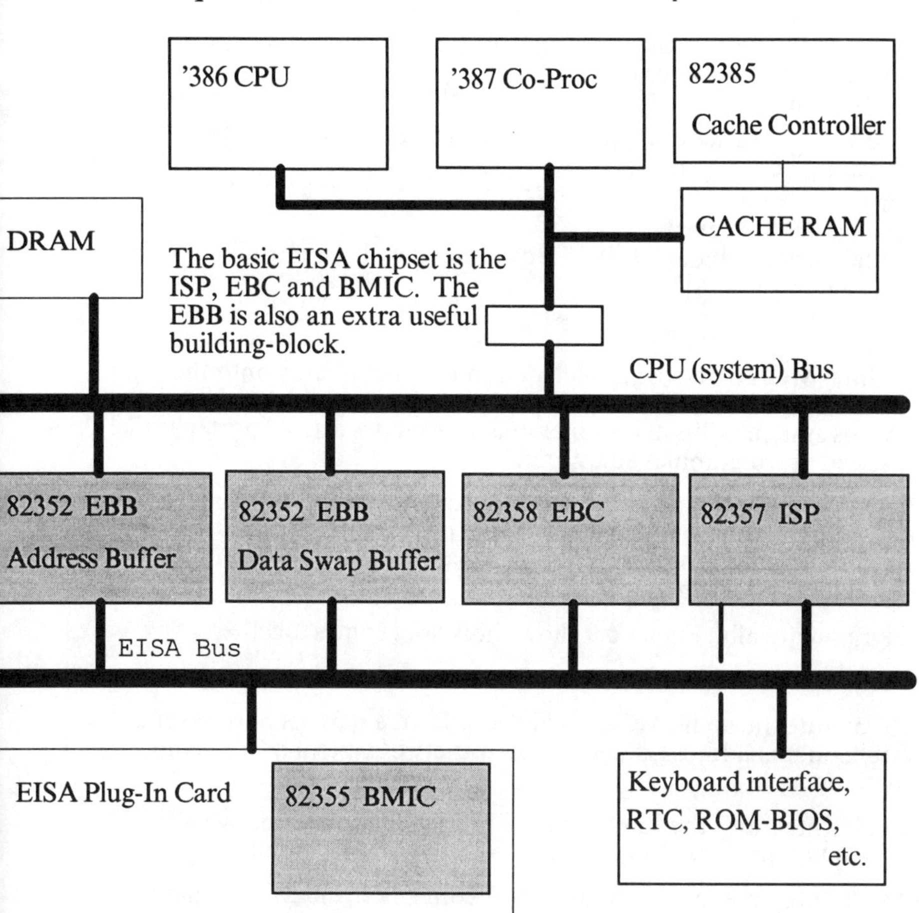

The 16-bit ISA bus provides only very crude "multimastering", meaning the ability to have multiple CPU cards, in which any one can take control -- they must be able to interrupt each other to achieve this. The EISA design implements multimastering very well, though we are groping ahead somewhat to try and think of applications for it. The ISA bus has intelligent I/O and secondary-processor cards that do very well without true multimastering.

The other great feature of EISA, compared with ISA, is the auto-configuring, meaning the elimination of flipping address-switches on the cards.

Intel manufactures a seven-chip set for MCA:

82303	Local I/O Support,
82304	Local I/O Support,
82307	DMA/CACP Controller,
82308	Micro Channel Bus Controller,
82309	Address Bus Controller,
82077	Floppy Disk Controller.

The 82307-9 are the three chips directly responsible for interfacing the CPU-bus to the MCA-bus.

For detailed information on MCA (also ISA and EISA), refer to the Intel "Peripherals" technical manual, order number 296467. However a very brief introduction will suffice here:

The Intel MCA chip-set has included some functionality onto the motherboard that would normally be placed on adaptor cards with the ISA-bus system. This extra functionality includes a serial port, parallel port, and video graphics adaptor.

The MCA bus is defined to support an "open architecture" (Intel's words, not mine) providing Multi-Master capability, Multi-Device arbitration with fairness, arbitration capability and easy configurability of the total system.

Diagrammatically, Figure 6.9 shows how it all comes together.

Briefly, here is the description of what each chip does:

82303: Integrates the MCA Card Setup Port, a parallel port, several peripheral bus-address latches, and a variety of system board setup functions.

82304: Integrates the 82306 Local Channel Support chip, two 8259 Interrupt controllers, and a wide assortment of TTL circuitry.

82307: Integrates a 16-channel DMA controller, and Micro Channel DMA Arbitration..

82308: The Data Bus Controller, complimentary to the 82309, controlling all 8, 16 or 32-bit data transfers.

82309: The Address Bus Controller, complimentary to the 82308, provides all address decoding, plus support for shadow ROM, and DRAM refresh.

FIGURE 6.9

MCA Chip-set.

All chips trademark Intel.

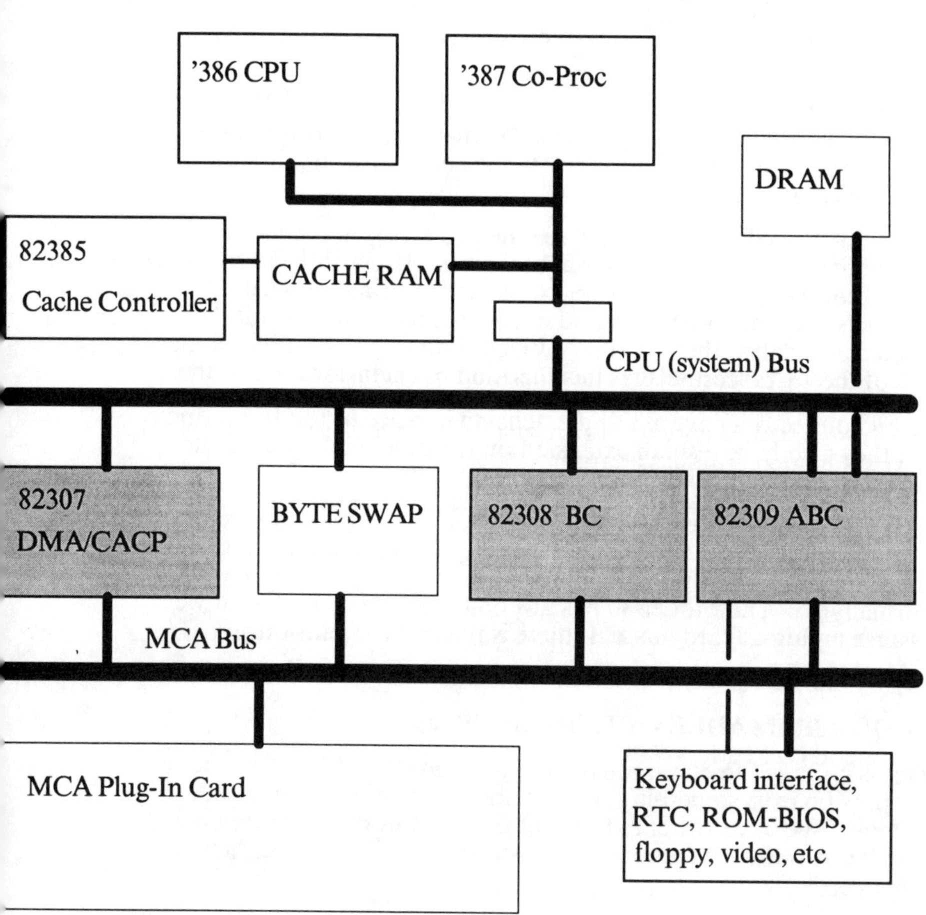

I have lumped together a whole pile of functions into one box -- various I/O interfaces on the motherboard are handled by special chips, such as the 82305 LIO, 82077 FDC, and 8742 keyboard controller. It is interesting to note that PS/2's put the VGA and floppy controllers on the motherboard, which of course does lock you into a fixed configuration.

Like the EISA, MCA has multimastering and auto-configuring.

MCA CONNECTORS:

MCA is normally thought of as being a 32-bit bus, however it was designed to handle data-buses of 8 and 16 bits as well, with the 82307 arbitrating.

Since the 286 CPU has a 16-bit data bus, the IBM model-50 has 16-bit MCA slots. The model-80, being a 386 machine, has three 32-bit slots and also four 16-bit MCA slots. So, the connectors are different, just as is the case with 8 & 16-bit ISA.

If you look inside a PS/2, you'll see the two types of connectors (386 machines). The 32-bit slot is longer than the 16-bit slot. Each 16-bit connector has a short extension-connector to bring it up from 8 bits to 16 bits (see Figure 6.10). The other end can have another kind of extension -- called the "Auxiliary Video Extension" -- on the Model-80, one of the 16-bit connectors has this kind of extension.

32-bit connectors have a 32-bit extension in place of the 16-bit one, but they also have a small extension on the other end -- called the "Matched Memory Extension".

Basically, the Matched Memory Extension allows plug-in memory cards to run with zero wait-states. There is a speed advantage to using the 32-bit slots for plug-in memory cards, so this is where they would normally go. The Model-80 has 2M on the motherboard, so if we assume a plug-in card has 8M, there is plenty of expansion left.

PROGRAMMABLE OPTION SELECT:

This is intended to eliminate the use of jumpers and DIP switches on adaptor boards, something that we are very familiar with in ISA systems. We have switches to select port addresses, interrupt-channels and DMA (Direct Memory Access)-channels, to avoid conflicts with other cards.

With MCA each card is addressed using a common block of eight I/O addresses. Each adaptor supplies a unique 2-byte identification code, and the MCA controlling circuitry looks up a table that identifies what kind of adaptor it is. The card can be told what I/O addresses and channels it can use. This even applies to ROM on the adaptor -- it can be located where there is no conflict.

BUS ARBITRATION:

Normally we think of the central CPU as being in control of everything, however it is possible for other devices to take over control of the system. DMA is an example of this -- it is present in even the

FIGURE 6.10

MCA Connectors.

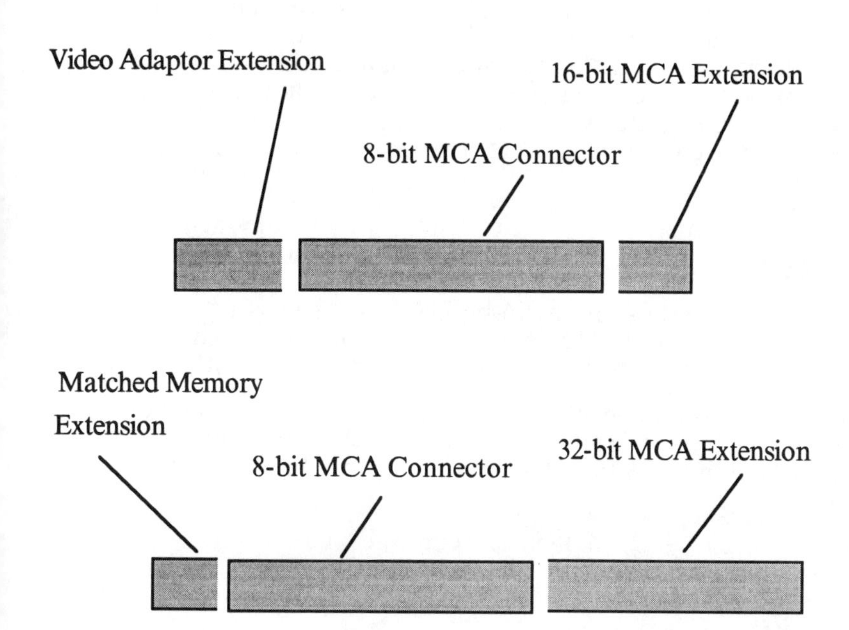

You can see from the above diagram that MCA is not just one connector, but a combination. Thus there is a certain degree of upward compatibility for MCA cards. But it's a pity that they had to dump the ISA bus -- though note that about half of the latest models of the PS/2 range are now offered with the 16-bit ISA bus. This was done due to market pressure, but IBM have stopped short of offering the EISA bus, since it is not an IBM-developed standard and is the arch enemy of their 32-bit MCA system.

It will be very interesting to watch over the next few years to see who wins the 32-bit expansion bus battle! Most likely both will hang in there, with a majority of systems being EISA -- since EISA has clear advantages (takes ISA cards, no licencing fees to IBM, etc).

earliest PC's, and is a chip that signals the CPU when it wants to take over, by a special request pin to the CPU-chip, and the CPU responds by going to sleep. The DMA chip can then transfer data to and from memory as fast as memory is capable, which is may be faster than transfers under program control of the CPU.

MCA supports eight DMA channels, but also has provision for any plug-in card to take over -- this could be another CPU. Some possibilities are digital signal processing CPUs and RISC CPUs, that offer enormous speed for their intended types of applications. Many of these plug-in CPUs are available, both for the MCA and ISA buses, but MCA has the edge in arbitrating between these different controllers.

INTERRUPTS:

These are similar to those on the 16-bit ISA bus. There is a functionally-equivalent 8259 chip or rather two of them, to give up to 15 interrupt requests, plus the Non-Maskable Interrupt (NMI).

A useful point about these interrupt lines is that on ISA systems you could only switch one adaptor card onto a particular interrupt channel. But with MCA the interrupt channels can be shared by many adaptors.

7

PARALLEL & SERIAL INTERFACES

"Parallel" interface can have a general meaning, however in this Chapter I cover only the parallel "Centronics" interface used for printers, since this interface is found on all PC's. Printers can also have serial interfaces, notably some laser printers (and other external devices such as mouse and modem communicate via the serial interface). Thus I found it convenient to group the parallel and serial interfaces into the one chapter.

Note that whenever I refer to the printer interface I mean the parallel interface, unless specifically stated otherwise.

THE PRINTER INTERFACE

Select one of these...

INTRODUCTION:

Have a look on the back of any PC and you'll find connectors marked "Printer", "Parallel" or "Centronics". These terms mean the same thing.

The printer interface is usually a parallel one, meaning that the 8-bit ASCII code goes to the printer over 8 wires.

The connector on the PC is usually 25 pins, called a DB-25 connector.

Note that the serial connectors (to modem, mouse or maybe a printer) are also usually a DB-25, (or 9) though of opposite polarity so that you don't accidentally plug the printer cable into a serial connector.

The printer-end of the parallel cable has what is called a Centronics connector, 36 pins, which you will be able to easily distinguish from the DB-25 type at the PC-end.

Obviously, with 25 pins and only an 8-bit ASCII code to transfer, there are lots of extra pins. Some of these are control signals to the printer, and some are status signals coming back from the printer.

There are appropriate registers in the printer-interface for this -- one status-register and one control-register -- you have direct hardware access to these ports, using **IN & OUT** instructions or you can be shielded from the hardware by programming the printer interface via **BIOS services**.

136

155

BIOS DATA AREA:

Below is the nitty-gritty detail of how the printer interface works and how the operating system and programs interact with it....

At start-up, BIOS checks out the hardware configuration of the system. On the IBM-PC, BIOS looks to see if there is a printer adaptor at port address 3BCh (on the mono display card maybe), then it looks at port 378h, then 278h.

If found, and IN THE ORDER FOUND, these addresses are placed in the **BIOS data area** in low RAM. This area is at memory address 0000:0400h to 0000:0600h.

0400h-0407h holds port addresses of up to 4 serial devices, followed by 0408h-040Eh which holds the port addresses of the printer adaptors.

ADDR	CONTENT
400	com1
402	com2
404	com3
406	com4
408	lpt1
40A	lpt2
40C	lpt3
410	equipment list

TABLE 7.1

9

0410h contains the equipment list, that is returned by INT11h, which contains, amongst other things, the number of printer-adaptors found by BIOS.

0408h holds the port-address of what DOS refers to as **LPT1**, while 040Ah holds LPT2 (or 0) and 040Ch holds LPT3 (or 0). It is important to understand this.

275

These are the various combinations of adaptors --

ADDRESS	CONTENTS								LOGICAL
0:0408	3BC	378	278	3BC	3BC	3BC	378	0	lpt1
0:040A	378	278	0	378	278	0	0	0	lpt2
0:040C	278	0	0	0	0	0	0	0	lpt3

TABLE 7.2

Only one of these columns is valid. So, 408 & 409 contain the 16-bit port address of LPT1, 40A & 40B contain LPT2, and 40C & 40D contain LPT3. But the port address is the first port only of the referenced printer interface. Obviously the interface has more than one port -- you would logically expect an output port, a status port and a control port -- and that is exactly what you get -- look at Figure 7.1.

Since the BIOS only looks for, and only records the address of, up to three printers, then that is our limit. There are a number of ramifications to this, one being that you should pay some attention to the DIP switches on the printer adaptor card when using more than one printer. These switches select which of the three port-address-ranges the adaptor is to reside at, and if there is only one printer adaptor it doesn't matter how the switches are set. From Table 7.2 you can see that the BIOS will record it as LPT1.

However if there are two adaptors, the one with the higher address will be recorded as LPT1, and the other as LPT2.

BIOS & DOS PRINTER SERVICES:

BIOS **INT17h** accesses the printer, and a value must be supplied in DX (0,1 or 2) to specify LPT1, LPT2, or LPT3. But, the DOS **INT21h/function5** accesses the default printer, which is normally

346
350

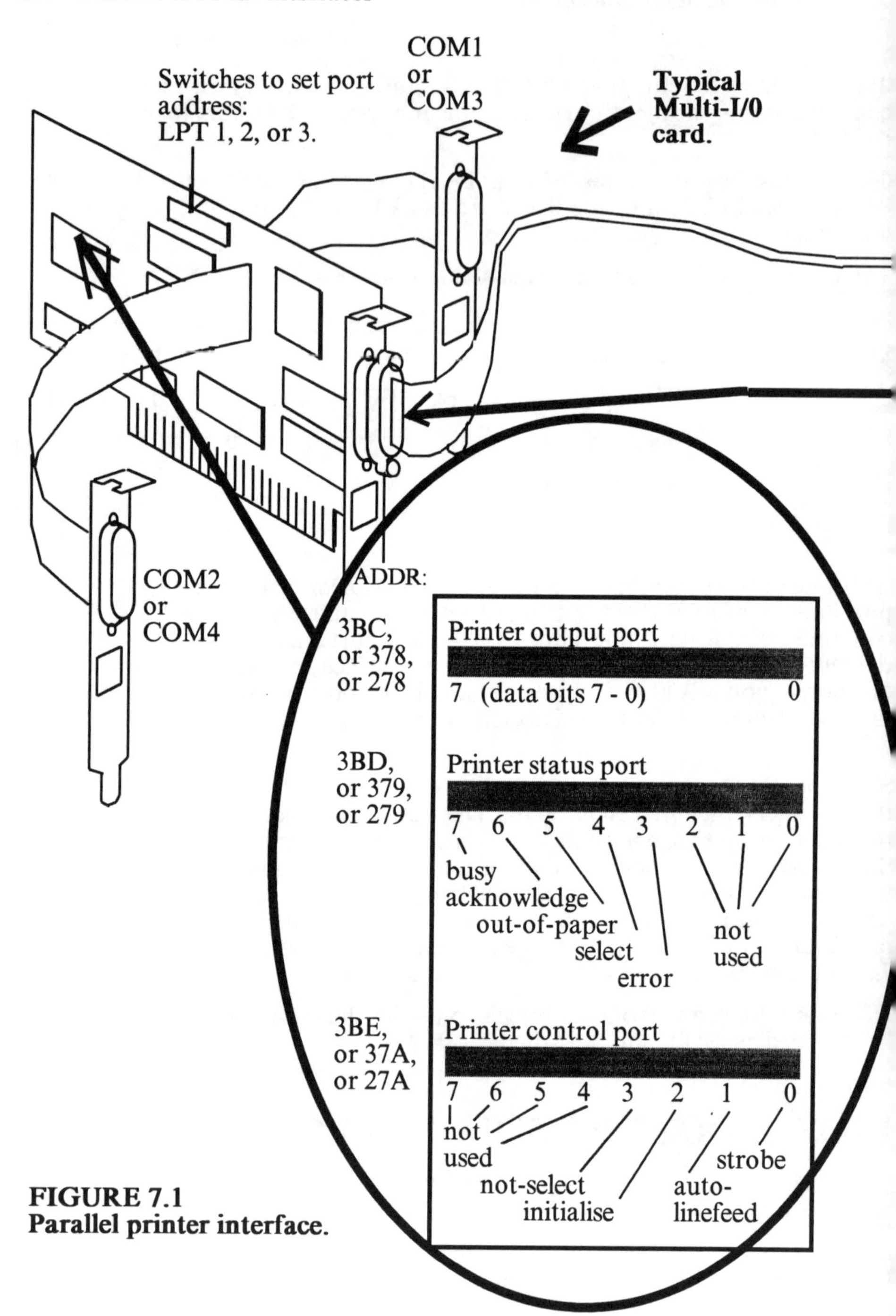

FIGURE 7.1
Parallel printer interface.

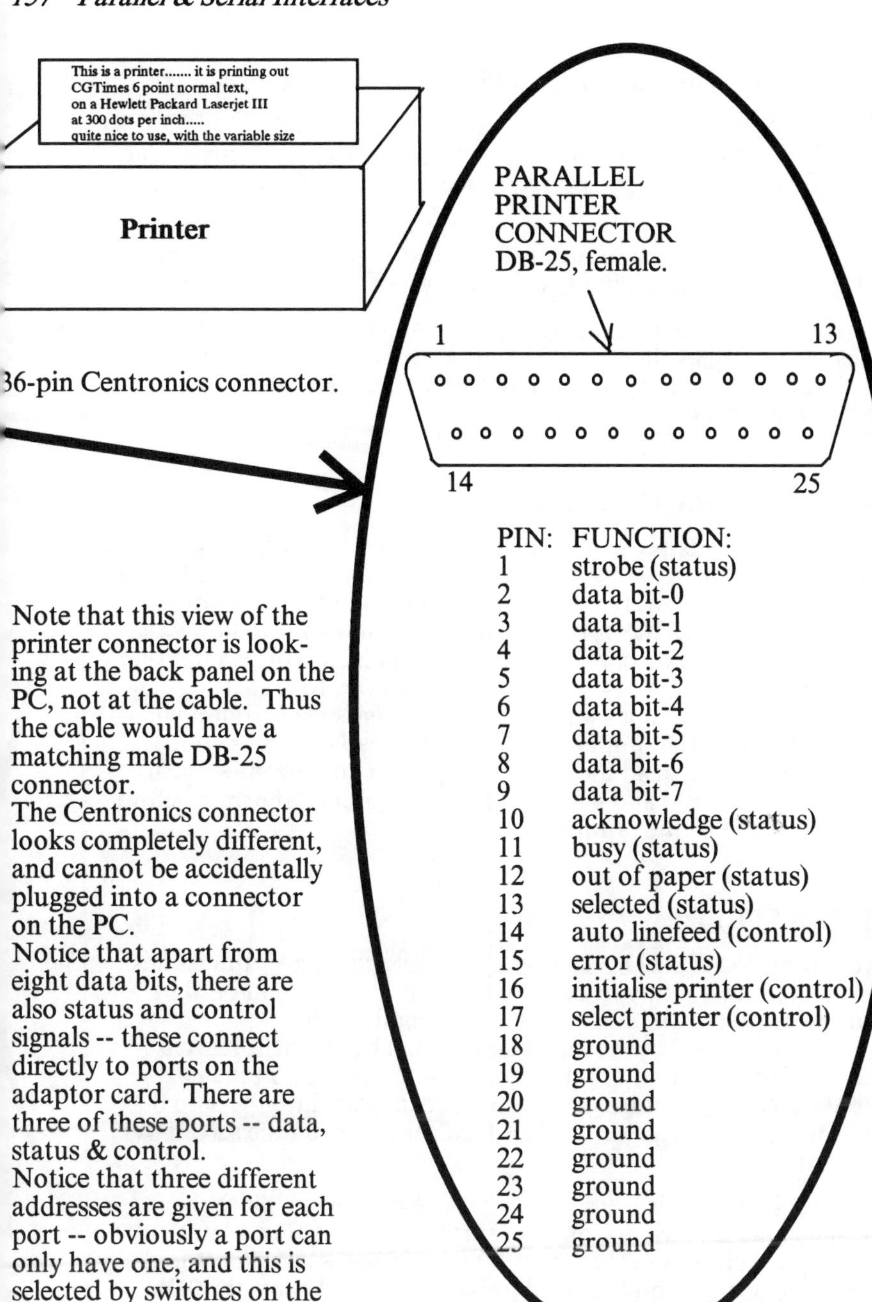

Note that this view of the printer connector is looking at the back panel on the PC, not at the cable. Thus the cable would have a matching male DB-25 connector.
The Centronics connector looks completely different, and cannot be accidentally plugged into a connector on the PC.
Notice that apart from eight data bits, there are also status and control signals -- these connect directly to ports on the adaptor card. There are three of these ports -- data, status & control.
Notice that three different addresses are given for each port -- obviously a port can only have one, and this is selected by switches on the card.

LPT1, but can be changed by DOS's MODE command to LPT2 or LPT3.

Some application programs only access the printer whose address is at 0:0408, that is, LPT1, either by directly accessing the adaptor's registers, or by INT17h.

Even DOS's mode command may not succeed in redirecting output from these programs to anything other than LPT1.

Solution -- swap the printer port-addresses in the **BIOS data area**: whatever is in 0:0408 will be treated by the application program as LPT1. A small utility program can do this, and in fact this is looked into in the worksheet.

154

PRINTER STATUS TESTING:

If you look at the details for **INT 17h** you will see that it has a service to return status information -- this is the same information as available directly in the status port, that could be read by an IN instruction. The advantage of the BIOS service is that you don't have to know the actual port address. You can find out such details as is the printer out of paper, on or off-line, busy, etc. The BIOS service to send a character to the printer does wait until the printer is ready, but it will hang the program if the printer never becomes ready. So it is good practice to specifically read the status and put up an error message if the printer is not ready, and give the user the option of aborting before sending characters to the printer.

346

AUTO-LINEFEED:

A useful point: **ASCII** 0Dh is a carriage-return character, and 0Ah is a line-feed character, but you don't necessarily have to send both of them to the printer at the end of a line. Normally with a wordprocessor the end of the line is determined by the right margin and the wordprocessor automatically continues the text on the next line -- but no carriage-return or line-feed are inserted into the actual file -- it is a "soft" carriage-return/line-feed generated on the screen by the software.

368

On the other hand, while using a wordprocessor you can hit the <enter> key and that will produce a "hard" carriage-return. The <enter> key generates the character 0Dh, but what is actually stored in the text-file depends on the word processor -- maybe just the 0Dh, or maybe both 0Dh and 0Ah characters are stored.

If you are using a programmer's text editor, or a general wordprocessor that can save a file as "ASCII only", the end of every line will have a hard carriage-return inserted, usually both characters 0Dh and 0Ah.

If you were writing a program that read a text file from disk and then sent it to the printer, you would usually send both CR and LF, though they may not be in the original file. The back of every printer has a set of DIP switches, and one of these turns "auto-linefeed" on or off. If off, which is the default setting usually, then send both CR & LF.

8-BIT VERSUS 7-BIT ASCII:

Some early dot-matrix printers only understood 7-bit ASCII, that is only the characters from 0 to 127 decimal. If you sent say 255, its eighth bit would be treated as zero which means that the printer would print character 127. Not very nice. Some antique software actually relies upon this, so to provide compatibility most modern dot-matrix printers have a DIP switch to select between 7-bit or 8-bit ASCII.

Of the 8-bit codes, there are various **character sets**. The most common for the PC is the standard IBM graphics character set.

370

SERIAL INTERFACE

On the back of your computer you should find at least one "serial" connector --- this provides what is technically referred to as the RS232 communication standard, and the connector itself is called a DB25 connector, with 25 pins, or in some cases a DB9 with 9 pins.

COM1-4:

I have already discussed how the **BIOS looks at the port-addresses** to ascertain which parallel and serial devices are connected. There can be up to four serial interfaces, COM1, COM2, COM3 and COM4, though in practice only two are used. There is a problem here -- if you look back to **Chapter Three** you'll see that there are INT 0Bh and INT 0Ch dedicated to the serial interfaces -- only two. INT 0Bh connects to COM2 and COM4, while INT 0Ch connects to COM1 and COM3. When a character comes in on a serial line and is ready inside the interface circuitry, to be read by the computer, the interface is capable of generating an interrupt. This works on the same principle as the keyboard interface, in which characters can be read-in asynchronously to whatever application is running. Perhaps the interrupt routine could put them into a buffer for later access by the application.

154

64

However unlike the **keyboard system**, serial interrupt handling is not an inbuilt part of BIOS or DOS -- it is entirely up to the application to hook into the interrupt vector table to perform interrupt handling. This is getting a bit out of our depth at this point -- modifying the interrupt vector table is discussed in depth in the chapter on resident programs.

137

Specific applications and device drivers will utilise the interrupt capability of the serial interface, but that is where the problem arises. Since COM1 & COM3, and COM 2 & COM4 share interrupt lines, there is a potential clash. In practice we are limited to two serial interfaces.

THE INTERFACE:

Inside the PC is a special I/O chip called a UART (Universal Asynchronous Receiver Transmitter), which is the interface between the serial connector and the CPU bus. It is rather like the PPI, except the external port in this case is a serial transmission line.

This means that the UART converts whatever it sends or receives between parallel byte form to serial byte form. So if you perform an OUT instruction, the UART will receive the byte, convert it to serial and transmit it one bit at a time down the serial line.

Strictly speaking, the serial connector only needs three lines, one for data-in, another for data-out, and a ground-line, however it is usual for the devices at each end of the transmission to signal each other --- just like you saw with the printer --- it had signals like "printer busy", "out of paper", etc.

So most of the 25 pins on the DB25 connector are used for this signalling, or "handshaking".

The RS232 specification is for asynchronous transmission, up to 110,000 bits per second, over a limited range.

INSIDE THE UART

Figure 7.2 shows the UART interface. Note that although the actual port addresses are given here, for the IBM-PC, it is usual not to communicate directly with the UART, but to go through BIOS or DOS services.

For BIOS it is **INT-14h**, which enables you to access all the registers, and send and receive characters. 344

The input and output registers should be clear enough. The Line Status and Control registers pertain to the UART itself, which is configurable by the Line Control register and whose status can be read by the Line Status reghister. The two extra registers, the Modem Status and Modem Control pertain to whatever is connected externally.

This need not necessarily be a modem, but traditionally it is, hence the naming of these two registers. These days we have all sorts of other devices connected to the serial interfaces, even mice. Basically the Modem Status register shows the status signals coming in on the external cable, while the Modem Control register provides control

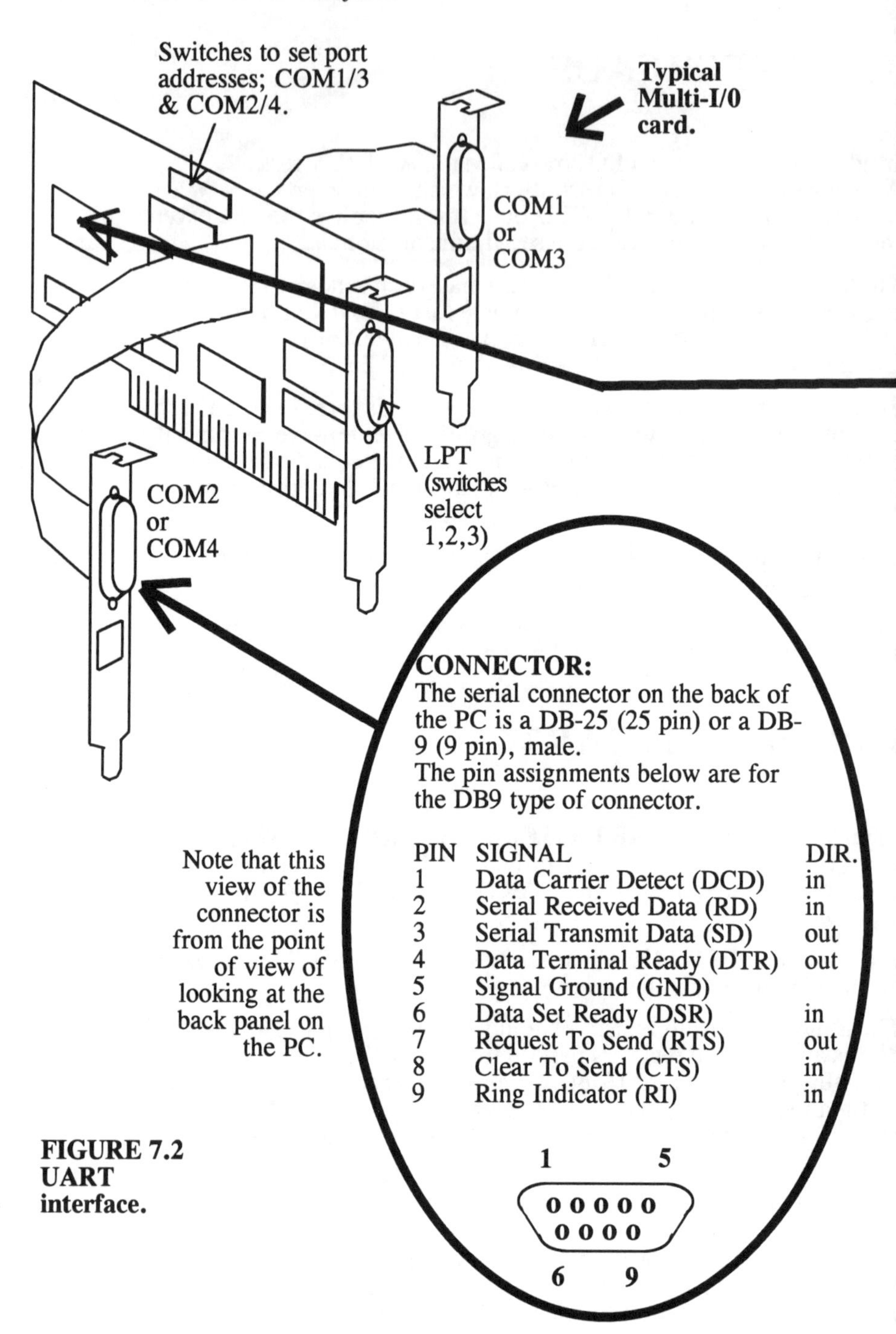

FIGURE 7.2 UART interface.

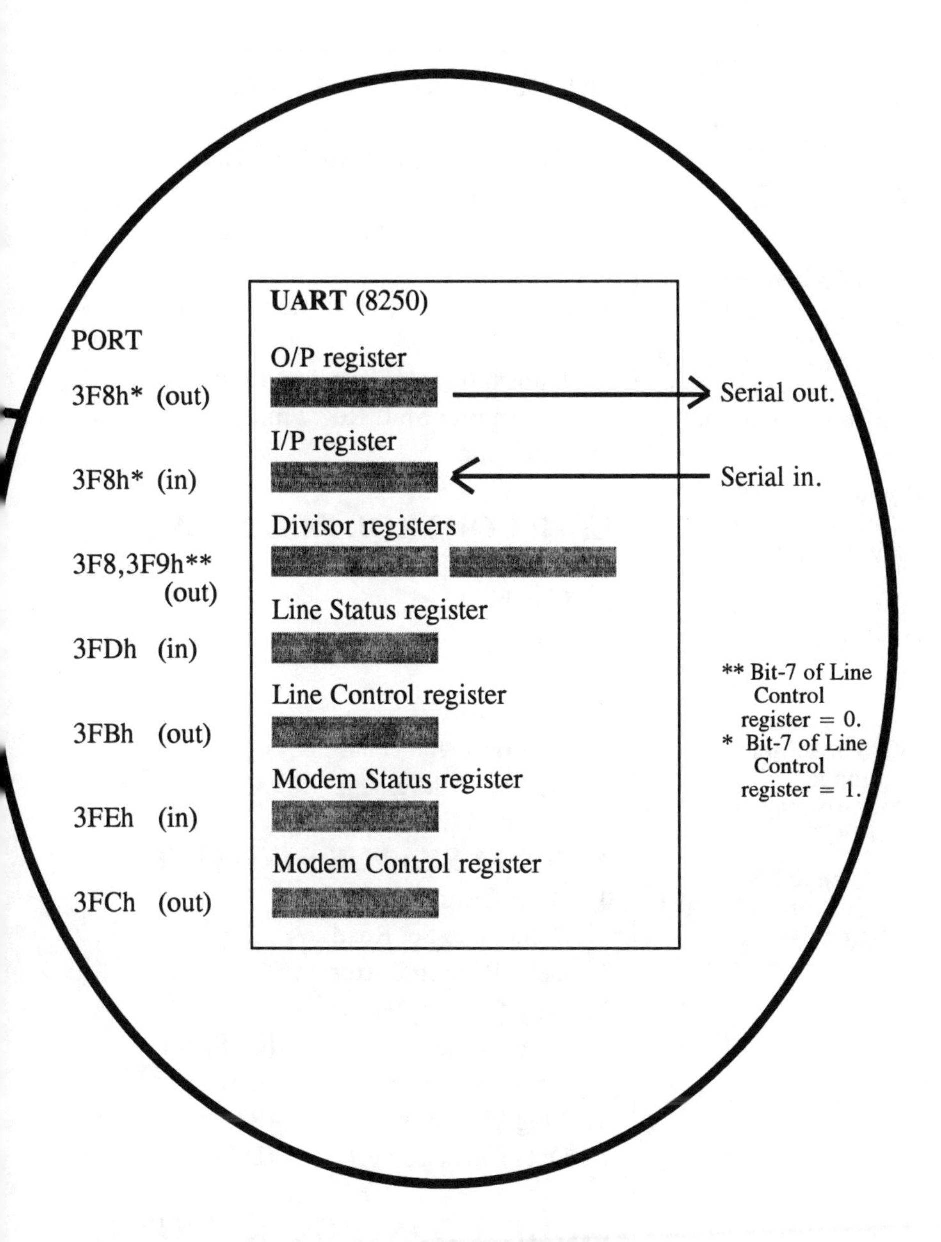

This is the insides of a UART, which is a single chip on the adaptor card. Note that the parallel and serial interfaces need not necessarily be on actual plug-in cards, but may be incorporated onto the motherboard -- it depends on the particular PC model and manufacturer.

signals going out to the external device -- you will be able to pick up all of these on the pins of the connector -- look at Figure 7.2.

Table 7.3 itemises the bits of each register. Notice that it's the bits of the Modem Control & Status registers that come out to external pins.

If you want more detail on how to program the 8250 UART and deeper explanations of the registers, a good reference is:

"8088 Assembler Language Programming: The IBM PC",

D.Willen & J.Krantz, 2nd Edition, Howard W.Sams, 1987.

BIT	MEANING	DB25 Pin
LINE STATUS REGISTER:		
0	Received Data Ready	
1	Overrun Error(chars coming too fast)	
2	Parity Error	
3	Framing Error (wrong no. stop bits)	
4	Break Detect	
5	Transmitter Holding Reg. Empty	
6	Transmitter Shift Reg. Empty	
7	Time Out	
LINE CONTROL REGISTER:		
0,1	Character Length	
2	Stop bits	
3	Parity	
4	Parity Type	
5	Stick Parity	
6	Set Break	
7	I/O Port Addressing.	
MODEM STATUS REGISTER:		
0	Delta Clear To Send	
1	Delta Data Set Ready	
2	Delta Ring Indicator	
3	Data Carrier Detect	
4	Clear To Send	(CTS) 5(in)
5	Data Set Ready	(DSR) 6(in)
6	Ring Indicator	(RI)
7	Data Carrier detect	(DCD)8(in)
MODEM CONTROL REGISTER:		
0	Data Terminal Ready	(DTR) 20(out)
1	Request To Send	(RTS) 4(out)
3	Set if interrupts to go to CPU	
2,4	Miscellaneous	

TABLE 7.3

PRACTICAL PROBLEMS:

Sometimes there can be a misunderstanding between the PC and the external device with regard to the definitions of the status and control signals.

For example, the modem or printer or whatever you have connected, may assert DSR (Data Set Ready) or CTS (Clear To Send), but not both, but if you try to read or send a character using the BIOS **INT-14h**, the computer will hang-up, as BIOS expects BOTH DSR and CTS to be set. Obviously, with a little monitor program that displays the status signals, you would pick up this problem straight away.

344

There are TSR's available to do this job, or you can use a "break-out" box that connects in-line with the serial cable and displays the lines on LED's.

Another problem has to do with data direction. A serial cable connecting a PC to a modem has pin-for-pin connections, but if we were to perform serial transmission between two PC's, a problem arises. In that case we need to crossover TD & SD, RTS & CTS, and DSR & DTR. Note that Table 7.3 shows pin numbering for DB25 connectors, while Figure 7.2 shows numbering for DB9 connectors.

WORKSHEET: PRINTER CONTROL

1.

It was mentioned in the theory section that it is possible to write a utility program that enables programs that print only to LPT1, to be redirected to LPT2 or LPT3.

Your job is to write a program that detects if LPT2 is present in the system, and if so swaps LPT1 and LPT2 (ie swaps the addresses in 0000:0408 and 40A).

2.

The program of step 2. is to be expanded so that a program called PRINTER.COM will select any printer you require as the primary (LPT1) printer.

The DOS command line will look like this---

```
PRINTER 3
```

Which means make printer number three into LPT1. The number after PRINTER can be any value between 1 and 3.

8

TIMER CIRCUITS

Here we have some fascinating time-related circuits in the PC: the 8253 Programmable Timer and the 6818 Real-Time Clock (with integrated CMOS RAM).

8253 TIMER

Like the **UART**, the timer chip is a standard type of chip --- you'll find something similar in any computer. The Intel 8253 Timer chip, or its **functional equivalent**, used in the PC basically consists of three counters, into which you can load a value and then start the counter decrementing on its own, independent of the CPU.

160 *144*

Before I go any further, here's the block diagram --- Figure 8.1.

This is not so complicated as it may first appear. Each of those counters can be loaded with a value. What happens is that when the CPU **OUT**'s a value to the register, say register-0 at port 40h, that value also goes into the counter.

136

Notice that the counters have their own clock source, of 1.19MHz. This makes them count down from whatever was loaded into them, independent of the CPU.

When they reach zero, the counters can simply stop, or reload automatically from the register and start counting down again. The essential point here is that when the counter reaches zero, it generates an output signal, that has occurred at a precise delay after the countdown was started --- obviously that delay was determined by the value previously loaded from the register to the counter.

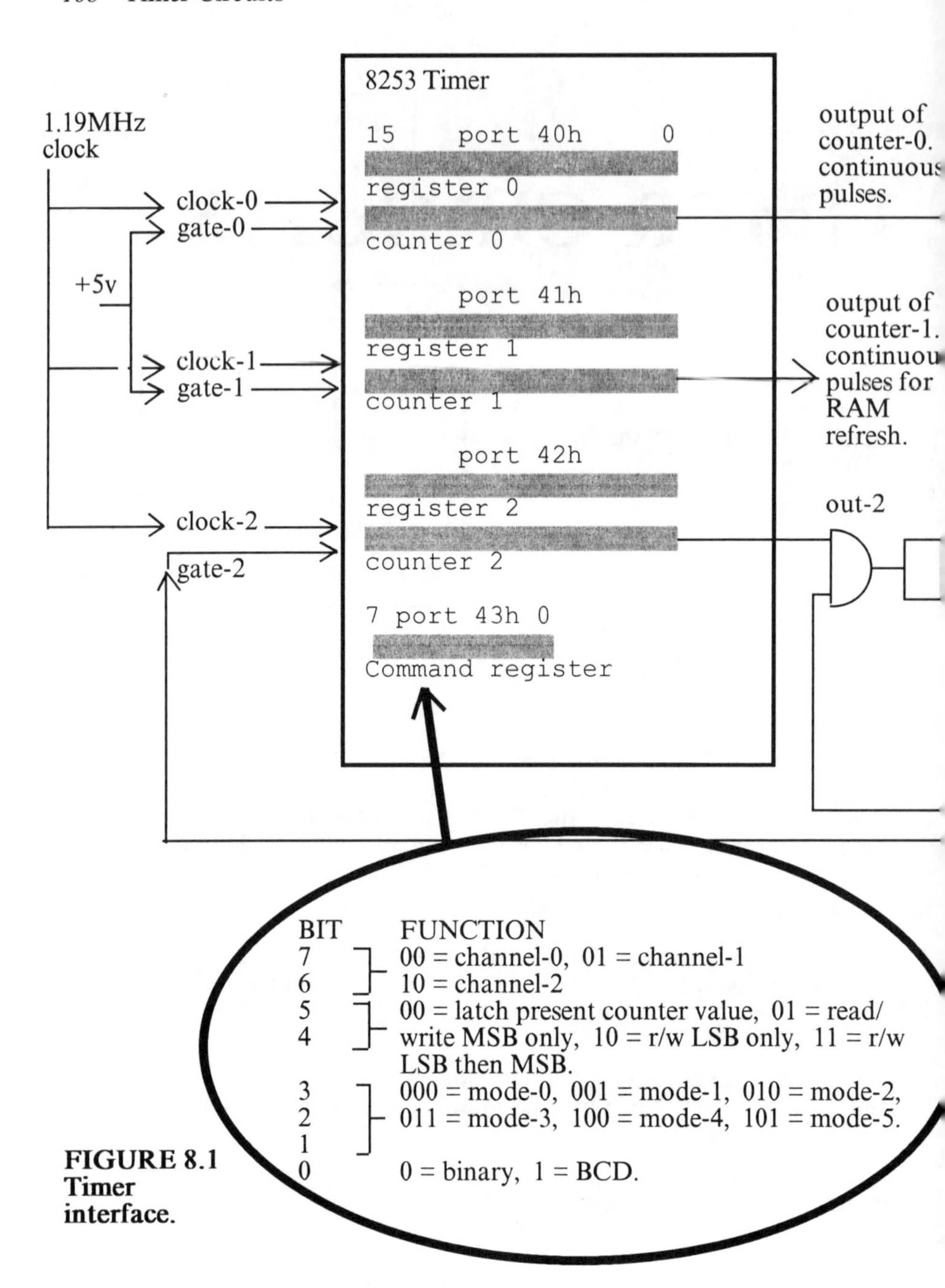

FIGURE 8.1 Timer interface.

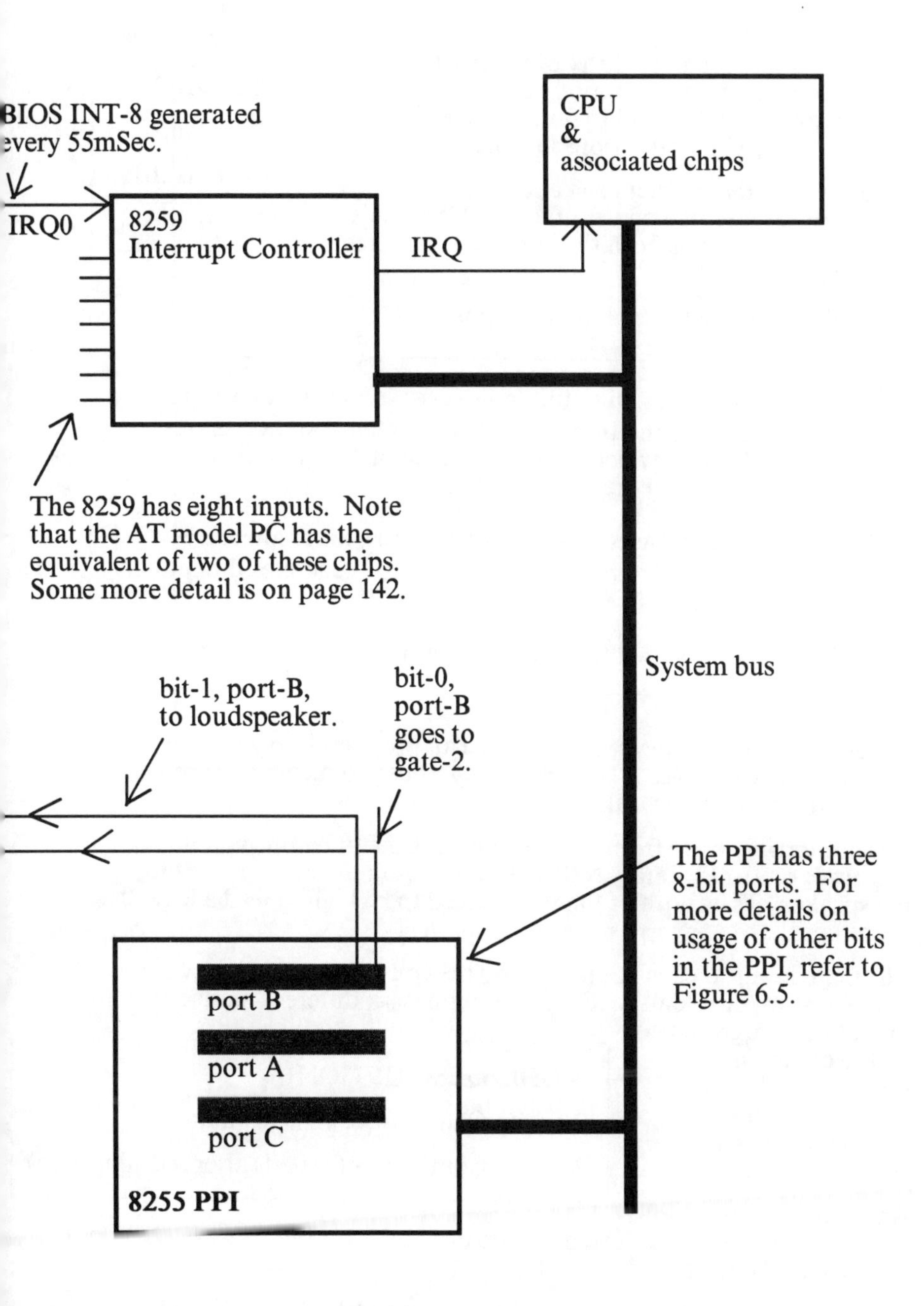
BIOS INT-8 generated
every 55mSec.
IRQ0
8259
Interrupt Controller
IRQ
CPU
&
associated chips
The 8259 has eight inputs. Note that the AT model PC has the equivalent of two of these chips. Some more detail is on page 142.
System bus
bit-1, port-B, to loudspeaker.
bit-0, port-B goes to gate-2.
The PPI has three 8-bit ports. For more details on usage of other bits in the PPI, refer to Figure 6.5.
port B
port A
port C
8255 PPI

Note that there is a peculiarity of the hardware --- the registers, with the exception of the Command register, are all 16-bit, and to send a value to them requires two OUT instructions like this:

```
MOV AL,BL
OUT 40h,AL
MOV AL,BH
OUT 40h,AL
```

Both bytes of the register exist at the same port-address, and two consecutive OUT's or IN's are required to access both the low and high bytes. Rather unusual.

In the PC, all three timers have a purpose ---

timer-0 generates an output pulse every 55mSec. This signal goes to the Interrupt Controller chip, and generates **INT-8**, which is the BIOS routine that has the job of updating the system clock.

341

timer-1 The PC uses dynamic RAM chips, that require a periodic refresh pulse. This signal generates that pulse, every 15.12‰Sec.

timer-2 This is used to generate tones to the loudspeaker.

Timer-2 is of most interest to us, as we can program it to generate pulses or square-waves of any frequency, thus producing interesting sounds from the loudspeaker.

It is not terribly clear from the diagram, but the timer output and bit-1 of port-B on the PPI are AND'ed and the result inverted and fed to the speaker. Thus both of these lines need to be high to feed a logic-0 to the speaker.

The Gate input to each counter starts the counter counting down, and also can stop, or reload it. Each counter has six different modes of operation, programmed by the command register, but basically the modes can be reduced to two main types:

MODE	DESCRIPTION
0,1,4,5	One-shot (counts down once).
2,3	Continuous (reloads after reaching zero).

Another generalisation is that these two modes further divide into pulse-output or squarewave-output modes.

For a more complete description, I refer you to **William & Krantz**. 161

Worksheet-(Music) does something interesting with the loudspeaker. 176

REAL-TIME CLOCK CHIP

IBM's original XT did not remember the time and date after being turned off, and required setting every time it was turned on -- a real hassle. The time and date is attached to every file by DOS when created and also when changed, which is a very useful feature, assuming of course that the PC has the correct time and date. With the introduction of the AT, IBM included a special chip made by Motorola, the 6818, that the BIOS looks for at power-on and reads the "real-time" date and time, consequently setting the BIOS clock.

The **Worksheet on Resident Programs** describes using INT 21h, **function-2Ch** to obtain the current time -- this DOS function simply reads the 6818 chip. The Worksheet also describes **BIOS INT-1Ah**, functions 0 and 02, that also return the time. *250* *353* *250*

INT-1Ah is also defined in the Appendices. *346*

The 6818 is also integrated into more recent **VLSI chips** in '286 & '386 systems. *145*

The 6818 includes an I/O-mapped RAM, with 64 registers, as shown in Figure 8.2. Don't be put off by this -- you normally think of memory as being memory-mapped, that is, part of the 1M (8086 CPU) map and accessable by the usual instructions such as MOV. Being I/O-mapped means that it is part of the **64K I/O-map** and only accessable by IN and OUT instructions. *134*

These are accessed by an OUT instruction to port 70h, specifying which address we want to talk to. Then an IN or OUT to port 71h accesses that particular register.

Thus there are two aspects to the 6818 -- it is a battery-powered clock and it also has the CMOS RAM. CMOS means that it has low power consumption, and the RAM retains its contents when the power is off, due to the battery. Look at Figure 8.2 and you'll notice that the RAM performs two major functions -- part of it holds the current time and date, and the other part holds configuration information -- see the box on page 124.

It's an interesting turn of events that the IBM PC, although being chock full of Intel chips, also has some Motorola parts, the 6818 being one of them, though in modern PC's only its functional equivalent is retained within VLSI chips.

It is very interesting to note that some of these registers are reserved, and apparently not used. Hmmm... don't believe it.... check it out first. It does open up interesting possibilities, as you could save some configuration setting of your own -- for example, if an application is

This is all I/O-mapped RAM, that we are referring to as registers:

Registers 0-8 are time & date.

Registers 10-13 are status on the 6818 chip itself,

while registers 14-51 are used by the BIOS for configuration settings.

6818 REGISTERS:

Addr	FUNCTION	DESCRIPTION
0	seconds	time, seconds, in BCD
1	alarm seconds	alarm, seconds, in BCD
2	minutes	time, minutes, in BCD
3	alarm minutes	alarm, minutes, in BCD
4	hours	time, hours, in BCD
5	alarm hours	alarm, hours, in BCD
6	day of week	day of the week, Sunday=0
7	day of month	day of month, in BCD
8	month	current month, in BCD
9	year	current year, in BCD
10-13	STATUS A-D	status registers A-D
14	diagnostic	status of BIOS diagnostics
15	shutdown	BIOS info defined at startup
16	diskette types	types of the 2 floppy drives
17	not used	
18	drive types	types of the 2 hard drives
19	reserved	not used by BIOS
20	equipment	info about hardware
21-22	low memory size	Kbytes below 1M
23-24	high memory size	Kbytes above 1M
25	fixed drive 1	extended type for drive-1
26	fixed drive 2	extended type for drive-2
27-45	reserved	not used by BIOS
47-48	checksum	checksum of addr. 16-45
48-49	high memory size	Kb's detected above 1M
50	century	the current century, in BCD
51	info flags	used by SETUP
52-63	reserved	not used by BIOS

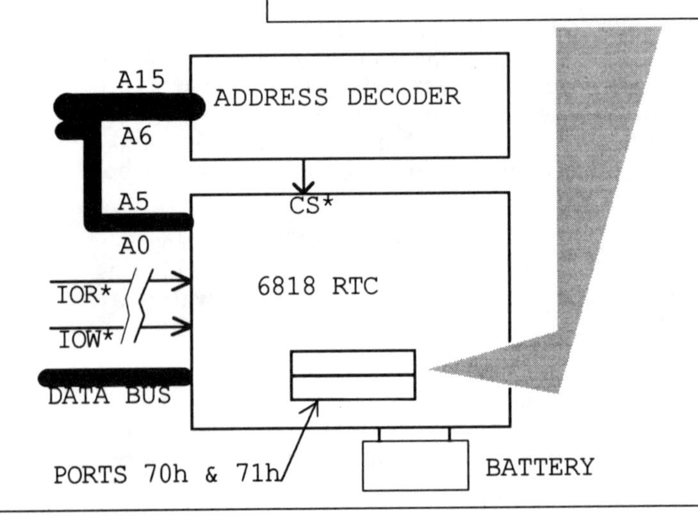

6818 REAL-TIME CLOCK

FIGURE 8.2

> **NOTE**:
> This description of the RTC is specific to AT-type PC's. Some PS/2 models have a modified configuration.

THE DIAGNOSTIC REGISTER:

BIT	MEANING
0-1	not used
2	invalid time
3	fixed disk failure
4	memory size doesn't match RAM
5	invalid hardware configuration
6	bad configuration checksum
7	RTC lost power.

THE EQUIPMENT REGISTER:

0	diskette drives installed flag
1	coprocessor present
2-3	not used
4-5	primary display type; 00=EGA/VGA, 01=CGA 40-col, 10=CGA 80-col, 11=mono display
6-7	no. floppy drives, 00=1, 01=2.

FLOPPY DRIVE TYPES:

0-3	second drive type
4-7	first drive type
	0 = drive not installed
	1 = 360K 5.25 inch
	2 = 1.2M 5.25 inch
	3 = 720K 3.5 inch
	4 = 1.44M 3.5 inch
	5-15 = invalid

HARD DRIVE TYPES:

0-3	second drive type
4-7	first drive type
	0 = drive not installed
	1-14 = see Table 8.1
	15 = extended drive type.

first installed from a master disk it can personalise that computer by writing to the CMOS RAM -- thus the program can check that it's on the right PC.

CMOS RAM SETUP -- SYSTEM CONFIGURATION:

The 6818 is not just a "timer" chip -- it also has RAM registers (mapped via I/O ports), in which the PC's SETUP program keeps system configuration information. The **power-up sequence** of the PC was introduced back in Chapter 1. The BIOS goes through a check-out sequence sometimes referred to as POST (Power On Self Test), which tests the integrity of the system RAM, plus other hardware, initialises chips such as the Interrupt Controller & Programmable Peripheral interface, and also reads the CMOS RAM settings. These settings are non-volatile, that is, they are retained when the power is off. They are set by means of a SETUP program, that may be supplied on disk with the computer, or is built-in to the BIOS ROM.

4

The latter is becoming increasingly popular, and the standard method for executing such a SETUP program is to press <CTRL-ALT-ESC> while the BIOS is doing the power-up sequence -- the PC then flips into the SETUP program, and system information such as number and type of floppy and hard drives, memory configuration, serial and parallel ports assignments, can be changed. In fact one of the first things the owner of a new PC should do is write down all the settings, should the CMOS RAM become corrupted -- an out-of-control program could change the settings, or failure of the battery.

There are lots of wonderful mysterious registers in the RTC -- let's have a look at the settings for disk drives. Register-16 specifies the two floppy drive types -- the top nibble is for the first drive, and lower for the second. Register-18 specifies the two hard drives, in two nibbles as above. The type-number can be from 0 to 14, specifying a particular disk size and configuration of tracks/sectors/heads. If =15, then an extended type number is held in registers 25 & 26.

The type-numbers for the hard drives may be what is called "logical" hard drive type numbers, which may differ from the actual "physical" **tracks/sectors/heads**, as the hard disk controller is able to map logical track/sector/ head requests from the BIOS into physical ones -- the requirement is that the total logical capacity should calculate to be

215

less than or equal to the actual physical capacity -- at least, some disk controllers are capable of this translation.

TYPE,TRACKS,HEADS,PRECOMP:	
1,306,4,128	22,733,5,300
2,615,4,300	23,306,4,0
3,615,6,300	24,977,5,none
4,940,8,512	25,1024,9,none
5,940,6,512	26,1224,7,none
6,615,4,none	27,1224,11,none
7,462,8,256	28,1224,15,none
8,733,5,none	29,1024,8,none
9,900,15,none	30,1024,11,none
10,820,3,none	31,918,11,none
11,855,5,none	32,925,9,none
12,855,7,none	33,1024,10,none
13,306,8,128	34,1024,12,none
14,733,7,none	35,1024,13,none
16,612,4,0	36,1024,14,none
17,977,5,300	37,1024,2,none
18,977,7,none	38,1024,16,none
19,1024,7,512	39,918,15,none
20,733,5,300	40,820,6,none
21,733,7,300	41,1024,5,none

TABLE 8.1 Logical HD Types.

Physical specs are different from logical due to the limited number of type settings that the BIOS can be set to, versus the greater variety of drives. Table 8.1 shows type numbers for the BIOS's of most modern '286 & '386 PC's. All of the types of Table 8.1 are 17 sectors per track and 512 bytes per sector. Some BIOSes have additional type numbers with different sectors/track, to try and match certain drives' physical spec's.

WORKSHEET: 8253 TIMER

The aim of this Worksheet is to show a method of creating sound at the loudspeaker.

1.

To make timer-2 produce a square-wave output, it needs to be programmed to mode-3, and a value written to register-2 to produce the appropriate frequency.
Have a look at the **circuit** --- you will see that PB0 goes into Gate-2 --- this is used to start the timer. Note also that although Out-2 from the counter will produce a square-wave, it will be also necessary to make PB1 high for it to get through to the loudspeaker.
It is best to see how this is all done by looking at actual code---

```
MOV  AL,0B6h ;program mode-3 into
OUT  43h,AL             ;timer-2.

MOV  BX,07C5h ;counter value for 600Hz
MOV  AL,BL    ;into register-2.
OUT  42h,AL
MOV  AL,BH
OUT  42h,AL

IN   AL,61h ;set PB0 and PB1.
OR   AL,03  ;(PB1 enables spkr),
OUT  61h,AL ;(PB0 starts timer-2).

MOV  AH,0   ;wait for a keypress.
INT  16h

IN   AL,61h   ;clear PB0 and PB1.
AND  AL,0FCh ;(PB1 disables spkr),
OUT  61h,AL   ;(PB0 stops timer-2).
INT  3     ;only if using DEBUG.
```

Try this program, and experiment with different frequencies.
Here is how to calculate the frequency---

FREQUENCY = 1,193,180/register-value
where FREQUENCY is in Hz (cycles/sec).

2.

Modify the above program to produce a changing frequency, hopefully a tune.
For this you will need to add to the above a delay, then stop the timer, then re-enter the program with a new value for reg-2, etc.

WORKSHEET: REAL-TIME CLOCK

Nothing particularly difficult about this Worksheet -- just become familiar with the 6818 chip.

1.

As an exercise, have a look forward to the Resident Programming Worksheet, at the **exercise to read the time**. 250
168 If you haven't done that Worksheet, don't worry about the TSR part of it -- just the program to read the time -- except now what I want you to do is write the program to read and display the real time by directly reading the 6818.
Note that for this exercise you will need a '286 or '386 system, or a recent XT.

2.

135 Are the unused registers really unused? What you could do is make a note of their current setting on a piece of paper, then change them, then reboot, then re-examine them.
Some clone-BIOS's may make use of the reserved registers, so it would be very wise to checkout many machines.

135
49
3.

We haven't got onto the chapter on disk I/O yet, but that doesn't stop us from looking at the settings in the CMOS 345 RAM. Find out the type number for the hard disk in your PC, and hence calculate the total capacity of the drive.
49 It should tally with what you know the drive to be.
341

9

THE MATHS COPROCESSOR

I don't intend this chapter to be a lesson on floating point arithmetic, though a brief recap won't hurt. Our main interest is how the PC can perform floating point operations for us, at the Assembly language level.

The box shows the steps to convert a decimal number to binary floating point:

DECIMAL TO BINARY:

decimal number:		+15.25					
Converting to binary:		8	+4	+2	+1 .	0	+1/4
		1*2^3 +	1*2^2 +	1*2^1 +	1*2^0.	0*2^(-1) +	1*2^(-2)
Answer:	0	1	1	1	1 .	0	1

This conversion is based upon the weighting of each binary digit:

```
x  x  x  x  x  x  x  x  .  x  x  x  x     <BINARY DIGITS
7  6  5  4  3  2  1  0  .  -1 -2 -3 -4    <POWERS-OF-2
                                           WEIGHTING
```

NORMALISATION:

The binary number has then to be normalised: +1 . 11101 * 10^11

That is, the binary-point is shifted so that there is a single binary-one digit to the left of the binary-point. However, so that the total value still computes to the original value, the normalised value contains a multiplation by a power of two, in this case 2-cubed (the "10" is in binary, so it is the same as decimal 2).

STORAGE IN F/P FORMAT:

The number is now in a suitable format for storage in memory and usage by a program. The precise format of its storage in RAM is covered below.

Hold on just a minute -- I presume that you know what "floating point" means -- just about everyone will have been exposed to the concept, perhaps knowing it as "scientific notation". Integer numbers, or integer numbers with an imaginary fixed decimal point, have a limit on their range, though with 32 bits it's not too bad. In fact its surprising what you can do with integer arithmetic, and it's fast. 2^32 equates to 4,300,000,000, but even so, floating point notation will give us a much bigger range from very small values to very large. Floating point does pay the penalty of a loss of accuracy compared with integer.

The discussion in this chapter focuses on the 80387 coprocessor, though the principles apply to the earlier ones. The 8087 is designed to go with the 8088 CPU, the 80287 with the 80286 CPU, and the 80387 with the 80386 CPU. The 80486 CPU has the coprocessor incorporated onto the chip, but it can be considered functionally equivalent to the 387.

The format of storage depends upon the level of precision that we require. The current industry standards are single-precision, double-precision and extended-precision. The formats are shown in Figure 9.1.

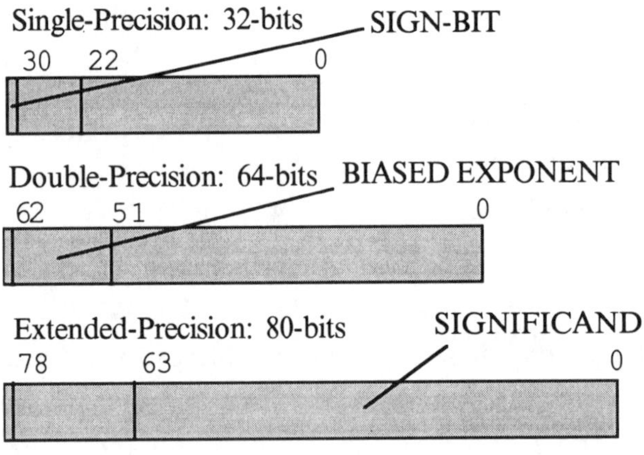

FIGURE 9.1

SIGN-BIT:

The number commences with a single-bit for the sign, being zero if positive. Note that we do not use 2's complement representation at all here.

EXPONENT:

The exponentional part comes next. In our previous example it is three, but it is actually modified slightly before being stored. As the xponent is not being stored in 2's complement representation, egative exponents (note: the larger the negative exponent, the smaller ne number, so we can work with tiny fractional quantities) must be epresented and the solution is to add a fixed bias onto the exponent make it into a positive number. In single-precision the exponent is ight bits in size, and a bias of 127 is added. Obviously the reverse ould have to be done when converting back.

'or double-precision the bias is 1023 and for extended-precision it is 6383 (decimal). In binary that would be 1111111b, 1111111111b and 11111111111111b respectively.

o, our little example had an exponent of 3, which becomes 3 + 127 = 30, or in binary it is 11b + 1111111b = 10000010b, and this is what ets stored.

IGNIFICAND:

'he significand is the rest of the value, with a qualification. What goes nto the significand field depends upon which level of precision. Since ne value is always normalised with a "1" to the left of the inary-point, there is no real need to actually store that "1". We lways know that it is there, so when converting back to the original alue we can always put it back in. This is what happens in single and ouble-precision -- the "1." in the normalised value is referred to as an implied binary point" and not actually stored. Only the fractional art, to the right of the binary-point goes into the significand-field.

ust to make life difficult or us, extended precision does store the 1." along with the actional part.

'igure 9.2 shows how the xample will look in oating point format, nd also how it is ctually stored in emory. Intel's andard is always to ore numbers starting ith the least-significant yte in the lowest emory address. This xample is using the 2-bit single-precision ormat.

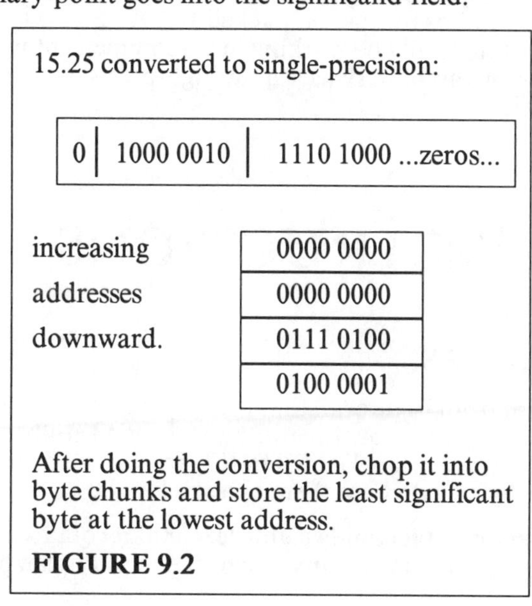

FIGURE 9.2

Note that the fractional significand is stored to the left of the significand-field.

RANGE:

You could now contemplate the range of values that the f/p representation can have. For single-precision the smallest value would be +/- 1.00 * 2^(-127), while the largest value would be +/- 1.9999*2^128. Work them out!

INTEGER ARITHMETIC

Yes, the coprocessor also does integer arithmetic. Since the main CPU does also, you might ask what's the point? One reason is more precision, since the coprocessor can do integer arithmetic at up to 64 bits in 2's complement straight binary and 72 bits BCD. The coprocessor can work at three levels of 2's complement precision: word (16 bits), short-integer (doubleword; 32 bits) and long-integer (quadword; 64 bits).

BCD arithmetic is very interesting -- it uses the lower 72 bits of the coprocessor's 80-bit register to hold 18 BCD digits, two per byte -- Intel refer to this format as "packed BCD". Bit-79 is a sign bit. We would not normally be working in 2's complement with BCD. So, the coprocessor can be very useful for high-precision and fast BCD arithmetic.

387 INSTRUCTIONS

REGISTERS:

You'll see from Figure 9.3 that there are eight 80-bit registers in the coprocessor, as well as three 16-bit status and control registers. The eight registers are labelled R0 to R7, and can be referenced as such, but usually we reference them as a stack.

Not a very big stack; only eight-deep, but it rotates around, so that we don't run out of stack. Any one of the registers can be the current top

FIGURE 9.3 Architecture of the Coprocessor.

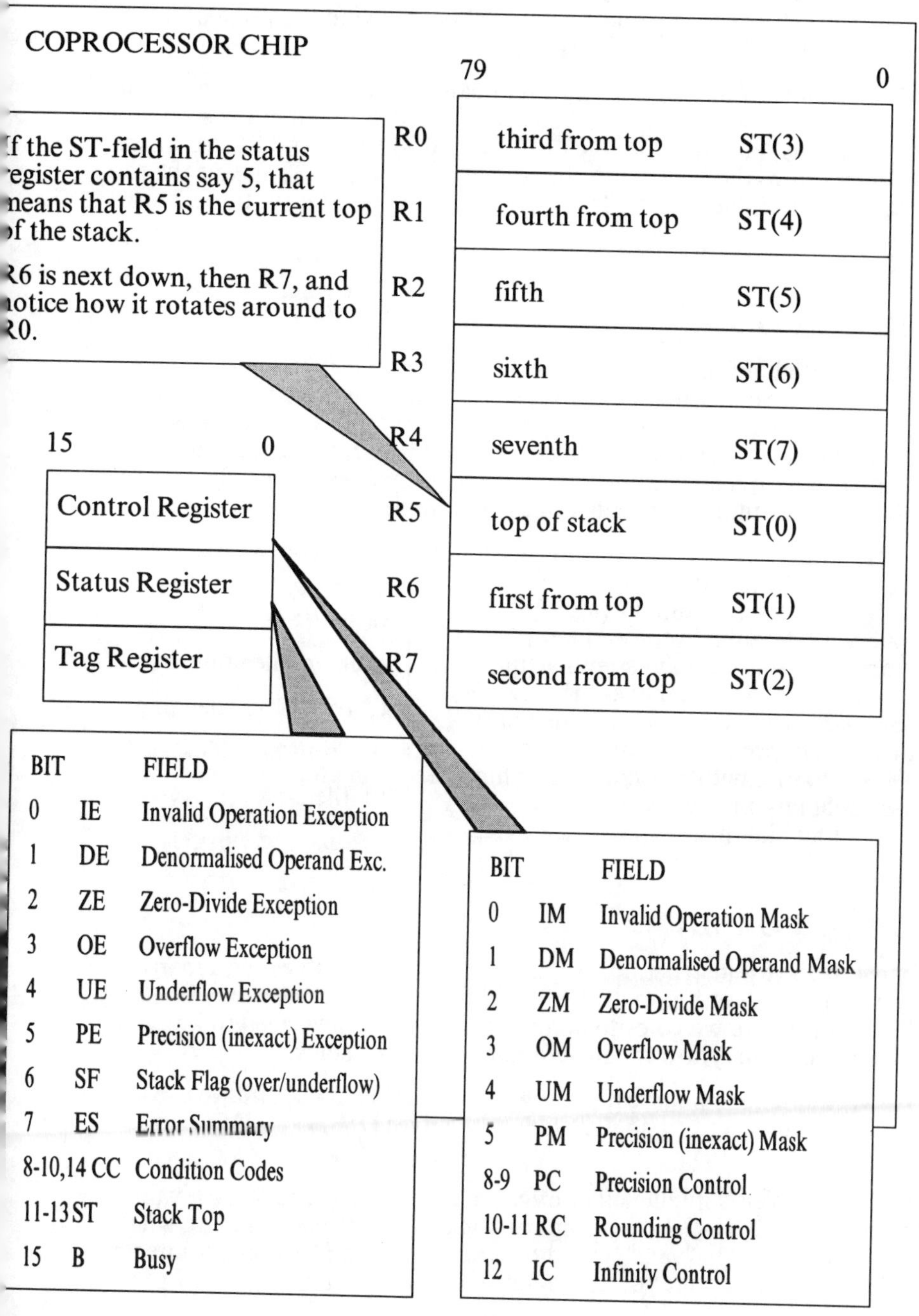

COPROCESSOR CHIP

If the ST-field in the status register contains say 5, that means that R5 is the current top of the stack.

R6 is next down, then R7, and notice how it rotates around to R0.

	79	0
R0	third from top	ST(3)
R1	fourth from top	ST(4)
R2	fifth	ST(5)
R3	sixth	ST(6)
R4	seventh	ST(7)
R5	top of stack	ST(0)
R6	first from top	ST(1)
R7	second from top	ST(2)

15 0

Control Register

Status Register

Tag Register

Status Register:

BIT		FIELD
0	IE	Invalid Operation Exception
1	DE	Denormalised Operand Exc.
2	ZE	Zero-Divide Exception
3	OE	Overflow Exception
4	UE	Underflow Exception
5	PE	Precision (inexact) Exception
6	SF	Stack Flag (over/underflow)
7	ES	Error Summary
8-10,14	CC	Condition Codes
11-13	ST	Stack Top
15	B	Busy

Control Register:

BIT		FIELD
0	IM	Invalid Operation Mask
1	DM	Denormalised Operand Mask
2	ZM	Zero-Divide Mask
3	OM	Overflow Mask
4	UM	Underflow Mask
5	PM	Precision (inexact) Mask
8-9	PC	Precision Control
10-11	RC	Rounding Control
12	IC	Infinity Control

of the stack, and the ST-field in the Status Register tells us which one. Figure 9.3 shows the example of the ST-field having the value of 5, meaning that R5 is the top of the stack.

Most of the x87 instructions automatically work on the top register or registers of the stack, but you can specify further down in the stack. Instructions reference the stack by means of the operand ST(n), where "n" designates the depth into the stack. ST(0) or just ST means the top register of the stack, and ST(1) means the next register (in this example it is R6), etc.

EMULATION:

It is not at all difficult to use the maths coprocessor. In fact there are also software emulators available, so that you can pretend that you have a coprocessor, from the application program's point of view -- the application will just run slower than with an actual coprocessor chip. Emulators are supplied by various companies -- notably Borland, as a utility with most of their compilers.

You should know whether your target system has a coprocessor or an emulator, though it is possible to write code that uses the chip if available otherwise defaults to the emulator. Normally you select at assembly-time which of the two you have -- the TASM command-line switch "/r" means that there is a coprocessor, while "/e" tells TASM to link with an emulator. Thus the assemble/link process would look something like this:

```
tasm /zi /r  filename
tlink /v  filename
tdstrip -s -c  filename
    last step .COM only
td  filename
    turbo debugger
```

DATA FORMATS:

Most of the f/p instructions work on the top of the stack, and many result in a push or a pop of the top value, from or to memory. However before we go onto actual code examples, we need to know how to get values into the program, and into the stack.

It's very simple -- we already know how to define data, and we use the same methods here. The Assembler directives **DW, DD, DQ and DT** are used. *100*

The Assembler is intelligent enough to know whether to store a value as integer, ASCII, floating-point or packed-BCD, by examining what you have entered. "val2" would be assembled as a plain binary integer value of 57 (note that you can enter minus signs -- if you had -57 then

Asm would treat this as negative 57 decimal and would convert it to the equivalent 2's-complement binary number). "val2x" on the other hand would be assembled as a floating-point number, single-precision. If the value contains a decimal point, it is treated as floating point. Also, if it contains an exponent-operator "E" it is also treated as f/p. For example 5.0 = 5E0, meaning 5.0 * 10^0.

```
;data segment....
val1   DW  57    ;word-integer (16-bit)

val2   DD  57    ;short-integer (32-bit), or
val2x  DD  5.7   ;f/p single-precision.

val3   DQ  57    ;long-integer (64-bit), or
val3x  DQ  5.7   ;f/p double-precision.

val4   DT  57    ;packed-BCD (80-bit), or
val4x  DT  5.7   ;f/p extended-precision.
```

DT is an interesting one. This is never used for holding an integer straight-binary value, as the precision is far more than we would require. If the dat-field is initialised as a whole-number, as is "val4" above, it is assembled in packed-BCD form. If it has a decimal-point or an "E"-operator, it assembles as f/p.

INSTRUCTION FORMATS:

The coprocessor instructions are listed in the **Appendices**. Notice that they all begin with the letter "F", so there's no danger of confusing them with the other CPU instructions. Most of them have the same addressing modes as the other instructions, but of course most of them are stack-oriented. 365

Firstly, a simple example, to show some operand options. The FADD instruction adds the f/p operand to the top of the stack ST(0).

```
fadd  val2x    ;add the single-precision value "val2x" to ST(0).
               ;(stack-pointer ST unchanged)

fadd  st(1)    ;add next down to top, result in top ST(0).
               ;(stack-pointer unchanged).

fadd  xt(0),st(1) ;same as above.

fadd           ;same as above. (implicitly uses XT(0) & XT(1))

fadd  st(1),st(0) ;adds ST(0) & ST(1), result into ST(1)
               ;(stack-pointer unchanged).
```

You see that we have lots of options for working with the various registers and with memory.

But -- note that the stack pointer is unchanged. Most instructions have three forms -- for example FADD is for floating point, but it has another form; FIADD, which does integer arithmetic, and another form; FADDP, which does f/p and then pops the top of the stack. In the latter case, the stack-pointer would increment and R6 would become the new ST(0). Here is a summary of the instructions:

DATA TRANSFER	
Push onto stack	FLD, FILD, FBLD
Pop off stack	FSTP, FISTP, FBSTP
Copy off stack	FST, FIST
Exchange	FXCH
Push constant	FLDZ, FLD1, FLDPI, FLDLG2, FLDLN2, FLDL2T, FLDL2E
ARITHMETIC	
Addition	FADD, FIADD, FADDP
Subtraction	FSUB, FISUB, FSUBP
Reversed subtract	FSUBR, FISUBR, FUBRP
Multiplication	FMUL, FIMUL, FMULP
Division	FDIV, FIDIV, FDIVP
Reversed division	FDIVR, FIDIVR, FDIVRP
Miscellaneous	FSQRT, FSCALE, FPREM, FPREM1, FRNDINT, FXTRACT, FABS, FCHS
COMPARISON	
F/p compare	FCOM, FCOMP, FCOMPP
Unordered compare	FUCOM, FUCOMP, FUCOMPP
Integer compare	FICOM, FICOMP
Compare to zero	FTST
Examine	FXAM
TRANSCENDENTAL	
	FSIN, FCOS, FSINCOS, FPTAN, FPATAN, FYL2X, FYL2XP1, F2XM1

TABLE 9.1

WORKSHEET: COPROCESSOR

Turbo Debugger is an excellent tool for examining the coprocessor instructions. You will need a PC with a coprocessor, either an '87, '287 or '387. The Assmbler defaults to the "worst case", which is a 8086 CPU and a 8087, unless you specifically start the source code with .286, .287 or .386, .387 directives.

A couple of pages back shows how to assemble, link and debug, so go ahead and examine the program here. The purpose of this Worksheet is very simple: to trace through a selection of coprocessor instructions and obtain a feel for how they work, particularly as they affect memory and the registers. Keep a close watch on the stack and observe how each instruction affects it. Don't forget to look at how 5.25 is assembled into memory.

```
comseg segment
   assume ds:comseg, cs:comseg
   org  100h
main  proc   far
   jmp start
val2   DD    5.25
val3   DQ    0
start: fld         val2  ;load
   fadd      val2    ;addition
   fst       st(1)   ;store
   fmul      val2    ;multiply
   fstp      val3    ;store & pop
   mov       ax,4C00h
   int       21h
main  endp
comseg    ends
   end       main
```

10
ADVANCED ARCHITECTURE

In for a penny, in for a pound .... Chapter Nine exposed you to the maths coprocessor, which can be considered as an advanced architectural enhancement for the PC, so now it's time to go the extra length and tackle today's CPU's. This chapter concentrates on the advanced architectural features of the '286 and '386, however it should be related at some stage to operating systems that utilise those features, which is done to a limited extent in this chapter. The book swings back to a dominant software theme in the latter part of the book, and there you will find details on **OS/2 and MS-Windows**. *293*

For now however, we need a thorough grounding in those architectural features of the '286 and most particularly the '386, that distinguish it from our old friend the 8086.

The '286 and '386 are upward-compatible with the 8088, so everything you have learnt in this course is relevant. The recent CPU's and operating systems to go with them tend to be much more complicated, so it is good to get going on the bottom rung.

Besides, there are about 30 million 8088-based PC's in the world, and your knowledge at this level will be in demand for many many years to come. There are about 8 million '286-based PC's, and the '386 is moving in quick, including the '386SX, which is a '386 with only a 16-bit external Data Bus. We also have the '486, which is a '386 with on-chip coprocessor and cache, and recently the '486SX, which doesn't have the coprocessor.

The outstanding feature of these later CPU's is, apart from speed, the in-built virtual memory management. read on...

EXTENDED & EXPANDED MEMORY

INTRODUCTION:

Extended memory is the term for memory above 1Mb. Conventional memory is the memory below 1Mb. Expanded memory is bank-switched memory that can be mapped into the conventional memory area. Figure 10.1 shows this.

Expanded memory, not shown in this diagram, is usually mapped into a 64K conventional memory region between the 640K and 1Mb boundaries.

PROGRAMMING CONSIDERATIONS

DOS APPLICATIONS:

Some DOS applications are designed to make use of expanded memory, but most do not. DOS applications cannot access above 1M vhen the CPU is running in eal mode. Only the '386 can uccessfully map DOS pplications into extended nemory, due to its paged nemory management.

Certain device drivers also use xpanded memory, such as a RAM-disk. Note however hat Windows on the 386 refers your system to have as nuch extended memory as ossible, and little or no xpanded memory, as Vindows is able to econfigure extended memory nto "pseudo" expanded as eeded.

BIOS SERVICE:

BIOS **INT 15h**, SERVICE 88h

345

This returns the amount of extended memory installed in the system.

INT 15h, service 88h;

Call with; AH=88h.

Returns; AX=amount of ext.mem (Kbytes).

ee the -- **Windows notes for the '386 >>>** *193*

REAL MODE:

199

The 8088 and 80286/386 running in real-mode can only have 20-bit ddressing and can only address up to 1Mb. When protected-mode is urned on, ie the memory management part of the 286/386 chips, ddressing above 1Mb is possible.

PROTECTED MODE:

199

t is possible, while running in real-mode, to temporarily switch to rotected-mode to access programs above 1Mb, then switch back to eal-mode.

Getting to protected mode involves a lot of housekeeping: in the 286 t involves setting the PE (Protect Enable) bit in the (MSW) Machine Status Word register, and setting up descriptor tables and loading the ddress of the GDT into the GDT pointer register.

The designers of the 286 provided no method for switching back to eal-mode, which was a serious oversight, howevcr it can be done by esctting the CPU. A certain value is stored in a special reserved BIOS rea as a signal to the ROM BIOS. The program then generates a ertain interrupt that resets the computer. The ROM BIOS, after its ower-on self-test, checks the special area, and sees that this is an ntentional restart, and simply returns control to the previously executing program. This is just a rough idea of the process, but the essential point here is that it is a messy technique and actually takes several milliseconds to accomplish, which is ages in CPU terms.

Fortunately the oversight was fixed on the 386, as only a certain bit needs to be set to switch back to real-mode, and the CPU doesn't need to be halted.

Have a look at INT 15h, shown here:

> **BIOS SERVICE:**
>
> BIOS **INT 15h**, SERVICE 87h
>
> This is an interesting function -- it moves a block of data between conventional memory (below 1M) and extended RAM.
>
> The CPU temporarily switches to protected mode to make the transfer, then back to real. This can be very useful for DOS applications, to relieve the 640K pressure.
>
> Call with AH=87h, CX=number of words
>
> to move, ES:SI=physical address of GDT.
>
> Returns; If operation successful;
>
> Carry-flag=clear, AH=0.
>
> If operation unsuccessful;
>
> Carry-flag=set, AH=status
>
> 01h RAM parity error
>
> 02h exception inter.error
>
> 03h gate addr.line20 fail

345

Since this is a switch from real to protected mode, BIOS INT 15h, service 87h also has to take care of housekeeping such as entering appropriate values into the GDT. It does require that a GDT already be in existence.

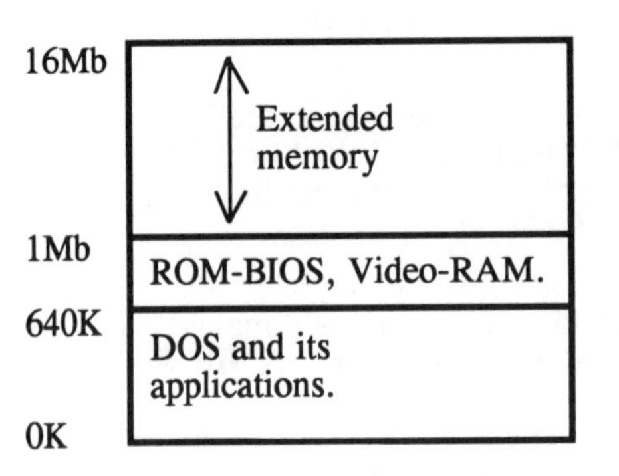

FIGURE 10.1 PC Memory Regions.

LEGEND:
- ■ '386 only
- ▣ '286 & '386 only
- ▢ '86, '286 & '386
- * invisible to programmer

NOTE:
The mathematics coprocesso[r]
are shown in Figure 9.3.

FIGURE 10.2 x86 registers.

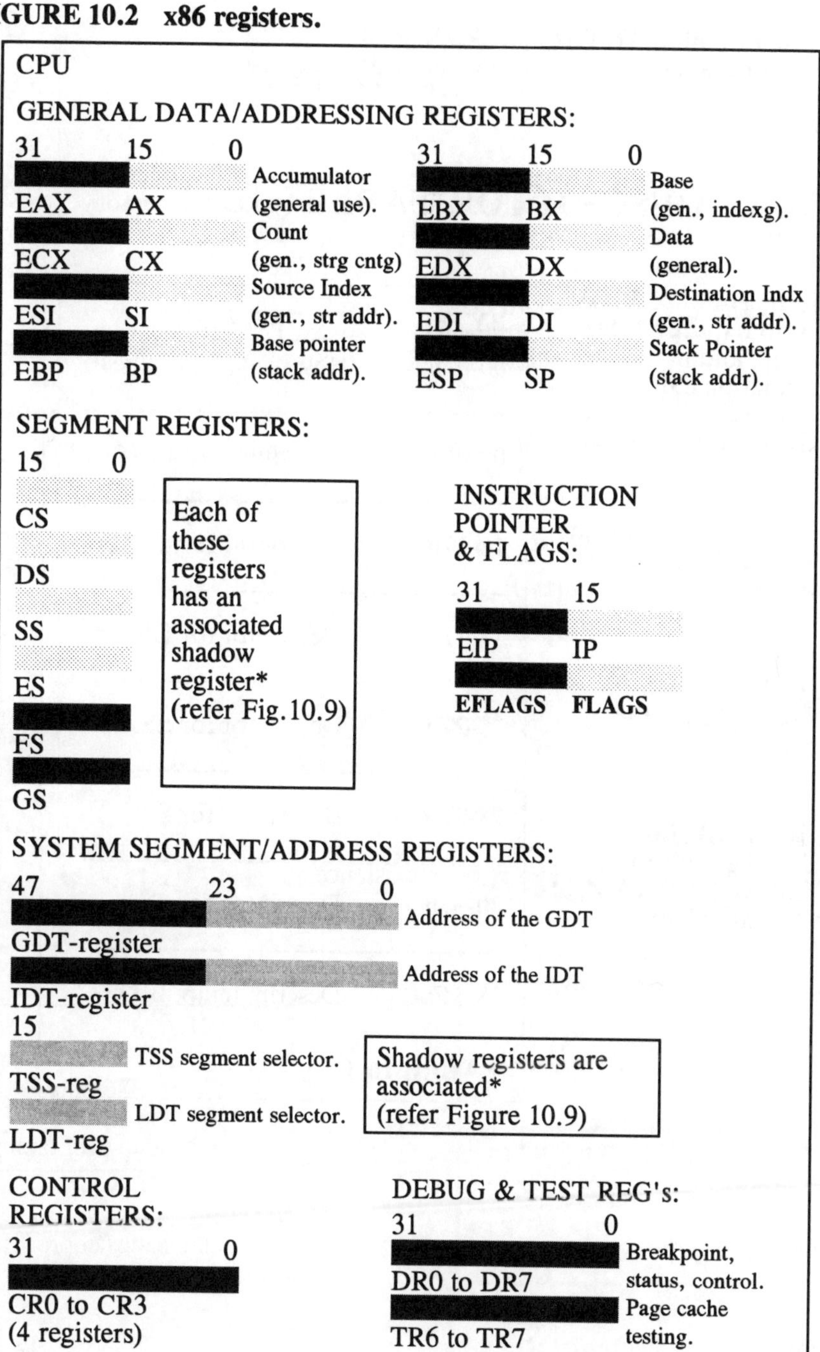

Refer also to: BIOS **INT 15h**, SERVICE 89h *345*
Allows a program to enter protected mode and stay there.

GLOBAL DESCRIPTOR TABLE (GDT)

202

The aforementioned BIOS services do require a GDT to be setup, and in the case of sub-function 89h, at least an IDT as well. The most basic GDT has this format:

BYTES	CONTENTS
00-07h	Reserved (should be 0).
08-0Fh	Descriptor for this GDT.
10-17h	Descriptor for the IDT.
18-1Fh	Descriptor for DS.
20-27h	Descriptor for ES.
28-2Fh	Descriptor for SS.
30-37h	Descriptor for CS.
38-3Fh	Descrip. temp. BIOS CS.

TABLE 10.1

The descriptor format is the standard one for selecting the physical address of a segment.

The format shown here, in Table 10.1, needs a little **modification for '386 systems**. *204*

There is a **Workshop** related to the topic of accessing extended RAM, at the end of this chapter. *214*

ARCHITECTURAL CONSIDERATIONS FOR MICROSOFT WINDOWS ON THE '386

Note that the architectural requirements for Windows/286 differs somewhat from Windows/386 or Windows3.0 configured for the '386, but I have glossed over the former as I consider that the near future overwhelmingly lies with '386 machines.

On a '386 machine on which I recently installed Windows, I configured the memory as:

System	640K
Expanded	0
Extended	1.384M

With Windows is supplied SMARTDRV.SYS, a disk-cache driver, that improves Windows performance and is a recommended addition. With Windows/286/386, it is installed by MEMSET.EXE, again supplied with Windows. The procedure is to exit Windows after you have installed it, and from the DOS prompt run MEMSET.EXE (it should be in the Windows directory). Do be sure to exit entirely from Windows, not just load a DOS-shell from the Windows Executive.

MEMSET installed SMARTDRV, first checking that there was adequate extended memory. It defaults to 128K and MEMSET inserts a line in the **CONFIG.SYS** file:

```
DEVICE=C:\SYSTEM\DEV\SMART.SYS 128
```

5

The path defines where abouts you have kept SMART.SYS. SMARTDRV automatically installs in extended memory, but if your system has expanded memory you can put a /A switch at the end of the above line to make SMARTDRV install into expanded memory.

Note that this installation procedure is more automated with Windows3.0.

EXPANDED MEMORY:

Some people are in the unfortunate situation that a memory board in their computer is hardwired as expanded memory (rather than extended), which Windows/386 cannot use for paged memory storage.

However you can put it to good use -- for those DOS applications that make use of it, and as RAM-drive or disk-cache.

On a '386 machine, the best situation is to have all of your memory as extended.

Windows assigns a portion of extended as "pseudo expanded", on a dynamic basis as DOS applications require, but this can get out of hand, as some DOS applications request a lot of expanded memory, so not enough extended is left to run other applications.

It seems best to fix the amount of pseudo expanded memory that Windows allocates. Note that this pseudo expanded memory looks just like real expanded from the applications point of view, and is also available for RAM-disks and other drivers designed to work in expanded mem.

The WIN.INI file in the Windows directory contains Windows setup configuration. You will find "emmsize=" in there.
Change this to 128 which will set the pseudo expanded memory to a fixed size of 128K:

```
emmsize=128
```

Note: make sure that this line has the value of 640;

```
windowmemsize=640
```

FIGURE 10.3

'386 Register Usage.

REGISTER	Use in Real Mode		Use in Protected Mode		Use in Virt-86 Mode	
	Load	**Store**	**Load**	**Store**	**Load**	**Store**
General registers	yes	yes	yes	yes	yes	yes
Segment registers	yes	yes	yes	yes	yes	yes
Flag register	yes	yes	yes	yes	IOPL*	IOPL*
Control registers	yes	yes	PL=0	PL=0	no	yes
GDTR	yes	yes	PL=0	yes	no	yes
IDTR	yes	yes	PL=0	yes	no	yes
LDTR	no	no	PL=0	yes	no	no
TR	no	no	PL=0	yes	no	no
Debug control	yes	yes	PL=0	PL=0	no	no
Test registers	yes	yes	PL=0	PL=0	no	no

NOTE:

PL=0: the registers can be accessed only when the current privilege level is zero.

* IOPL: the PUSHF and POPF instructions are made I/O privilege level sensitive in Virtual-86 mode.

ARCHITECTURE OF THE 286/386

INTRODUCTION

Select one of these....

This section focuses on the '386, since it represents the future thrust, and specifications refer to it unless the '286 is specifically named.

The '386 has an external physical address bus of 32 bits, which means it can address 2^32 = 4.3 billion bytes of memory.

The data bus is also 32 bits, which speeds up access, though note that byte-addressing is still used, for compatibility with earlier microprocessors.

I/O addressing is still the same as earlier members of the '86 family, using the lower 16 bits of the physical address bus, along with the special I/O control signals. 16 bits allows up to 65,000 I/O addresses.

REGISTERS:

All the familiar registers are there; **AX, BX, CX, DX, SI, DI, BP, SP**, which has been done for compatibility -- have a look at Figure 10.2, which shows the registers for the whole family, including their sizes. 16

Note that the 80386 has 32-bit registers, that are simply extensions of the above.

FIGURE 10.4
Concept of virtual memory & machines.

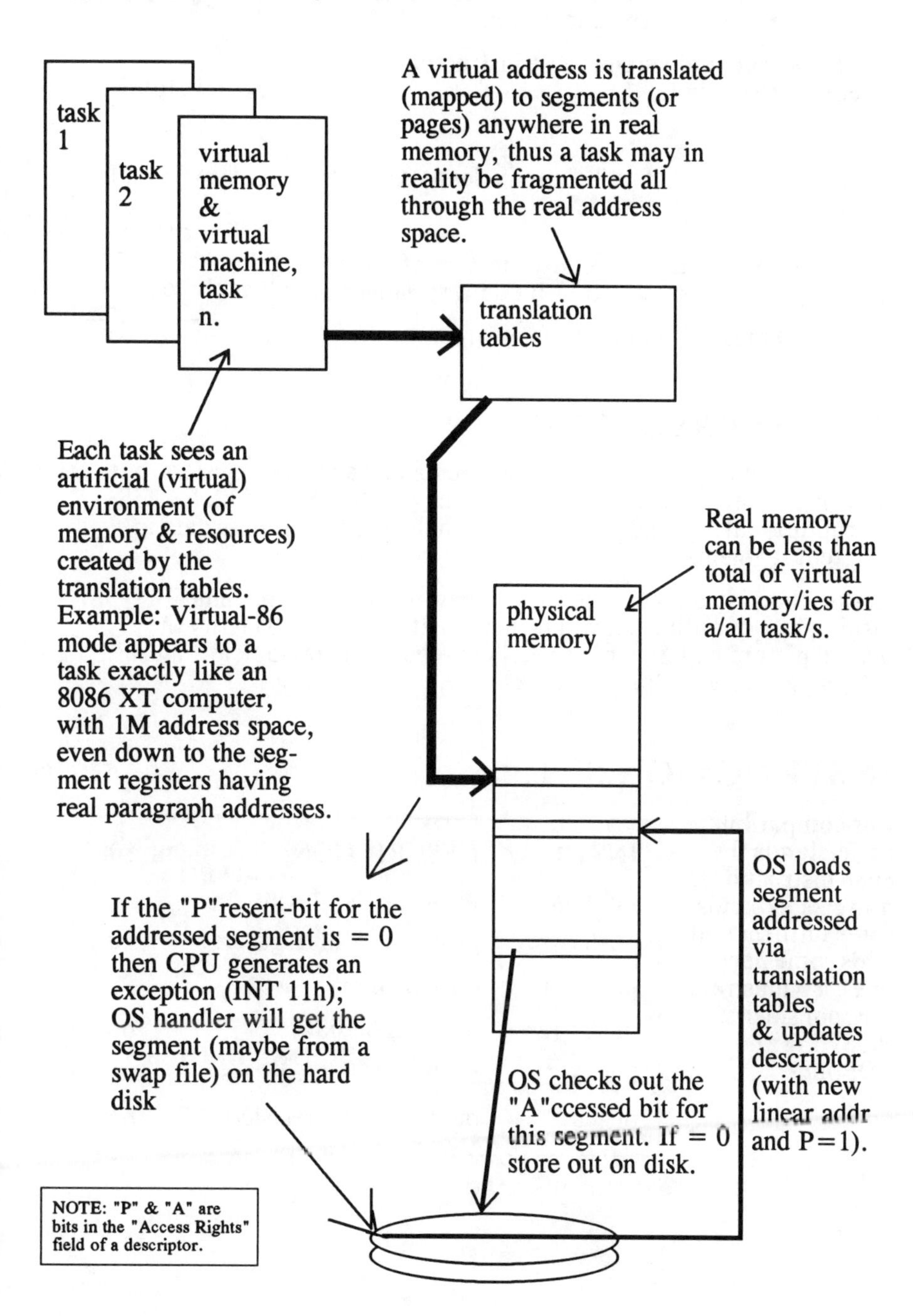

You are familiar with the concept of the 16-bit register AX being accessed in halves;

```
mov    al,0
```

Or in total;

```
mov    ax,0
```

The 80386 can understand these instructions, but also extends the principle;

```
mov    eax,0
```

The "E" prefix denotes a 32-bit register.

Note that in Assembler (for any member of the '86 family) you can also define 32-bit data variables;

```
var1   dd   0
```

100

where DD means "Define Doubleword".

SEGMENT REGISTERS:

For compatibility reasons these have remained as 16-bit registers, but some more have been added. Now we have; ES, CS, SS, DS, FS, GS. The additional segment registers are usually used to address data in different segments.

Rather than introducing the various new registers in a piecemeal fashion as we continue, it will be helpful at this point to clarify the overall picture with regard to registers -- have a good look at Figure 10.2, if you haven't done already.

INSTRUCTION SET:

360

For compatibility, understands the 8088 instructions, however expands some of them and adds some new ones. To illustrate this, consider PUSHing and POPping;

INSTR.	DESCRIPTION	8088
push ax	pushes a 16-bit register	
push eax	pushes a 32-bit register	no
push var1	push memory	
push 0123	push **immediate**	no
pusha	push all 16-bit registers	no
pushad	push all 32-bit registers	no

33

ADDRESS RANGE:

PAUSE for a moment and think about this:

```
mov    al,es:[di]
```

Our understanding of this from the 8088/86 point of view is that the content of DI is used to calculate the address from which the data is fetched into AX;

physical address = **ES**x16 + [DI]

35

That is, the physical address is the segment value multiplied by 16 (effectively moved left 4 places) to make a 20-bit base-address, to which the offset in DI is added. Since the offset is a 16-bit value, we have an addressable range within this segment of 65,000.

HOWEVER the 80386 has 32-bit registers, so;

```
mov    al,es:[edi]
```

Has an offset of 32-bits, which means that the offset can be up to 2^32 = 4.3 BILLION. So who needs segments? The offset alone can address the entire physical address range. Segmentation is still a useful feature however.

REAL MODE:

189

This means that the virtual addressing capability of the 80386 is disabled. This also disables the multitasking capability. Physical address calculation reverts back to that employed on the 8086 (described above), and the interrupt-vector table resides at segment zero in memory just as for the 8088, so MSDOS and 8088 programs should run quite happily. This is however crippling the '386.

VIRTUAL MODE:

189

There are special features built-in to the CPU, that the operating system makes use of. Each task must be protected from the other -- memory allocated to each must not overlap, no task must access another task's memory area unless specifically allowed to, and no task must mess-up the operating system and I/O. Taking care of all of this is called memory management.

Protection between tasks is accomplished by having an address translation table for each task. The program may think that it is reading address F000:0408 (ie it is a "virtual address"), but the table translates this into the area of memory set aside for the task, isolated from all other tasks.

The '286 employs memory management by segmentation, while the '386 improves upon this by adding another mode, memory management by **paging**, as well as a special **8086 virtual mode**. The latter is of particular interest for multitasking DOS applications. *206*

MEMORY MANAGEMENT BY SEGMENTATION

This applies to both the '286 and '386, as the latter is designed to be upwards compatible with the entire '86 family.

Index...

SEGMENT REGISTERS:

In real mode, the CPU behaves just like the 8088, and the segment registers contain actual physical paragraph addresses.

In '286 virtual mode, the values in the segment registers no longer directly represent physical addresses. We refer to the values in these registers as SELECTORs.

LOCAL DESCRIPTOR TABLE:

When the operating system loads a program into memory, it also loads appropriate values into the segment registers. The operating system also creates a LOCAL DESCRIPTOR TABLE (LDT) in memory, into which it puts the actual physical segment addresses of the program.

Get this picture clear in your mind..... The physical addresses are no longer in the segment registers. Since this is a multitasking

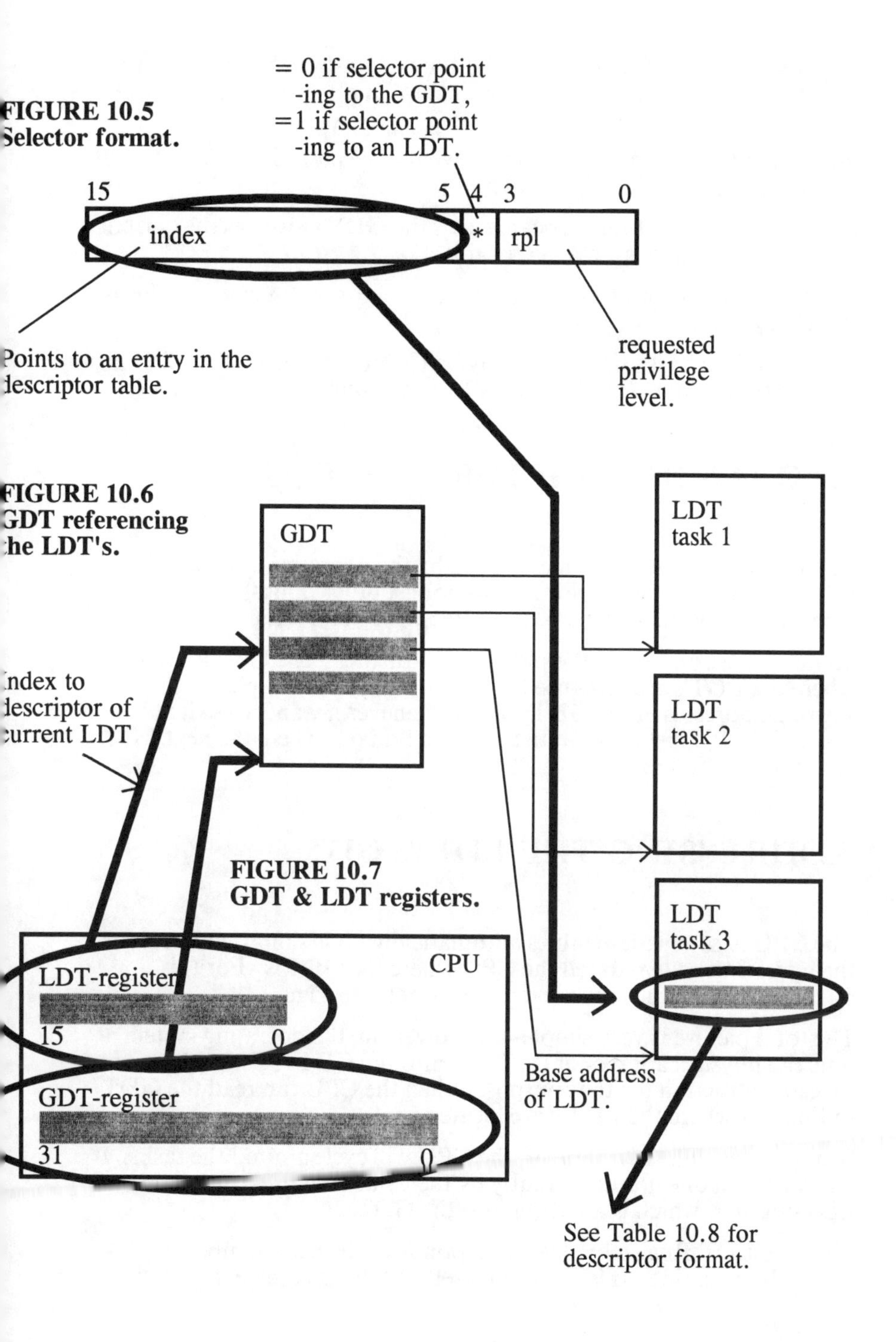

FIGURE 10.5
Selector format.

FIGURE 10.6
GDT referencing the LDT's.

FIGURE 10.7
GDT & LDT registers.

environment, an LDT is maintained for each task (program), and the selector values in the segment registers are simply offsets into the LDT. have a look at Figures 10.5 to 10.8

Just pause for a moment and clarify what a selector looks like. It's not just an address -- refer Figure 10.5.

Note that a segment register can access the GDT as well as the current task's LDT -- there is a reason for this.

Note too the four-bit field for privilege-level for that segment -- this is discussed later.

Thus changing tasks involves changing to another LDT. The CPU has a neat way of doing this, but firstly let's introduce the GDT.

GLOBAL DESCRIPTOR TABLE (GDT):

192

There is only one of these maintained by the operating system. The GDT contains physical addresses (amongst other things) of various resources, in particular the base-addresses of the LDT's.

So now pause and build the picture a bit further. The CPU knows where the LDT's are, because the operating system has placed their starting addresses in the GDT. Thus whenever it wants to switch tasks, the CPU just looks in the GDT to find out where the next LDT is --- refer to Figure 10.6.

ADDRESSING THE LDT & GDT:

The CPU accesses these tables automatically. It is simply a matter for the operating system to tell the CPU where the GDT is. For this purpose the CPU has special registers--- refer to Figure 10.7.

The total picture is very simple--- at power-on, the operating system puts the physical address of the GDT into the GDT register (there's a special instruction for that purpose), then the CPU can read the GDT to find out where the LDT's are located.

In a multitasking environment, the CPU will cycle around the tasks. It knows which one it is at currently by the value contained in the LDT-register, which is an offset into the GDT.

Thus the LDT-Register value corresponds to the task-number currently executing. It is not an "offset" exactly, as each entry in the

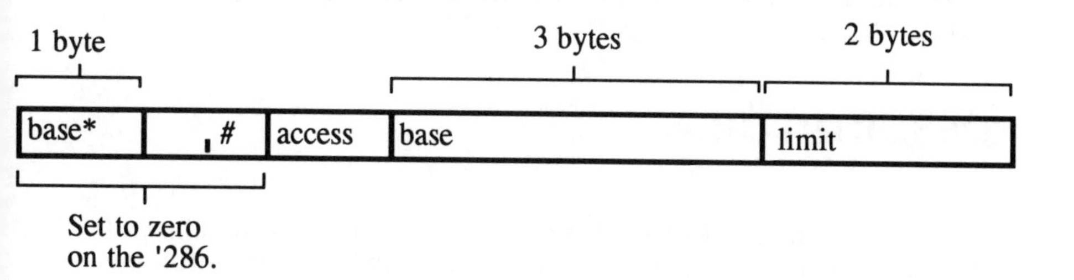

FIGURE 10.8

Descriptor Format.

Alongside is the legend for the above descriptor.

Descriptors reside in LDT's and GDT's -- refer back to Figure 10.7 to see how the descriptor within the GDT can reference a descriptor within an LDT, which in turn can provide the physical address and other information for a segment.

*	The segment base (starting) address for the '286 is only 24 bits, while for the '386 is 32 bits (*=high part).
#	The limit (size) of the segment, in bytes, which can only reach 64K with the '286, but virtually no limit with the '386 -- the higher part of the segment size resides here (#).

ACCESS-BYTE:

DPL-field	(2 bits) determines the privilege level of the segment.
P,A-bits	Present & Accessed bits enable the operating sys. mem. management.
R,W-bits	Read&Write bits set read /write contraints on the segment.
C-bit	Conforming bit.
ED-bit	Set if segment is a stack.

GDT is more than one byte, but is a pointer to the n-th entry in the GDT.

DESCRIPTORS:

192

Each entry in the GDT or LDT is called a Descriptor. It contains not just a physical address, but also vital information for the multitasking environment.

The basic **format of the GDT** is described elsewhere, but we can pause at this point and see what a descriptor looks like -- refer to Figure 10.8.

192

With reference to Figure 10.8, the legend-box explains some of the descriptor fields. The "access" field is interesting. The bits contain various status information.

SWICHING YOUR CPU INTO VIRTUAL-MODE:

You don't necessarily need OS/2 or similar for this. Plain old DOS has functions that your application program can use to switch into virtual mode, and take advantage of memory management and multitasking, all under DOS.

Jump off for a look at DOS functions for switching into protected mode >>>>

188

Before doing this in your program under DOS however, you would need to do what a multitasking operating system does automatically --- set up a GDT.

The basic format of a GDT is described elsewhere >>>>

192

Note:

There are other complexities in implementing multitasking or virtual memory management under DOS and I don't recommend you tackle it from scratch. Various modules are available commercially to assist here. Better yet, use an operating system designed specifically for this purpose.

FIGURE 10.9 Shadow registers.

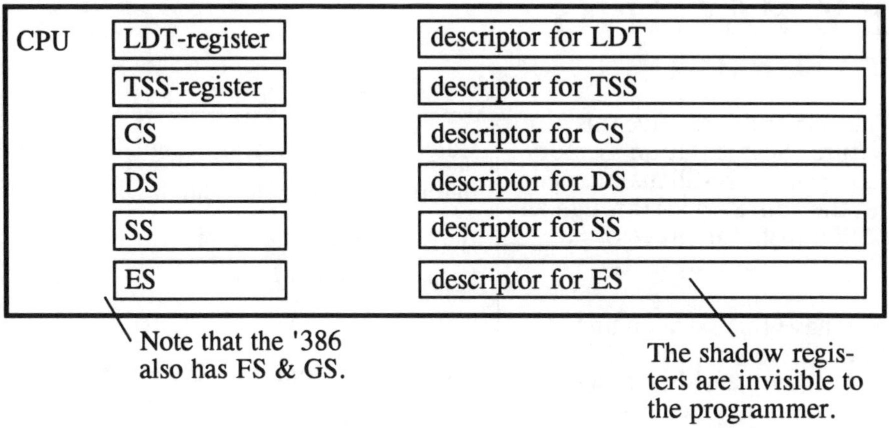

CPU		
	LDT-register	descriptor for LDT
	TSS-register	descriptor for TSS
	CS	descriptor for CS
	DS	descriptor for DS
	SS	descriptor for SS
	ES	descriptor for ES

Note that the '386 also has FS & GS.

The shadow registers are invisible to the programmer.

SHADOW REGISTERS:

There is a major problem with these tables--- every time the CPU needs to access memory it will have to get the physical segment address from the current **LDT**. This is going to slow execution down enormously.

200

The cure is more complexity inside the CPU. Each segment register has a shadow register, and each shadow register contains the current Descriptor.

Get this--- the shadow register contains the Descriptor, part of which contains the physical paragraph address. This may seem philosophically wrong somehow--- these highly evolved chips threw the actual physical addresses out of the segment registers into LDT's and the GDT. Now they have sneaked back in, as shadow registers.

So this is the picture --- refer to Figure 10.9.

So what was the point of throwing the paragraph-addresses out of the segment registers in the first place? The answer to this is protection. Your program can't get at the shadow registers, so you can't access physical memory directly and possibly stuff up the multitasking environment.

Now for the speed issue. When the CPU changes tasks, it reads the GDT and LDT and loads the shadow registers. Automatically. So from then on it has the physical addresses inside the chip and can go at full speed.

MEMORY MANAGEMENT BY PAGING

The '386 and '486 have this feature. Segmentation memory management is still maintained, but the address goes through an extra translation process:

Why have this extra paging unit? There are various reasons, not least being that memory managment of segments, of any size from 0 to 64K, is awkward for the operating system. Far better for the swapping in and out of chunks of program in a multitasking environment if those chunks are all the same size, and preferably small.

The paging unit does this. It breaks a segment up into 4Kbyte "pages", each of which can be mapped anywhere in the physical memory.

Calculation of address using LDT descriptor, as per the '286, however the '386 contains a 32-bit base-address field.
|
The address from the LDT is not a physical address, as it has to go through another translation process. In this case it is referred to as a "linear address". It is 32-bits.
|
Paging unit. Produces actual physical 32-bit address.

The precise mechanisms involved with memory management are quite complicated, and not the central focus of this particular book. Suffice to say that the "linear address" forms an offset into "page tables", that contain the actual physical address of the page.

The CPU has various extra registers for maintaining the paging mechanisms, most importantly CR3, which contains the base-address of the Page table Directory. This is the picture -- Figure 10.10.

CR3 register tells the CPU where the Page Table Directory is. The Linear Address is split into fields, part being a Page table Directory offset, pointing to an entry in the Directory which contains the base address of a particular Page Table.

Bits 12 to 21 of the linear address are used as an offset into the Page table.

FIGURE 10.10
Page tables.

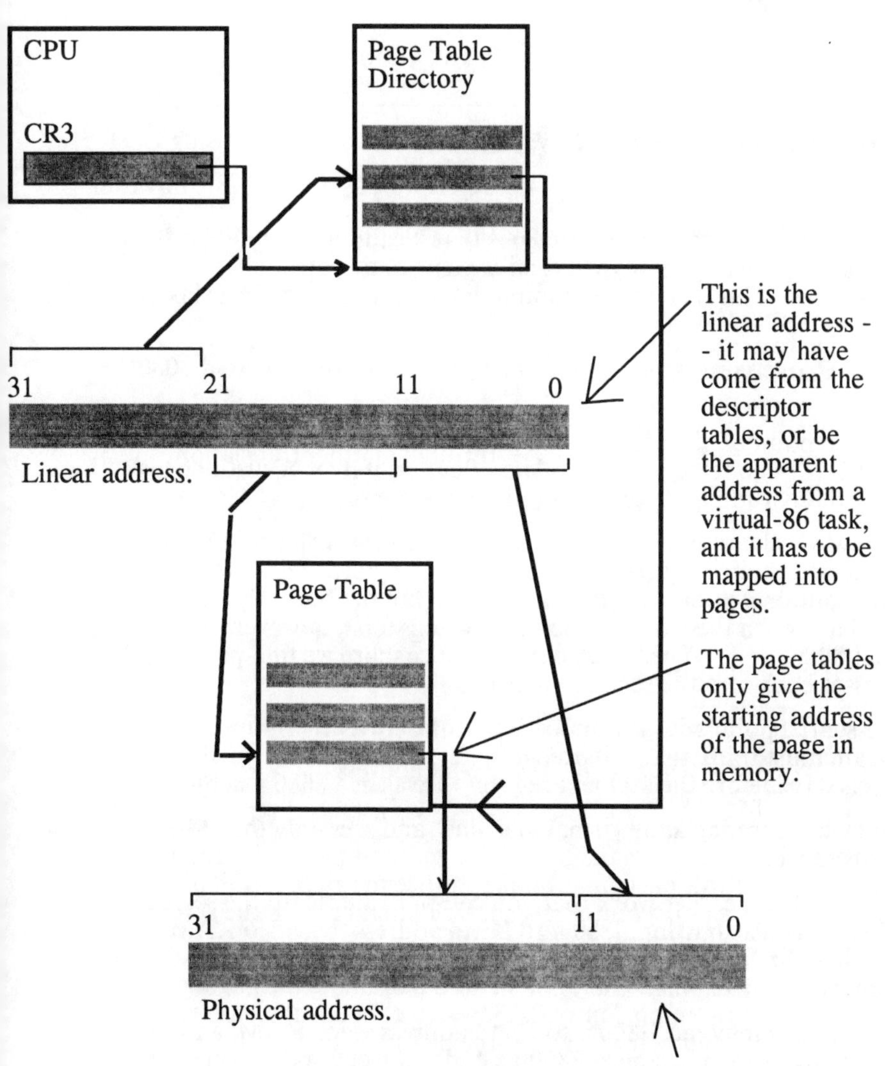

The entry in the page table contains bits 12 to 31 of the final physical address, while bits 0 to 11 of the linear address require no translation and become part of the physical address.

VIRTUAL 8088/86 MODE

A serious disadvantage of the 80286 is that it cannot emulate the 8086 while taking advantage of virtual-addressing and protection mechanisms. Thus AT-model computers mostly run merely as faster XT's.

The 80386 overcomes this limitation, with what is called virtual-8086 mode.

From the point of view of each program, the system looks just like an IBM-PC XT-model, only faster. And of course it may be just one task among many running together on the '386 system.

It is now a rather curious turn of events: when the '286 or '386 operate in protected modes as described above, their segment registers no longer contain actual paragraph addresses (but of course they did sneak back onto the CPU, in the shadow registers), however the virtual-8086 mode comes a full circle, as once more we find paragraph addresses back into the segment registers!

The essential point with this mode is that the currently running program must think that it is executing in a 8086 machine, in all respects. Therefore the segment registers are as in a 8086 machine.

Each task is running as a "virtual machine" and sees only the 1Mb address space.

You know from earlier work that you can put values into the segment registers, such as putting B800 into ES to address the video RAM. Well, virtual-8086 mode is completely happy with this, but don't forget that this is a "virtual machine", not an actual one.

Although you may put B800 into ES to address video RAM, and the virtual address then becomes B800h x 16d + offset as per normal 8086 CPU's, the address that actually comes out of the '386 CPU is something else. The virtual address goes through page tables, so can be translated anywhere in the entire RAM address range of the '386.

Interestingly, descriptor tables are not used -- the 20-bit virtual address goes straight into page tables.

FIGURE 10.11 Paging Mechanism for Virtual-86 Mode.

Instead of putting the 20-bit linear address onto the address bus, as for real-mode, Virtual-86 mode uses the upper 8 bits of this address as a lookup in the current table -- note that the table entry contains the base-address of the page, which is combined with the lower 12 bits of the linear address to form the actual 32-bit address. It is this final 32-bit address that the CPU puts out for a memory access.

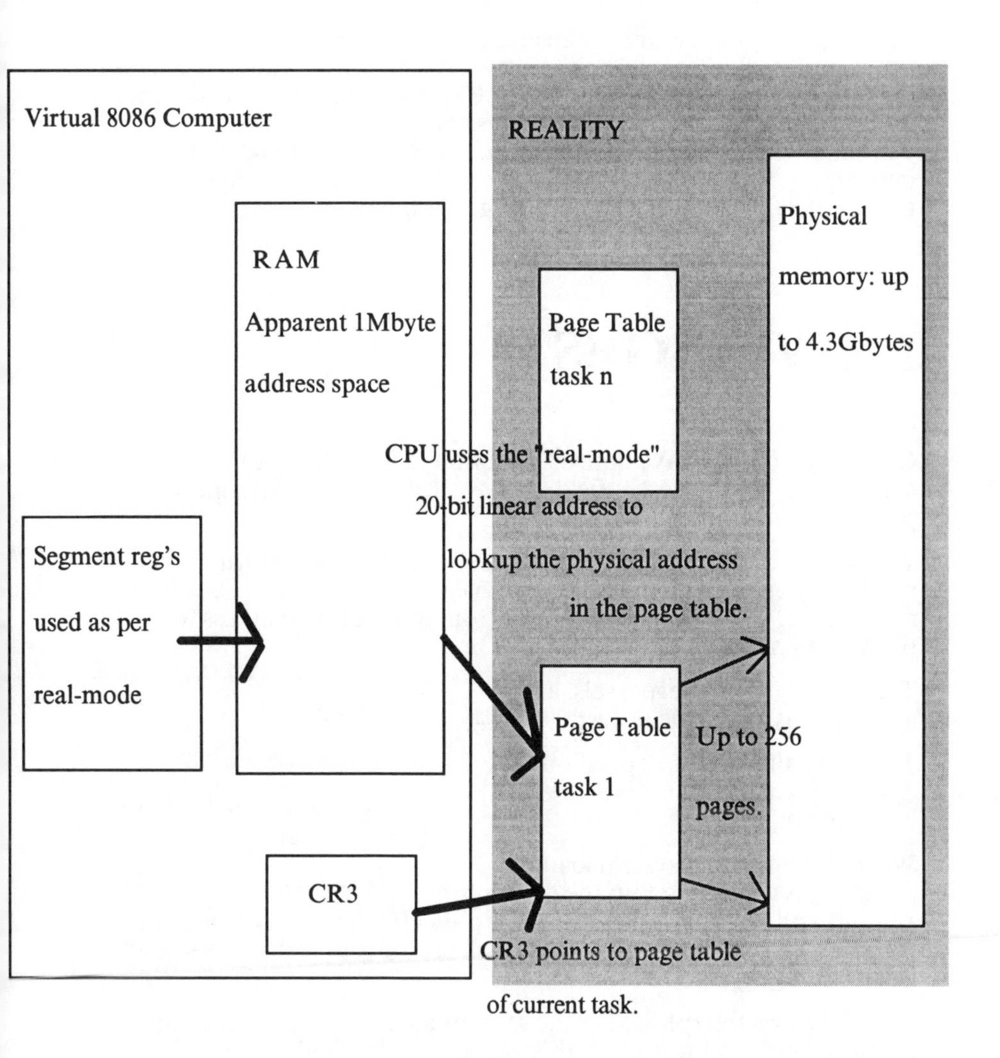

So what happens if your program writes directly to video RAM at segment B800? This is up to the operating system, which most likely will create virtual-screens for each task, set up anywhere it wants to in RAM. Only the current foreground task will have actual screen output -- done simply by copying the virtual-screen contents to the display-RAM during a task-switch, and changing the page table entries for the new task so video output goes directly to the display-RAM.

This is all very clever, and means that all DOS applications will run in a true multitasking environment. A DOS application can even access the interrupt vector table at 0000:0000 and alter vectors, yet the table itself can be located anywhere in physical memory, and is a table dedicated to that one task -- the operating system, if it uses the interrupt table, has the original version located at actual physical address 0000:0000, which cannot be got at by tasks.

PRIVILEGES

One thing you will have noticed about the **descriptor** is that it contains within the access-field, 2 bits called the dpl -- descriptor privilege level. *204*

The corresponding on-chip selector also has the same information, referred to as the rpl -- requested privilege level. This is a protection mechanism, to prevent applications from unauthorised access to places they shouldn't go.

There are four privilege levels, and applications are at the lowest:

0 -- kernel
1 -- system services
2 -- custom extensions
3 -- application

The exact allocations depend on the operating system, but this is the usual breakdown.

When the operating system loads a program, it will also set up the descriptors, and put appropriate values into the dpl-field. The CPU will read the Local Descriptor Table and load the shadow registers and the selectors (segment registers).

The CPU uses the rpl-field in the selector as the program's current privilege level, and will check this against the dpl-field in the descriptor. The rpl's value must be equal to or less than the dpl for access to be allowed.

FIGURE 10.12 Translation Lookaside Buffer.

The Translation Lookaside Buffer is simply a cache of the 32 most recent page table look-ups, thus speeding performance. The TLB is located inside the CPU and minimises the performance degradation of having to perform an external table fetch every time a memory operation is required. The concept is similar to the shadow registers used in segmentation.

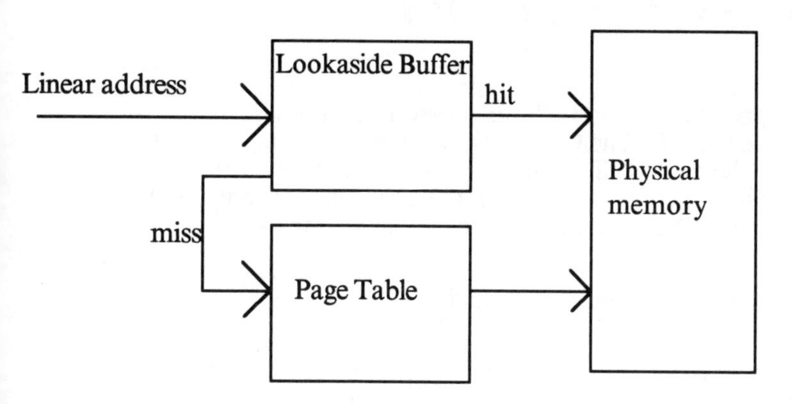

Actually, the TLB uses what is called a "content addressable", or "associative" memory, a technology that allows faster lookups. There is no conventional address & content -- rather only two adjacent contents, organised like a table of two columns. The "address" input to the TLB directly references the first column -- if a matching entry exists in the first column, then the output "contents" from the TLB will be the adjacent entry in the second column.

This is done directly in hardware and is very fast. If the address input does not have a matching entry in the first column, then there is a miss -- of course the TLB is much more than just an associative memory, with various control functions. Every time a page table is read, the page index and the content are read into the two columns of the associative memory -- older entries are discarded.

Thus the CPU has a very fast technique for reading the page table -- an entry only needs to be read once from the external memory, and from then on is within the CPU.

It does this checking before loading the shadow register.

Note that the operating system may set the rpl to a higher value than the program's current privilege level (cpl) when accessing routines with less privilege than the current program.

TASK SWITCHING

Task switching has been described previously as the process of changing to a new LDT. The CPU looks into the GDT and finds the base address of the next LDT, then loads its LDT-register with the new address. The selectors need not change since they are only indexes into the LDT. The CPU will then automatically load the shadow registers from the new table.

The paging process does something similar.

However there are all sorts of complications with a task switch, such as how to save all the CPU's registers. To save the current state of a task, before it is switched out, yet another table is required, in fact one of these is required for each task.

The table is called the Task State Segment (TSS). It is a complete segment, with a corresponding descriptor contained in the GDT. Thus the GDT contains not just descriptors for the LDT's as described earlier.

The CPU has yet another register, called the TSS-register, that is an index into the GDT, pointing to the descriptor for the current TSS -- refer Figure 10.13.

The format of the Access-field in the descriptor distinguishes the descriptor as a TSS-descriptor rather than an LDT-descriptor.

Basically, the TSS saves all the CPU's registers, the current TSS-register and LDT-register values, and maths coprocessor registers (if there is one).

A little note at this point: other information can also reside in the GDT, such as what are called "Call-Gates", that are far calls particularly to operating system services. These Call-Gates can cross privilege levels.

And another little note: the INT instruction transfers control to an operating system service, or maybe a custom routine, usually at a more privileged level, but this is allowed. A special table of these vectors is ıaintained, called the Interrupt Descriptor Table (IDT), and the CPU ıaintains yet another register, the IDT-register, that contains the base ddress of the IDT.

'hus the interrupt vector table can be located anywhere in memory.

'he chapter on advanced operating systems goes into **Call-Gates**. *306*

FIGURE 10.13 Task State Segment.

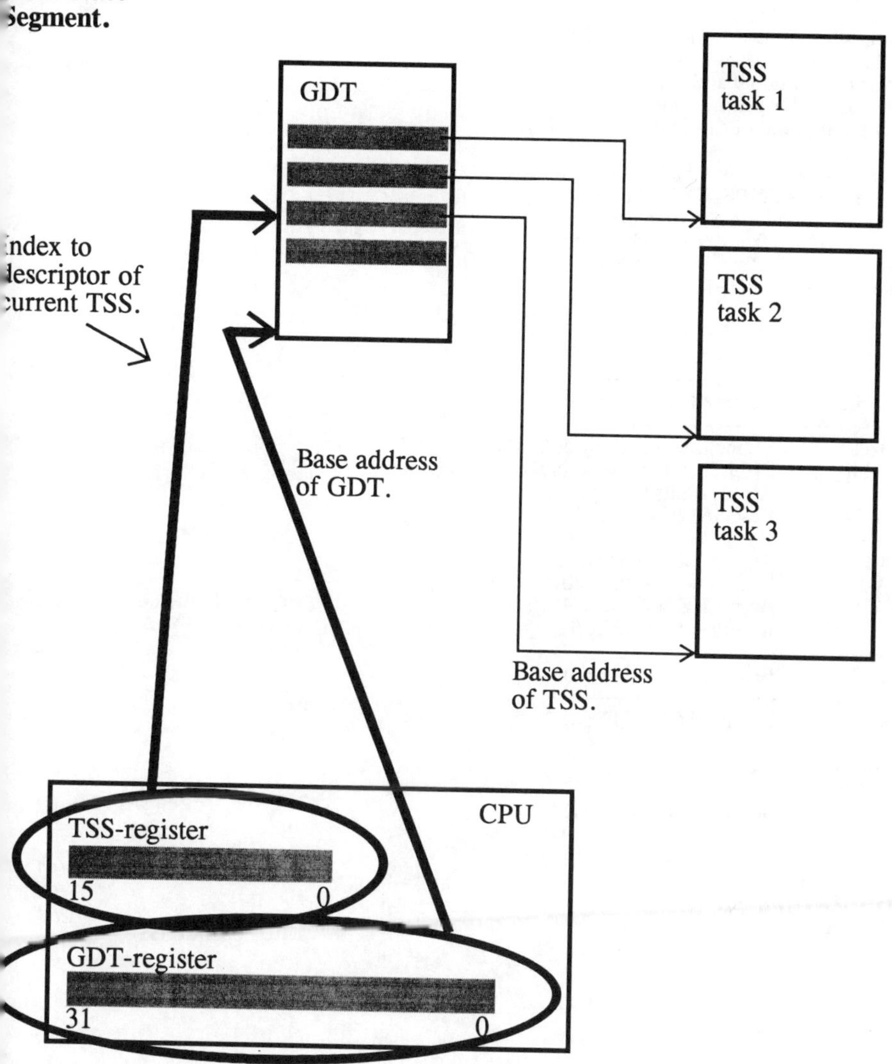

WORKSHEET: EXTENDED MEMORY

Running the CPU in protected mode requires a lot of setting up, and we will not reinvent the wheel, since many suitable operating systems already exist, including extensions to DOS.
A most useful BIOS service is INT-15h/f-87h, which copies blocks of data to and from conventional and extended memory -- very useful for getting code and data temporarily out of the 640K, such as TSR's.

The Source Listings, Chapter 20, contain some code -- EXTEND.COM.
Analyse it, and use it -- then do the reverse -- load from extended to convent.
Note that Prior to calling the BIOS service, the GDT was created as follows:

BYTES	DESCRIPTOR CONTENTS
00-07h	Reserved (should be 0).
08-0Fh	Reserved (should be 0).
10-11h	Segment length in bytes*.
12-14h	24-bit linear source address.
15h	Access rights (always 93h).
16-17h	Reserved (should be 0).
18-19h	Segment length in bytes*.
1A-1Ch	24-bit linear destin.address.
1Dh	Access rights (always 93h).
1E-1Fh	Reserved (should be 0).
20-27h	Reserved (should be 0).
28-2Fh	Reserved (should be 0).

*at least 2xCX-1.
NOTE:
This should work on both the '286 & '386.

References:

INT-15h/f-87h *190*
Basic GDT format *192*
Format of descriptors *204*

11

DISK I/O

The last five chapters have
een following a distinctly
ardware-oriented theme, and
t is time to swing back toward
he software. You will find the
est of this book to have a
trong software theme, with
his chapter somewhat in the
niddle -- here we explore the
lisk architecture and how we
ise the BIOS and DOS to
ommunicate with the disk.

BIOS-LEVEL DISK I/O

The main distinction compared with DOS-level disk I/O is that BIOS
INT 13h) gives direct access to disk sectors, whereas DOS functions
perate at a much higher level. We always work at the DOS function
evel for disk access, except when something sneaky is involved.

343

DISK STRUCTURE

On a standard-density floppy disk, there are 40 tracks numbered 0 to 39, and 9 sectors per track (numbered 1 to 9), each sector being 512 bytes. Track 39 is the innermost on the disk. Side 0 of the disk is underneath (opposite the label) and side 1 is on top.

FORMATTED DISK

When formatted, the disk is structured into 4 sections;

1. **boot record**, 216
2. **File Allocation Table**, 216
3. **File Directory**, 218
4. data.

A physical picture of the layout of track 0 for 360K floppies is shown in Figure 11.1.

Note that a second copy of FAT is kept in sectors 4 & 5.

BOOT RECORD;

A single sector, located sector1, track0, side0. Contains a bootstrap program for loading DOS. ALL formatted disks have this.

FILE ALLOCATION TABLE;

Located sector2, track0, side0. Shows physical location of each disk file. TWO copies of F.A.T. are kept on disk. Size can vary from 2 sectors on floppys up to 82 on a hard disk. Since there are many different formats of disks, that is, single-sided, double-density,

FIRST BYTE	DISK STRUCTURE
FF	2 sides, 8 sectors/track, Directory: side1,sectors1,2, number of DIR entries: 112.
FE	Single-side, 8 sectors/trk, Directory: side0,sect.4,5,6, number of DIR entries: 64.
FD	2 sides, 9 sectors/track, Dir: side0, sectors6,7,8,9, side1, sectors1,2,3, 112entr
FC	Single-sided, 9sectors/trk, Dir: side0, sectors6,7,8,9, Dir entries: 64.
F9	Quad density, 9 or 15 sector
F8	Hard disk.

TABLE 11.1 First Byte of FAT

FIGURE 11.1 Track 0 layout, floppy.

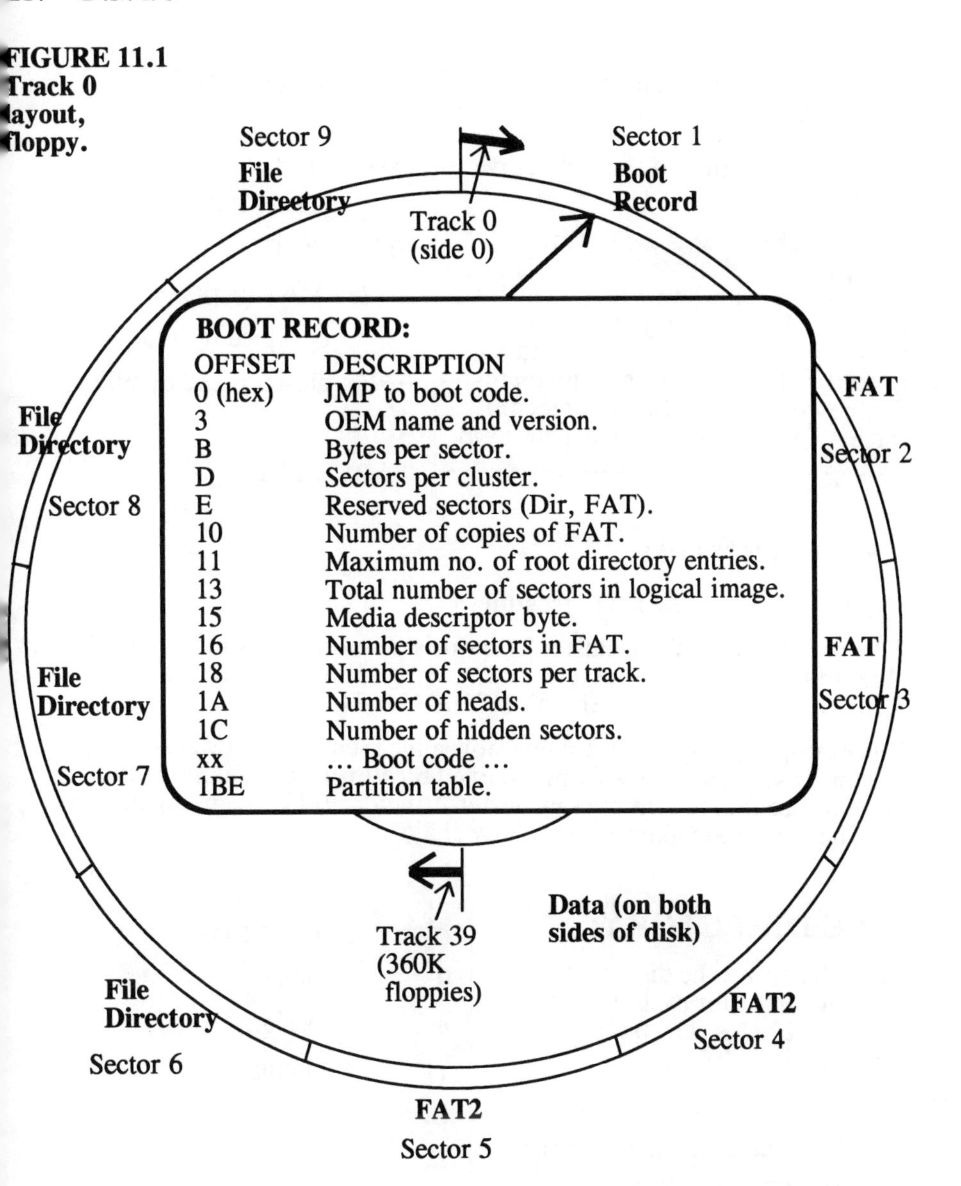

quad-density and so on, the size of the File Directory (and the FAT), its position on the disk, plus other factors, vary. The first byte of FAT shows the structure of the disk, as per Table 11.1.

For 360K floppies, 2 sectors are grouped into a "cluster", as the disk mechanism reads and writes a cluster at a time, for efficiency. The clusters are numbered from 1, corresponding to sectors 1 & 2, up to the maximum for the type of disk. Each number in the FAT indicates the current status of a cluster;

ENTRY	DESCRIPTION
0	cluster is free
FF7	"bad" cluster (FORMAT marks these).
02-->	occupied by a file
FFF	cluster is end of a file.

TABLE 11.2

FAT SRUCTURE:

Figure 11.2 shows the FAT structure.

Files can be stored from cluster 2 onwards. The first entry in FAT is an "Identification" value, that tells us the storage-format for the disk. Refer to DOS functions 1Bh and 1Ch that read this value.

The example of Figure 11.2 shows how a file is entered -- it starts in cluster 4 (which we know from the File Directory), and looking in the table we see that it continues in cluster 7, then 8, 9, 46, 47, ending in 47. The entries are likened to a "daisy chain".

FILE DIRECTORY;

Lists all files on the disk, and starting sector for each file. Each entry is 32 bytes. The basic structure is;

OFFSET	DESCRIPTION
0	filename
8	extension
11	attribute
12	reserved
22	time
24	date
26	starting **cluster** number
28	file size

TABLE 11.3

The first byte of the filename field indicates the status of the file. If this entry is not in use the byte may contain E5h; 00h indicates that it is not in use and all subsequent directory entries are empty. Other values in this position have different meanings.

IGURE 11.2
'AT Structure.

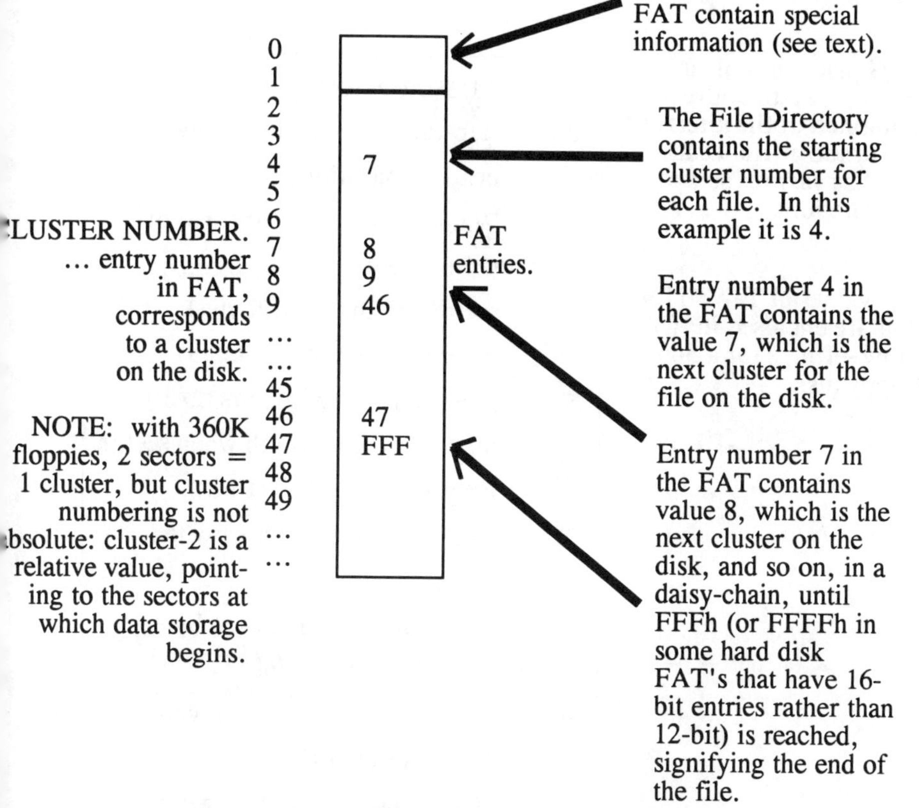

'rom the fourth byte onwards, FAT entries reference clusters, and are each 2 bits in length -- though for hard disks each entry may be 16 bits. As far s I'm aware, for disks with 1 cluster = 2 sectors, the two sectors are physi-ally located directly opposite each other -- that is, on opposite sides of the latter. It follows that hard disks with say two platters would most likely mploy 4 sectors per cluster. Although the extra platter has doubled the apacity, the FAT could still be the same size, with the tradeoff that file orage has the smallest quantum of one cluster -- the bigger the cluster the ss efficient is space usage.

DISK CONTROL PARAMETERS:

DOS places a table in memory, at an address contained in the interrupt vector table (**int 1Eh**), that has various setup information;

The values in Table 11.4 that are enclosed in "( )" show settings for a 360K floppy disk.

OFFSET	DESCRIPTION
0,1	step-rate (6mSec),dma mode (on), head unload-time.
2	Wait-time until motor turns off (25h =2sec).
3	sector length (2 =512bytes).
4	record number per track (9).
5	gap size between sectors (2Ah).
6	maximum data length when sector length not specified (FFh).
7	gap size between sectors when disk formatted (50h).
8	data value stored in each byte when formatted (F6h).
9	head-settle time, after moving to new track (0Fh =15mSec)
A	time allowed for disk to get up to speed. Measured in 1/8secs (02 =1/4sec).

TABLE 11.4

347

BIOS INTERRUPT SERVICES:

INT13 is for disk access. There are six services. Refer to--
Reference, INT-13h.

343

DOS DISK I/O

Three methods are looked at in this section...

METHOD USING FILE CONTROL BLOCK (FCB)

This method was superceded from DOS version 2.00 onwards, with the introduction of file-handles. A description of accessing a disk file using a FCB follows;

DOS COMMAND-LINE "TAIL";

On the DOS command-line, when a program-name is followed by more parameters, when the program is loaded into RAM the parameters are placed in the Program Segment Prefix (PSP). Example of DOS command-line;

```
C> DSK2SCRN B:DEMO.TXT
```

Where DSK2SCRN is the program to be executed.

Interestingly, parameters following the program-name are put into TWO places in the PSP; offsets 05Ch and 081h. The area commencing at 05Ch is in a special format, for setting up of a File Control Block, necessary to open the file specified (if the command-tail specifies a file). The format is;

OFFSET	CONTENT	EXAMPLE
05Ch	drive number	2
+1	filename (first parameter)	DEMO
+9	extension (second param.)	TXT

TABLE 11.5

Checkout what goes into 06Ch, if you wish.

Offset 081h in the PSP simply holds the command-tail as-is, without any formating. This area is 128 (decimal) bytes. Actually, offset 80h contains a count of the number of bytes in the command-tail, and 81h is usually a blank-character, since that is what is typed immediately after the program name. The command-tail will terminate with 0Dh, which is the <enter> key.

Example;

OFFSET	CONTENT	EXAMPLE
081h	parameter-string	B:DEMO.TXT

TABLE 11.6

FILE CONTROL BLOCK;

This is a special area used for opening a disk file and accessing data in it.

The format of a File Control Block is;

OFFSET	SIZE	DESCRIPTION
0(hex)	1(byte)	drive number
1	8	filename
9	3	filename extension
0C	2	current block size
0E	4	record size (bytes)
10	4	file size (bytes)
14	2	file date
16	10	...reserved...
20	1	current record no.
21	4	file-relative record no

TABLE 11.7 FCB Format

When we open up a file, most of these parameters get filled by DOS, however we do have to put in some parameters before the file is opened; these are the drive number, filename and extension. Note that the drive number is 0=default drive, 1=A:, 2=B:, and 3=C:.

The example program DSK2SCRN.ASM (on the Companion Disk, and listed in the Appendices) shows how we can setup the FCB prior to opening the file.

Note that with this example program, and the above dialogue, the implication is that the filename to be opened is provided from the DOS-command-tail, however, this is only one instance. From within our current program we can create a FCB and put any filename we wish into it prior to opening the file. Note also that the FCB is setup by us in the data segment of our program -- don't be misled into thinking it is in the PSP.

RECORDS & BLOCKS;

For convenience we break a file up into RECORDS, and a record can be any size we specify, from 1 byte to 32767 bytes. It is entirely up to us, and has nothing to do with how the data is stored on the disk. A BLOCK is defined as 128 records.

The first block in the file is block 0. The current record number is relative to the start of the current block.

The file-relative record number is relative to the start of the file. The first file-relative record in the file is record 0.

SEQUENTIAL FILE ACCESS;

The sample program DSK2SCRN.COM (the source listing, DSK2SCRN.ASM, should be on your distribution disk/s) shows this.

SEQUENTIAL_READ, **function14h**, reads one record at a time, and each time it does, updates the file-relative record number in the **FCB** automatically, so that the next time the function-call is made the next record will be read. 344 221

This allows us to go sequentially through the file, from any starting point. The opposite function to this is **function15h**, (SEQUENTIAL_WRITE). 345

Note that all functions mentioned here require DS:DX to point to the FCB.

Note also that the DTA is implicitly addressed, set by an earlier function, **no.1Ah, SET_DTA**. 346

RANDOM FILE ACCESS;

Function21h, READ_RANDOM, and **function22h**, WRITE_RANDOM, will read or write one disk record to/from the DTA. The file-relative record number in the FCB must be set to the record of interest. Of course the area set aside for the DTA must be big enough to hold the record. The file-relative record number in the **FCB** is not changed by this operation. 353 221

Function28h, READ_BLOCK, and **function29h**, WRITE_BLOCK, read or write the number of records specified in register CX, starting 353 from the file-relative record number in the FCB. This transfers large chunks, and the DTA must be big enough.

STANDARD INPUT/OUTPUT

DOS 2.00 onwards makes reference to "standard input" and "standard output".

Certain functions, such as function1, **KEYBOARD_INPUT**, were redefined to accept input from the standard input, which could be the keyboard, or a file, or some other device. **Function2**, DISPLAY_OUTPUT, was also redefined to output to the standard output, which could be a printer, screen, or a file.

350

350

The distinction between files and devices such as printer and console has become blurred.

Physical standard input or output devices can be any of these;

CON:	keyboard input, screen output.
PRN:	printer LPT1 output.
AUX:	auxiliary (COM1).

DOS enables us to redefine standard input and output on the command line, by this format;

```
program-name <input-device >output-device
```

The example program DSKSCRNB.COM shows this principle. The program is the same example given earlier, in which a file is read sequentially, processed, then output to the screen. However in this case the DOS redirection symbol < is being used to redirect standard input from a file rather than the keyboard.

Note that the filename can include a drive and path specification on the DOS command-line. Note that since output is to the screen in this example, >CON: is optional as a second parameter, since it is the default. Note the much shorter program.

FILE HANDLES

These DOS functions work with DOS version 2.00 onwards, and make obsolete all the disk access functions that require the FCB.

The FCB was designed before pathnames, so can't handle them, which was a major reason it was superceded, apart from the complexity. Here is a means of opening a file;

```
;..........................................
;data area....
filespec db "c:\wordproc\galaxy\letter.t      100
                                               221
            xt",0
handle   dw   0
....
;code area....
....
....
 mov  dx,offset filespec                       100
 mov  al,0                                     355
 mov  ah,3Dh                                   355
 int  21h
 mov  handle,ax
....
....
;..........................................
```

Function3Dh, OPEN, supercedes func. 0Fh, and expects DS:DX to be a string with the pathname & filename, terminated by 0 (called an ASCIIZ string). Various information must also be provided in AL, but for simplicity we will only consider bits 0-2, which must contain an "access code" as follows;

CODE	MEANING
0	open for reading.
1	open for writing.
2	open for both reading & writing.

TABLE 11.8 Access Code

The function opens the file and returns a file "handle", a number in AX. If the operation failed, an error code is returned in AX (marked by the carry-flag set). From now on the file can be specified by its handle.

HANDLES:

A program can open many files/devices, and each will be assigned a handle number by DOS. The first five handles are **reserved** by DOS;

HANDLE USE	DEFAULT
0 standard input	CON: (keyboard)
1 standard output	CON: (screen)
2 standard error output	CON: (screen)
3 " auxiliary device(AUX:)	COM1:(serial)
4 standard printer (PRN:)	LPT1:(printr)

TABLE 11.9 Reserved Handles 275

Thus those DOS functions that require a handle in register BX can be made to access the keyboard, screen, printer or serial port by putting one of the above values into BX.

If **functions3Ch or 3Dh** are used to open a disk file, the handle assigned by DOS will be some number between 5 and 20 inclusive.

RANDOM/SEQUENTIAL READ/WRITE;

Having opened a file with function3Dh (or 3Ch) we can then read from or write to it.

Function 3Fh, READ_HANDLE, expects a handle in BX, the number of bytes to read in CX, and the Disk Transfer Address in DS:DX. After the operation, AX contains the actual number of bytes read. If AX=0 the end of file has been reached. If carry flag set, AX contains an error code. Example;

```
;............................................
;data area...
dta     db 0    ;Disk Transfer Area.                100
...                                                 355
 mov  bx,handle      ;READ_HANDLE
 mov  cx,1           ;    /
 mov  dx,offset dta  ;    /                         100
 mov  ah,3Fh         ;    /                         355
 int  21h            ;/(char-->DTA)
...
;............................................
```

The opposite operation is function40h, WRITE_HANDLE.

Note that these two functions are suited to sequential access also, as they automatically move the filepointer to the next byte. This introduces the filepointer....

FILE POINTER;

This is an essential aspect of random file access. The above functions utilise a file-pointer to ascertain where in the file to read from or write to. This is very different from DOS1.xx's records and blocks.

The file pointer specifies the number of bytes from the beginning of the file, and is returned in DX:AX after **function42h**, MOVE_FILE_PTR. 356

Function42h expects an offset in CX:DX and a "method code" in AL.

If AL=0 then the offset becomes the new file-pointer value. The offset in this case is an unsigned number.

If AL=1 then the offset is added onto the existing file-pointer value. The offset in this case is a two's complement 32-bit number.

If AL=2 the offset is from the end of the file (new file-pointer = total file size - offset). Again offset is two's complement.

To simply increment the file-pointer;

```
;.........................................
...
 mov  cx,0    ;offset.
 mov  dx,1    ;/
 mov  al,1    ;method code.
 mov  bx,handle
 mov  ah,42h
 int  21h
...
.....................................
```

356

Note that it is quite possible to move the filepointer beyond the beginning or end of the file, and DOS will not return an error message. To avoid using function-42h to accidentally move the filepointer beyond the end of the file, you can use this function to find out the file size --- can you figure out how?

For sequential usage note that functions 3Fh and **40h** update the file pointer automatically. That is, if you use 3Fh to read a single character, the filepointer will increment by 1, so next time you call 3Fh the filepointer will already be pointing to the next character in the file. 355

WORKSHEET: DISK I/O

1.
Rewrite our example program to use **functions3Fh and 42h**. The DOS command-tail is only to require the source filename;

355

A> programname filename

(Drive and path allowed with filename).

Note that the command-tail will be found in the PSP at offset 081h. Use **function 3Eh** to close a file.

355

This Worksheet is not so difficult. You can use the example programs DSK2SCRN.ASM and DSKSCRNB.ASM as guides, except of course your program must use the DOS-handle method.

NOTE
A solution to the above has been supplied as DSKSCRNC.ASM.
Optional further exercises are as follows --

2.
Modify the above program so that when the program is executed it displays only the first 25 lines of the file, and by pressing the <Page-Down> key the next 25 lines display.

3.
If that was easy enough, expand the program so that by pressing the <Page-Up> key the display will go back 25 lines.
A hint here is to save the filepointer values where the first line starts, by pushing them onto the stack.
A <Page-Down> can push a value onto the stack and a <Page-Up> can pop it off.

12
PROGRAM DESIGN: STRUCTURE & OBJECTS

Asm is an unstructurerd language, unlike C and Pascal, however that does not mean we can justify the writing of "spaghetti-code". On the contrary, structure is entirely up to us, in the design phase, and Asm programs can be very nicely structured.

Of course some of the structured flow-of-control constructs do not exist in Asm, but we can simulate them, and it could be argued that in smaller sections of code nice-looking structure doesn't matter. A crude JMP over major sections of code can also be quite useful at times, so we should not be structured fanatics.

A good basic rule is to make extensive use of procedures (and I hope that students pick up good programming practice from my example programs). This used to be the only advice I gave my students, along with encouragement to plan beforehand, perhaps with "Pseudocode" and a hierarchy chart of the procedures. These days however we are being told that to be "with it" we must use objects. Object Oriented Programming (OOP) is "in", but can we apply these principles to Asm, and is there any point in doing so? The constructs of C, for example, have been added to and extended to encompass OOP concepts, giving us C++, but with Asm we only have the basic instruction set to work with, plus the current crop of Assembler directives and operators. Will we be torturing Asm, and ourselves, by trying to force OOP onto Asm programming?

Note that I decided not to write about conventional structured techniques in this chapter, but OOP is another matter, as to use it requires special knowledge of some of Asm's higher-level features.

OOP BACKGROUND:

Right from the start let me say that OOP is not the answer for all programming problems. In fact it has somewhat limited usefulness for the kind of applications for which we usually write Asm code. Problems that are rigidly sequential are especially unsuited to OOP. Often we may find it practical to implement only part of a program using OOP techniques. A fundamental problem with OOP is that it goes against our main reasons for using Asm: speed and compactness, yet the advantages in the design stage, plus maintainability and reusability, may outweigh the disadvantages in many cases.

I have found OOP to be amazingly useful, even at the Asm level, which has quite surprised me ... with the qualification that its use lies in mixing procedural code and object-oriented as needed. So much so that I felt it necessary to add this chapter to the latest edition of my textbook. However the task of describing how to practically use OOP is not an easy one. I have studied a number of books on the subject, and found that it took some time before the concepts crystallised into true understanding. Part of the problem is the proliferation of terminology, and worse still, different authors define some terms in conflicting ways. "Class" and "Object" for example. I did find a book with the promising title of "Object Oriented Assembly Language", however it did not answer the particular questions I was asking. The reference I liked most came from a single article in Dr Dobb's Journal; "Object Oriented Programming in Assembly Language", by Randall Hyde, March 1990, pp. 66-73, 110-111, though it's not for the OOP neophyte.

OOP neophytes should start here. This chapter ignores the confusion of terminology and goes straight to the basic principles, with simple code examples. There are only three terms I want to use: Class, Object and Instance. Wherever I have used another strange word, it should not detract or distract from the learning of the material. If you want a thorough treatment of all the terminology, concepts and programming techniques, there is an excellent OOP visual design tool called ObjectCraft, that comes with a nice introductory manual: ObjectCraft Inc., 2124 Kittredge Street, Suite 118, Berkeley, CA 94704, USA.

OOP PRINCIPLES:

feel that the best way to teach OOP is by example. So, let's say that you wanted to write a program that draws little shapes on the screen. Of course it could do a lot more as well. What we have to do is identify every little item in the program, such as a shape, as an "object". Furthermore we should try to identify objects that are related to each other; that inherit properties from each other. Obviously the sharing of code saves space (but there's much more to inheritance).

You could for the time being consider "class" and "object" as having the same meaning, which is quite true in many circumstances. Class can more truly be thought of as the definition of an object. The object we are labelling as a shape includes all the code and data associated with that shape. We could start the design of our program by sketching this -- have a look at Figure 12.1.

TOP-DOWN OOP:

The oval represents the object, while the rectangle represents a data variable associated with the object, and the rectangle with the arrow-head at one end is code associated with the object. What we are doing here is top-down design. I started off in the most general terms, at the maximum level of vagueness if you like, by drawing an oval representing the shape, and what data and code I think any shape should have. Perhaps I might want to draw many different kinds of shapes in my program, but it is important initially to think of the totality, of what pertains to all shapes. What I thought all the shapes would want is vertical and horizontal coordinates, to set the size and proportions of a shape. Hence I put VERT and HORIZ variables onto SHAPES. Then I thought that all shapes need to know where they are to be placed on the screen, hence ROW and COL. SIZE is code for accessing VERT & HORIZ, and PLACE is code for accessing ROW & COL. Finally I considered that all shapes would need a routine to actually draw the shape on the screen, given all the parameters -- that I called REDRAW (I've referred to it as a "dummy method", which I've explained below -- keep reading. There is another unanswered question at the moment -- why have I defined two methods SIZE and PLACE to "access" the variables?).

Most OOP intro. textbooks give examples of objects that you can very readily think of as being almost physical entities, such as "shape" followed by sub-classes of "box", "oval" and "triangle". Note however that an object need only be a logical concept or grouping of data/code, not necessarily a visual entity. Here I am following the classical line.

I gradually worked from the general to the specific, splitting SHAPES up into the particular shapes I wanted -- in the Figure I chose just two; BOX and CIRCLE. Now a most important concept -- our object BOX, having being defined as a subclass of SHAPES, inherits all of SHAPES' data and code. A complete copy of SHAPES' data is made for BOX, but the original SHAPES' method-code is not copied, since the data contains pointers to it .... in the case of REDRAW, I want BOX and CIRCLE to have their own redraw routines, and the dummy REDRAW pointer in SHAPES will ensure that the subclasses can have different procedures but all with the same name. That is, I put REDRAW onto SHAPES, knowing that all subclasses would need a method called REDRAW. Make the note that all subclasses are able to use the code from higher levels, and inherit all data structures with the same names as earlier classes, but unique to the current object. Alternatively, a subclass can rewrite a method yet it will still have the same name as before. Practice will show the importance of this. A little note about BOX -- I

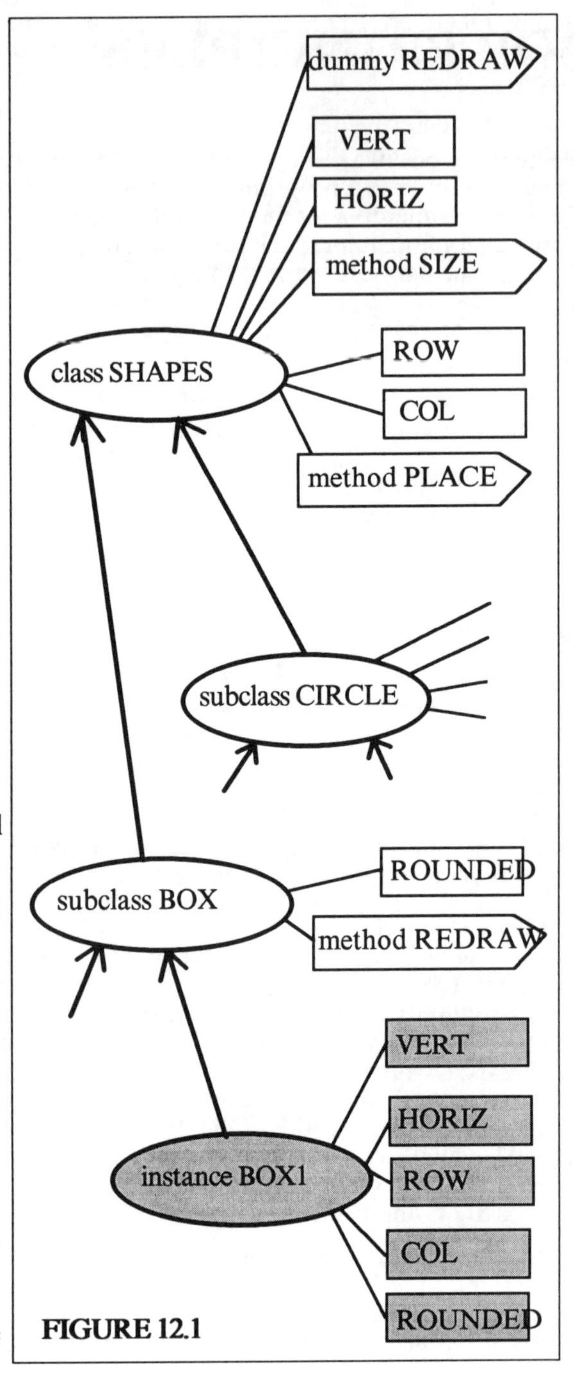

FIGURE 12.1

attached ROUNDED to it, being a parameter specifying rounded corners -- I did not put it onto SHAPES as it is not generic to all shapes.

The classes describe data structures and code for the objects, but to draw a box at a specific location requires an "instance" of BOX. For each box that we want to simultaneously display, we will require a specific instance, with different names, perhaps BOX1, BOX2, etc.

An instance, when in existence, will have an actual data area created for it, in the data segment or heap, which can be destroyed when the particular instance of BOX is no longer required. The dynamic creation of instances in memory, and subsequent destruction, is something you should plan for in the program, however with this simple example I have only implemented static instances.

STRUC DIRECTIVE:

```
;data segment....

BOX       STRUC
NAME      db "0123456789"
SIZE      dw 0
LOCATE    dd 0
BOX       ENDS          ;end of structure
   ......
BOX1      BOX <"BidBox",32,1200>
BOX2      BOX  <"ResultBox",58,4015>

;code segment....

     mov    ax,BOX1.SIZE

     mov    bx,OFFSET BOX1
     mov    ax,[bx.SIZE]

     mov    ax,[bx+10]
```

We do need to use some higher-level constructs available in Asm. STRUC works just like data structures in higher-level languages, and is very useful. There's nothing revolutionary about it; it's just a convenient way to define arrays of data with various fields. The listing shows the data structure called BOX. BOX is just a label for the starting address of the data, while NAME, SIZE and LOCATE label each field. It is most important to note that Asm equates these field-names as offsets from the <u>start of the structure</u>, not the segment. Having created the structure we can then assemble specific instances of it -- in this case we have created BOX1 and BOX2. The "< >" delimiters enable us to initialise the data, with "," delimiting fields -- "< >" without anything between would leave the data fields set to whatever BOX defined them as, and two commas together means do the same for just that field. For example if I rewrote the definition of BOX1 as follows:

```
BOX1  BOX  <"BidBox", ,1200>
```

.... then the SIZE would be left as 0.

The code portion shows how to get at the data. Note the "dot" operator; this is there for compatibility with C, but Asm treats it exactly as it does the "+" operator. The four examples all do the same thing; load BOX1's SIZE into AX.

MACROS:

The student should have encountered the concept of the macro in higher-level languages. I mention it here as my example OOP code makes use of a macro. Unlike a procedure, the macro expands in-line when the program is assembled. Inefficient from the point of program size, but fast as it avoids the time overhead of procedure call and return.

```
;macro definition....
;(in code segment, outside procs.)
    .....
NOWIS   MACRO    instance_label
    mov   bx,SEG instance_label
    mov   es,bx
    mov   bx,OFFSET instance_label
    ENDM
    .......
    ......
;usage of the macro....
    NOWIS  BOX1
    ......
```

"NOWIS" can be any label, and is the name of the macro. Simply putting this label in the code causes the expansion of the macro at that point. This example shows how a parameter can be passed to the macro (more than one can be passed); "BOX1" becomes "instance_label" inside the macro.

CONSTRUCTING AN OO PROGRAM

An object consists of data and code. By use of STRUC we can declare such a data & code structure. The listing here shows how SHAPES has the data variables VERT, HORIZ, ROW, and COL, and pointers to methods, labelled REDRAW, SIZE and PLACE -- the actual procedures would be located somewhere in the code segment.

No problems so far. Now consider BOX, which is a child-object of SHAPES, and inherits SHAPES' data and methods. An invaluable aspect of Structures is that they can be nested (this is a qualified statement), which allows us to place the structure of SHAPES inside BOX. The "< >" delimiters allow initialisation of the data; in this case it is left at the default values set by SHAPES, except for the REDRAW_BOX routine.

Notice the naming convention I have given to the methods, for example PLACE_SHAPES. This is so that when you see the procedure in isolation somewhere in the code, you will immediately see its prefix describing its action

```
stack1      SEGMENT stack  'stack'
    db      128  DUP(0)
stack1      ENDS
;...............................................
data        SEGMENT  'data'
    ......
SHAPES   STRUC
REDRAW  DW  ?          ;dummy method.
VERT        DB  5
HORIZ      DB  5
SIZE        DW  SIZE_SHAPES
ROW         DB  0
COL         DB  0
PLACE      DW  PLACE_SHAPES
SHAPES   ENDS
            ;Note; use DD for pointers if
            ;multiple code segments.
    .......
BOX STRUC
    SHAPES  < REDRAW_BOX,,,,,, >
ROUNDED  DB  0
BOX  ENDS
    .....
;create an instance of BOX....
BOX1        BOX   < >     ;could initialise
BOX2        BOX   < >     ; parameters.
    .....
NOW         EQU  [bx]     ;or es:[bx] see below.
    .....
data        ENDS
;...................................................
code        SEGMENT  'code'
    ASSUME  cs:code
    ......
```

; *listing continued next page ....*

or what it does, followed by the structure or class it is associated with.

For the specific case of an actual box to be drawn on the screen, I have created an instance BOX1, with data initialised appropriately. Note that I have defined an alternative procedure for REDRAW, named REDRAW_BOX. The methods will use the data fields ROW, COL, VERT, HORIZ & ROUNDED, but note that the correct data in the instance we are currently working on will only be accessed, unless we specify otherwise. Thus data of the same name in other instances is not touched. This is very useful and fundamental to OOP -- how it's done will become clear.

Let's say the code is currently working on instance BOX1, and calls method PLACE. Furthermore let's say that this method wants to read variable ROW, which is a reasonable requirement. Trouble is, variable ROW exists in four different places, but of course we want the method to access this variable in BOX1. This is where some of OOP's inefficiency comes in. Some kind of pointer has to be passed to every

;listing continued from previous page....

```
NOWIS   MACRO  instance_label
;refer to previous page for macro to load
;es:bx, if need access multiple data segments.
    mov    bx,OFFSET instance_label
    ENDM
    ......
;..................................................
main        PROC  FAR
    mov    ax,data
    mov    ds,ax
    ASSUME  ds:data
    .......   .....
    NOWIS  BOX1
    mov    dx,0105h        ;row & col
    call   NOW.PLACE
    .....
    call   NOW.REDRAW
    ......
    ......
    mov    ax,4C00h        ;back to DOS
    int    21h
main        ENDP
;..................................................
PLACE_SHAPES  PROC  NEAR
;the new row and column coordinates are
;passed to PLACE via DX.  DH=row (0-24)
;DL=column (0-79).
    mov    NOW.ROW,dh
    mov    NOW.COL,dl
    RET
PLACE_SHAPES  ENDP
;..................................................
REDRAW_BOX  PROC NEAR
;no parameters passed to this one.  It just
;uses ROW, COL, VERT, HORIZ
;& ROUNDED to redraw the box.
;note again that NOW override is used to
```

; listing continued next page ......

```
;listing continued from previous page....
;access only the data at the currently pointed
;-to instance.
      ......
;some code here to draw box on scrn.
      ......
REDRAW_BOX ENDP
;.....................................................
SIZE_SHAPES  PROC  NEAR
;perhaps this could have some parameters
;passed to it, to update VERT & HORIZ,
;then return with a pass/fail in AX.
      ......
      .....
SIZE_SHAPES  ENDP
;.....................................................

CODE      ENDS
      END  main
```

Complete Listing as OBJECT.ASM on Companion Disk & Appendix D.

method from the calling code, and every method has to use this pointer to access the correct data structure.

In practice it's not difficult. NOWIS is the macro that places the pointer in BX and this macro must be inserted before a method-call. Also, inside the method, every reference to a data field must use NOW override (NOW is equated to [BX] -- see the data segment definition). In procedure "main" look at what I have done -- I set the pointer to BOX1 by passing it to the macro, then called method PLACE. NOW.PLACE is the same as DS:[BX+offsetPLACE] -- in case you find this a little bit confusing, don't worry, as the technique itself is straightforward.

There's nothing to stop me from passing parameters to PLACE, by the stack or registers, which doesn't appear to violate any OOP rules. We haven't decided what method-PLACE is supposed to do -- let's say that it receives parameters from the calling procedure and just updates ROW & COL, then returns, perhaps with a pass/fail message in AX. This brings me to another important principle of OOP -- our code must not directly access the data of another object. To modify ROW & COL, which we could quite easily do -- but mustn't -- we must call a method declared as part of the object containing ROW & COL. Hence we have to call PLACE to change data in BOX1. The reason for this restriction is that all code that can affect the data must be attached to the object, so that it is completely self-contained and fully defined. This greatly aids modularity, transportability, predictability and maintainability.

In the listing you'll see that I have called REDRAW to draw the box with the new coordinates. The pointer has already been set to BOX1, so no need to do it again.

I could of course have the program do a lot more, but this suffices to show the principles of objects. To round off the description of the program we now need to look at the actual coding of the methods. They are just procedures.

The main procedure passed the new row and column coordinates to PLACE via DX -- this is an arbitrary decision. Inside PLACE I only need two MOV instructions to update ROW & COL -- note the use of NOW to provide [BX] override -- so that data in BOX1 only will be accessed. In theory I could access data in BOX2 (or any other object) from within the PLACE_SHAPES procedure or from main, or from anywhere, simply by an instruction like this;

```
movBOX2.ROW,dh
```

But I must not. Instead I must use NOWIS to point to BOX2 and then call method PLACE. Look at the incredible overhead just to execute two instructions! The macro, followed by procedure call and return. Welcome to OOP!

IMPORTANCE OF "NOW" PREFIX:

One more important point, mentioned earlier but its significance may have escaped you. In "main" I have called REDRAW, but recall that I gave BOX its own redraw procedure -- logically the same thing would be done for CIRCLE, which means that we have two REDRAW procedures. Yet we use the same name for all of them. Higher-level languages refer to it as "polymorphism", but with Asm it's not so transparent -- we have to manipulate NOW.

I have used the override NOW to reference the current object. It is a bit of a nuisance to have to precede all method-calls and data accesses by the NOW prefix, but there is a useful outcome in terms of readability. Anything without the NOW prefix you will know is a call or data-access to conventional non-object code and data. In a practical program there is likely to be a mixture. Don't ever forget the NOW override, and don't ever try and call a method that is not associated with the current instance, as specified by NOWIS. Asm has no way of checking for this kind of design integrity -- it's up to you.

CONCLUSIONS:

OOP has taken modularity one step further. Inheritance of data structures, while protecting the data of each object from that in other objects, plus inheritance of methods while retaining this data integrity, is the essence of OOP. My class called BOX can be used to create other subclasses and/or instances -- it is a very clean way of drawing multiple boxes on the screen, without any conflicts of data or code. BOX is also eminently reusable in future programs, extremely easy to read and easily maintained. OOP is in fact a complete program design & maintenance methodology, and highly recommended.

A final, but most important note: the example program listed in this chapter doesn't actually work, so don't try it as-is. There are some little refinements that need to be made for a particular Assembler, so use the program OBJECT.ASM on the Companion Disk. This program is much larger, with many more useful comments, and has comments on differences between MASM's and TASM's handling of structures. Just a couple of points here;

1. MASM doesn't let you nest structures, while TASM does, so the nesting of SHAPES into BOX requires a kludge with MASM. Initialising of instances in both cases is a kludge. .... ah-ha! ... just before going to print with this edition I had a quick look at the spec's for the new MASM version 6.0, and guess what .... it supports nesting of structures!

2. MASM & TASM don't allow forward address references within a STRUC definition, which may mean that the listing of the definition of SHAPES as shown in this chapter, needs to be modified.

3. STRUC field-names must be unique, which goes against our ideal requirements for OOP. TASM has an "ideal mode" of operation that defines field-names as local to the structure, but imposes a restraint on how the fields of instances can be accessed from the program, which means that the NOW override won't work as-is.

LINKING WITH C++

C++ function members can be written in Assembly language, and in-line Asm code works okay too. I have given an explanation of this in **Chapter 14**. 264

WORKSHEET: OOP & ASM

1.

The example program OBJECT.ASM on the Companion Disk is to be expanded. Note that it currently assembles correctly with TASM, and requires a modification to the nesting of SHAPES into BOX to be assembled by MASM -- see comment in file.

The program is to display four boxes, one at each quarter of the screen, and all different sizes.

2.

Add another variable to SHAPES; COLOUR. This colour variable will be inherited by BOX, and procedure REDRAW_BOX is to make use of it when drawing a box. The program is to have the four boxes each a different colour.

3. **ADVANCED WORK**:

Create a new top-class called KEY (not a sub-class) that accepts keyboard entry and displays it in the current box. The current box is to be selectable by typing the keys 1, 2, 3, or 4 (so these are not sent to the display).

Class KEY will need a method TRANSFER to input the key and send it to the screen. You could create a data field attached to KEY, called CHARACTER, to temporarily hold the character, plus another variable that specifies which box is the current one for output. This latter variable could be called SWITCH and would have the value 1, 2, 3, or 4.

TRANSFER would have code to read a character from the keyboard, determine if SWITCH is to be updated, and if not look at the value of SWITCH to determine which box the character is to go to. It would be proper OOP for any output to the box to be via a method attached to SHAPES; create this and call it CHAROUT. TRANSFER can pass the parameter CHARACTER to CHAROUT via a register.

Main will have to call NOW.TRANSFER of instance KEY1, after setting NOWIS KEY1.

13

RESIDENT PROGRAMS

This Lesson brings a number of important concepts together, including how to modify the interrupt table, to make a program resident, and to multitask under DOS.

Contents of this Chapter:

INTRODUCTION TO TSR's

This is a fascinating topic. It does represent a quantum leap in your work through this book, but well worth learning about.

This section describes three different techniques--

1. True multitasking using **INT-8**, the 55mSec timer interrupt, *341*
2. A resident program that pops up by utilising **INT 9** vector to check for a "hot-key", *342*
3. Ditto, but using **INT-16h**. *345*

There are three example programs provided to show each of these:

INT8.ASM	INT9.ASM
INT16.ASM	

A resident program is one that you load in the normal way, by typing its name at the DOS command-line, and DOS then loads the program, which then executes. The resident program, also called a TSR (Terminate & Stay Resident), has two executable portions:

install portion,
runtime portion.

INSTALL PORTION:

The install portion is what executes when the TSR is first loaded, and doesn't do very much. It mostly just alters one or two of the vectors in the interrupt table.

Let's say it alters **interrupt-9**. This entry in the table points to a routine in BIOS ROM, which is the routine that handles all keypresses, reading the keyboard, converting the scancode to ASCII, and putting the keycode into the keyboard buffer, ready for a program to read the character via **INT-16h**.

69

345

INT-9 is a hardware interrupt, generated every time a key is pressed or released. This is fully explained in the chapter on the keyboard interface.

342

What the install portion does, is change the address in the table to point to its own runtime-portion, but also saving the old address in its own data area.

Do you see what will happen? -- whenever a key is pressed or released, control will go to the runtime portion of the TSR, not the original BIOS routine.... have a look at Figure 13.1.

One final thing the install portion does is exit back to DOS using a special interrupt that leaves the TSR resident. Normal exits back to DOS releases the memory occupied by the program, so it is once more free, but TSR's want to stay in memory permanently.

Summarising this, whenever a key is pressed or released, control goes to the TSR, which checks to see if the character is that required to pop-up the TSR. Usually this is some special key combination, such as <ALT-Z>. If not, the runtime portion simply jumps to the original BIOS routine, so keyboard handling continues as normal.

Thus it is as though the TSR isn't there at all -- it only becomes active when it detects the correct keypress. Then the runtime portion does

FIGURE 13.1 TSR installation & structure.

Key pressed/released: hardware INT-9 generated. CPU looks at entry no.9 in table. (TSR's that are activated by the keyboard usually make use of INT-9 or 16).

Start of memory; address 00000.

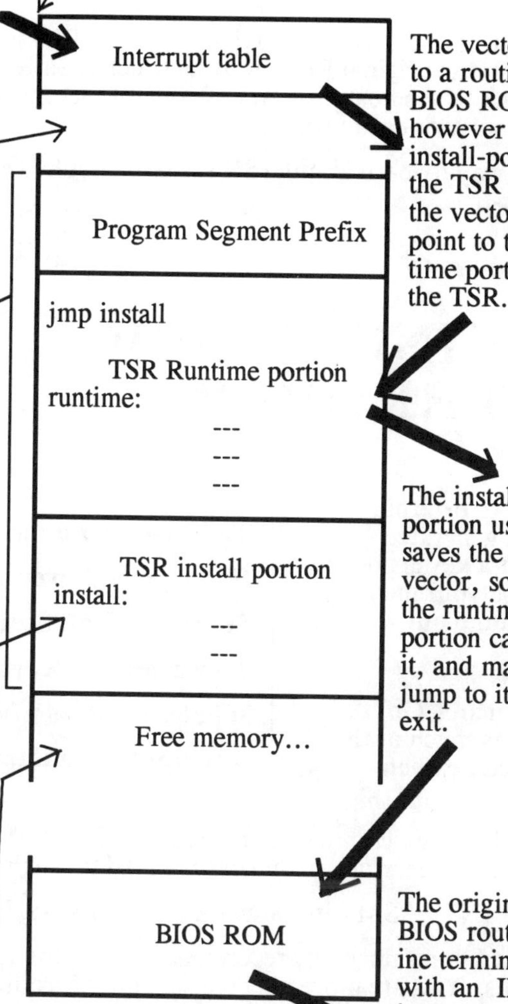

Interrupt table

The vector points to a routine in the BIOS ROM, however the install-portion of the TSR alters the vector to point to the run-time portion of the TSR.

This part of the memory map has BIOS/DOS data areas, resident DOS, and device drivers.

Program Segment Prefix

The TSR is first loaded by DOS as per any other program. Internally however it is structured into two executable portions. Note that the PSP, of size 100h, is created by DOS when the program loads and is not part of the disk file.

jmp install

TSR Runtime portion

runtime:

The install-portion usually saves the old vector, so that the runtime portion can call it, and maybe jump to it upon exit.

TSR install portion

install:

When the program first loads, execution starts at the install portion. This portion alters the appropriate interrupt vector/s then uses a special software interrupt to return to DOS while leaving the TSR resident (DOS normally deallocates a program upon exit). Since the install portion only needs to execute once, upon return to DOS all memory past INSTALL: is made free.

Free memory...

BIOS ROM

The original BIOS routine terminates with an IRET instruction, which returns control to whatever was executing prior to the interrupt.

Free memory is where another application can load. When an application is running, the TSR is still in memory and can be invoked. In the case of INT-9, all keypresses will invoke the runtime portion, which typically looks for a hot-key -- if not found, control continues on to the original vector.

whatever it is meant to do. Most of you will have encountered TSR's in some form or other.

When the runtime portion does detect the correct hot-key, it does its thing, and when "put away" goes back to the program running prior to the interrupt.

It can do this in one of two ways-- by an IRET instruction, or by jumping to the original BIOS routine which itself terminates with an IRET back to the host program. Which of these two options to use depends on various factors.

The best way to learn about TSR's is by example, and we'll look at INT-9 first.

MAKING USE OF INTERRUPT-9

INT-9 is an external interrupt generated whenever a key is pressed. To refresh your memory on this, jump out:

To brush up on the Interrupt table	*62*
For a general overview of INT-9	*69*
Summary (Ref. Section) of INT-9	*342*
To Review the Keyboard Interface	*137*
What CPU does when interr. occurs	*139*
Structure of an interrupt routine	*139*

There you are! Go through as much of that lot as need be, then proceed.

I've put the entire commented source code for INT9.ASM into this chapter, as it is instructive to carefully read through it.

I called it INT9.ASM, since it makes use of INT-9, logically enough.

Note that I don't normally recommend INT-9 for TSR's, as it can be dangerous. You are more likely to stay out of trouble by using INT-16h. However INT-9 is the only option for certain applications.

Microsoft publish an "MSDOS Encyclopaedia" that gives a skeleton TSR -- the listing is about a dozen pages long! -- a lot of special checking is included and I recommend that you study a reference like this before developing serious TSR's that make use of INT-9 or INT-8.

245

For more explanation of this >>>>

Now for the listing. Note that if you have the Companion Disk for this book, it will also be on that. It is important to bear in mind that it is a skeleton program only -- the **listing** is given near the end of this Chapter.. *248*

ANOTHER APPROACH TO TSR POP-UP

The method used in INT9.COM is very hardware-dependent, since it requires direct communication with the keyboard and Interrupt Controller's registers.

Also a routine invoked by INT-9 can easily cause problems, due to the non-multitasking nature of DOS. DOS functions are not re-entrant, and this poses constraints on use of DOS services within the interrupt routine. If you invoke the interrupt routine while the computer is in the middle of a DOS routine, and your routine also calls a DOS routine, expect trouble. Your routine could also be invoked in the middle of some time-sensitive operation, such as disk access; again possible disaster.

Thus use INT-9 with extreme caution, or not at all.

Another, indirect, method is to use **INT-16h**. This is the BIOS service used by all programs and DOS itself to access the keyboard buffer. INt-16h reads the buffer AFTER INT-9 has put characters into it. Thus they will have been processed in some way by INT-9. My INT9.COM program needed to use INT-9 as it had to grab the scancodes directly from the keyboard. *345*

If your TSR redirects INT-16h via itself, it will be invoked everytime a program or DOS calls that service. In practice this is quite okay.

Even for programs that only use DOS services, not BIOS services, still DOS itself translates all DOS keyboard calls down to BIOS INT-16h calls.

One of the main reasons INT-16h is safe is that DOS or a program will only try to read the keyboard at a time when nothing time-critical is happening in the system.

Let's cut this short. I've put some code **listing** near the end of this Chapter to show this. You will note that it avoids direct access to the hardware, which is a plus-point for portability. *249*

Note that even with INT-16h there are some DOS functions that you should avoid, due to the peculiar ways in which DOS works -- Int-21h/Function-9 for example. It would appear that the conflict potentially arises with any DOS console I/O function, so avoid these.

MAKING USE OF INTERRUPT-8

DOS was never designed for multitasking. Popping up a TSR is not true multitasking, as only one program executes at a time. DOS does have one special multitasking built into it --- printer spooling, for which there is a special DOS function call, however for true multitasking of programs we have to go to DOS shells such as Microsoft Windows.

There is however a simple method using **INT-8**, which is a hardware interrupt that occurs every 55mSec. If this is redirected via a TSR, then we have multitasking.

341

INT8.ASM demonstrates "multitasking" by using a resident program and the timer-interrupt. A resident program opens many possibilities, and can be made to execute at the "same" time as another program. This is achieved by using int08 to call the resident program. Int08 is generated every 55mSec, and updates the BIOS clock.

Our INSTALL routine can change the interrupt-8 vector in the interrupt table, to divert to the RUN_TIME routine, which would in turn transfer control back to the proper BIOS routine after doing whatever it wants. However, IBM/Microsoft considered that programmers would want to access the 55mSec timer, so provided int1Ch "USER_TIMER_INT", which is called by int08 routine after it has done its own housekeeping.

Normally int1Ch consists of simply an IRET instruction, but we can divert it to our own routine, which would terminate with an IRET.

Note that our RUN_TIME routine could do many other things; maybe display the date or time on the screen continuously if we wished, rather than a message, in which case our routine would have to access int21h, functions 2Ah and 2Ch.

The program INT9.COM accessed the interrupt table, but due to the danger of an interrupt occurring while writing to it (which we got around by a CLI), IBM/Microsoft provided INT21h functions 35h and 25h to do the job. This program uses these. Here is an extract of INT8.ASM:

```
run_time:   ;displays message on scrn.
;note; routine must be kept very short,
;as it is recalled every 55mSec.
;best to drive video ram directly.
; ...push all regs onto stack....
 mov  ax,0b800h ;video ram segment.
 mov  es,ax    ;    /
 mov  si,offset message                    100
 mov  di,0     ;video offset.
 mov  ah,0f0h  ;attribute.
 mov  cx,001dh ;loop count.
next_char: lodsb ;display a char.          42
 stosw              ;    /                 42
 loop   next_char                          39
 iret   ;back to wherever.
install:
 mov    al,1Ch ;get interrupt vector.
 mov    ah,35h ;     /                     354
 int    21h    ;     / (--> ES:BX).
 mov    int_offset,bx   ;save vector.
 mov    int_seg,es      ;    /
 mov dx,offset run_time ;loadnewvector
;COM file, so DS already set okay....
 mov  al,1Ch           ;     /
 mov  ah,25h           ;     /             353
 int 21h               ; / (DS:DX-->).
 mov  dx,offset install ;point free mem,
 int  27h              ;leave resident.    348

;..................................
```

```
;INT9.COM   Barry Kauler, March 1989.
;This program introduces two programming
;principles...
;1. How to make a resident program.
;2. How to install a custom int routine.
;The intention of this program is to
;provide a standard means of exiting
;back to DOS from any program.
;When any key is pressed, a hardware
;interrupt 09h is generated.  If the
;key was ESC the application program may
;interpret it as a command to "go back"
;a step.  This routine detects three
;consecutive presses of ESC and responds
;by exiting entirely from the program.
;The program has two portions, an
;install, and a runtime portion.
;Executing the program from the DOS
;command level will cause the install
;portion to run. It changes the Interupt
;Vector table, so that an interrupt
;will jump to a different user-created
;routine. Once the redirection is done,
;control reverts to DOS, but uses
;INT 27h, which leaves this program          34
;resident in memory.
;Note that INT 27h requires the next
;free memory address in DS:DX.
;Note too that the install portion
;removes itself after executing.
;The user-created int. routine reads the
;keyboard scan code, and detects three
;consecutive ESC's. After checking the
;scan code it does nothing else and
;passes control to the original int09,
;unless three ESC's are detected, in
;which case it exits to DOS.
;The new interrupt routine is labeled
;RUN_TIME. RUN_TIME remains resident
;until computer is rebooted.                 4
;Any programs loaded subsequently to
;installation of INT9.COM will go into
;the area defined by INSTALL as free
;after RUN_TIME.
;note that at runtime, int09 will cause
;the segment and offset to be loaded
;into CS:IP from the interrupt-table,
;and control will go to RUN_TIME, but
;DS could be anything.  Thus it needs to
;be set equal to CS at the beiginning of
;RUN_TIME for data addressing to work.
;.....................................
com_seg segment                              101
 assume ds:com_seg,cs:com_seg                102
 org    100h                                 102
int9        proc   far                       102
 jmp    install
;data area...
int9_addr dw    0,0                          100
```

```
esc_cnt  db    0                                         100
run_time: ;entered due to any key press.
 pushf          ;save flags
 push ax        ;save register.
 push ds    ;     /
 push cs    ;ds needs to be made =cs.
 pop ds     ;
 in  al,60h ;read keyboard scan code.                    135
 cmp al,81h ;release ESC key?(bit7 set)                  44
 je  continue ;do not reset ESC_CNT.                     32
 cmp al,1      ;is it pressing of ESC?
 jne unfinish ;      (scan code =1).
 inc esc_cnt  ;record consec. ESC's.                     47
 cmp esc_cnt,3 ;test limit.
 jne continue ;do not reset ESC_CNT.
 in al,61h ;keyboard ack housekeeping.                   135
 or al,80h ;     /                                       49
 out 61h,al ;     /                                      135
 and al,7fh ;     /                                      49
 out 61h,al ;     /
 mov al,20h ;signal end of int to 8259.                  64
 out 20h,al ;     /
;note that int. has left stuff on stack.
 add sp,6 ;stuff pushed start of routine                 47
 add sp,6 ;should get IP,CS,F's off stck
 sti      ;enables interrupts.                           139
;note that normal exit from interrupt is
;IRET,but we are aborting.
;note also that INT20h won't alwayswork
;so use this method...
 mov al,0         ;back to DOS.
 mov ah,4ch      ;     /                                 357
 int 21h         ;     /
unfinish: mov  esc_cnt,0   ;clear count.
continue:
 pop ds ;restore original (unknown) DS.
 pop  ax
 popf
;awkward problem here as JMP uses DS
;-- need CS overide.
 jmp  dword ptr cs:int9_addr ;go to                      53
;original int09 (far jump).
;.....................................
install:
;reconfigures int09 in address table.
 mov  ax,0 ;point to int09 in addr table
 mov  es,ax          ;  / (segment)
 mov  di,24h         ;  / (offset)
 mov  ax,es:[di] ;save orig. int09 addr.                 35
 mov  int9_addr,ax   ;       /
 mov  ax,es:[di+2]   ;       /                           34
 mov  int9_addr+2,ax ;       /
 cli            ;disable interrupts,
;to avoid a disaster.
 mov  es:[di],offset run_time ;new int09                 100
 mov  es:[di+2],cs         ;  addr.
 sti           ;enable interrupts.                       139
 mov  dx,offset install ;tell DOS free
 int  27h ;addr, exit but keep resident.                 353
```

```
;extract from INT16.ASM.....
;data area....
int16save       dw 0,0
dump            dw 0  ;scrap.
;...............................
runtime16:
;a little theory on interrupts-- an int
;causes 3 16-bit values to go onto the
;stack -- flags, cs, ip, with ip on top.
;interestingly, a far-call--- CALL xyz
;FAR --- puts cs & ip on stack but not
;flags.
;All BIOS routines terminate with a FAR
;IRET, which expects flags,cs,ip on
;stack.
;the calling program will have put a
;value in AH to select a subfunction of
;int-16, so must sort this out...
;You will notice some stuffing around
;with the stack in the code, as at exit
;it must be exactly as it was when
;runtime entered.
;
;What we are going to do here is call
;the original int-16h routine. the
;INSTALL portion of this program will
;have saved the old int-16h interrupt
;vector in a data area called INT16SAVE.
;A problem is that this BIOS routine is
;terminated with a FAR IRET, ---
;to make sure the stack is right for
;this, PUSHF is placed before the CALL..
;
;Have a good look in the Appendices on
;how INT-16h works.  You will see that
;it has various subfunctions, selected
;by a value in AH.  This value will
;determine what we now do...
;..........
 sti      ;allows interrupts.                139
 push ax   ;**NOTE AX SAVED HERE**
 cmp ah,0                                    44
 je readkey
 cmp ah,10h
 jne notreading
;
readkey:
 pushf
 call dword ptr cs:int16save ;read key       53
 cmp ax,2C00h    ;test for ALT-Z
 jne nothotkey
 pop ax   ;since we pushed it above.
 jmp yesthisisit
nothotkey:
 pop dump ;get AX off stack to variable
 DUMP. AX now has keycode req
 -uired by main program.
 iret     ;back to main program.
notreading:
 mov ah,1 ;refer to BIOS INT-16h
;literature.
 pushf
 call dword ptr cs:int16save  ;test key      53
 jz notaltz    ;zero-flag set if no key      32
 cmp ax,2C00h          ;test for ALT-z       44
 jne notaltz                                 32
;Since it is ALT-Z, unload it from the
;keyboard buffer....
 mov ah,0
 pushf
 call dword ptr cs:int16save ;read char.     53
 pop ax
 jmp yesthisisit
;
notaltz:
;TSR not activated, so go on to normal
;int-16 handling....
 pop ax  ;get stack original condition.
 jmp dword ptr cs:int16save                  53
;note this is a JMP, not a CALL.
;takes control back to main prog
;
yesthisisit:
;a tsr must be very careful with regs...
;should push them all here, then when
;program exits, pop all regs, then
;back to original program...
 push ax
 push bx
 push cx
 push dx
 push bp
 push si
 push di
 push ds
 push es
;
;give some thought to the segment
;regs... DS requires setting....
 push cs
 pop  ds
 jmp code_starts
;..............................
codestarts:
....
.... ;this is the guts of the TSR.
....
;to get back to main program--
...pop all regs in reverse
...order to above....
....
;In this case do not IRET back to
;main program.  Instead jump to
;original BIOS interrupt  -- this is
;because the main program invoked the
;interrupt with some intention, to read
;a key or check keyboard status, so we
;.....  look on Companion Disk.
```

WORKSHEET: RESIDENT PROG's

On your distribution disk you've got:
INT9.ASM
INT8.ASM
INT16.ASM

So there's plenty of material to work with.

1.

Your task is to do what was suggested in the **comments of INT8.ASM** --- write a program that displays the time at the top of the screen.

Both BIOS and DOS have services for setting and reading the time and date. This is the DOS service for reading the time ---

INT21h/function**2Ch**, returns the time, in the following format---

REGISTER	CONTENT
CH	hour
CL	minute
DH	seconds
DL	hundredths of seconds

The values are normal binary numbers.

The BIOS services are a problem, as it depends what version of DOS and what machine you have.
INT-1Ah,AH=02, reads the clock time, but not on plain XT machines.
A basic BIOS service that should work on all machines is **INT-1Ah**,AH=0, which reads the number of 55mSec "clock ticks" since you turned on the power.
Returns---

REGISTER	CONTENT
CX	High word of count.
DX	Low word of count.

AL=0 no 24-hr overflow since power-up.

This is the service you will use for this Worksheet.
Note that PC's later than the very early models have an inbuilt **battery-powered clock**, and when the PC powers-up it reads this clock and sets the BIOS clock 171 to the real time. Thus INT-1Ah will return the real time.

Your program will use INT-8 so that it displays the "clock ticks" as a continuous background task.

You should note a slight complication here--- the count is supplied as a binary value, but to display it on the screen it will have to be converted to ASCII decimal digits. 246

I have supplied a routine to do this, but it may need some modification to suit your needs--- >>>> 128
A problem with this conversion routine is that it will only handle binary values in DX:AX up to a certain amount, beyond which the DIV instruction in the routine will give a divide overflow. 353
You could work out a way for the conversion to handle higher values.

****WARNING1:****
This program is to be a TSR, but I strongly suggest that you first write it as a non-TSR. That is, don't make it resident, and don't modify the INT-8 interrupt vector.
The reason for this is that once you start messing around with the interrupt table there can be unfortunate repercussions to the rest of the system if there is a bug.
Also TSR's are very difficult to debug.

346 ******WARNING2:********
Do not call a DOS-service from within your INT-8 routine, only BIOS-services. If you do, DOS may crash. Even avoid BIOS calls if possible.
My advice is to boot up on a floppy disk and have all programs on the floppy -- do not access the hard disk at all.

14

LINKING MODULES

Ve are now delving into ome more advanced ıspects of programming. A ıuick look at other advanced" software topics overed in this book:

'his chapter can be livided into these main ections:

INTRODUCTION

Vhen you write a sizeable program, it probably won't just be one nassive source file, but a number of separate files, and possibly some rewritten library files. Also there may be more than one programmer vorking on the project. Thus for sizeable projects, linking of modules vill be involved. Most likely the modules will be a mixture of Asm and ıigh-level, so you must know how to link these. Note that modern Assemblers from companies such as Borland and Microsoft, pay particular attention to compatibility for linking, and there are often **implified segment directives** that you can use. These directives are *107* designed for smooth integration between the high-level and Asm modules of that particular vendor's compilers and Assemblers.

Borland for example have, apart from the model directives (.SMALL, .MEDIUM, etc) that ensure segment names and attributes are suitable for linking, special directives to optimise linking with particular compilers -- these even insert code for proper handling of the stack, to remove the problem of how you manipulate the stack to get at the parameters passed to and fro.

This is all very well, and you are welcome to use these, however for the learning process we absolutely need to study what is going on at the fundamental level, so the description in this Chapter sticks with the standard directives.

Okay, here are the sections dealing with the linking of Asm modules:

GROUP directive:

Constrains segments of a program to have the same starting address The general format is;

```
name   GROUP   segment [,segment]
```

Where "name" is any label, and "segment" is the name of a segment.

This means that although the source code may have different segments declared, as per normal .EXE format, at assemble-time they will all be given the same address.

Example of usage;

```
comseg  group   data2, data1
...
data1   segment
...
data1   ends
...
data2   segment
...
data2   ends
```

PUBLIC directive:

Declares variables or labels public, so that they can be accessed from other modules. Note that during linking, public symbols in different modules but with the same name are resolved to a single address. Example;

```
public   var1, main1
...
var1     db     0
...
main1    proc   near
...
```

100

102

SEGMENT Directive:

The general definition for the SEGMENT directive is;

```
label SEGMENT [align-type] [combine-spec] [class-type]
```

We have been using the SEGMENT directive for all our coding, but not worrying too much about some of the qualifiers that can be tacked onto it. You will have seen from some of the code that you've written, that you put the "**STACK**" qualifier after the stack SEGMENT declaration -- this perticular qualifier is called the combine-spec.

105

The combine-spec is mainly of interest to the Assembler, and can be PUBLIC, STACK, COMMON, or MEMORY.

You may have come across some lines of code like this:

```
stack1 segment stack 'stack'
```

The last qualifier, in single-quotes, is called the class-type and is of interest to the linker and also the Codeview (or Turbo) debugger, and can be 'CODE', 'DATA' or 'STACK'.

The label is whatever you want -- the example just above has called the segment "stack1", though note that for correct linking you should use **standard names** across all the modules -- this is one advantage of the simplified directives.

298

Align-type is rather technical -- it is optional usually, and can be BYTE, WORD, PARA, or PAGE. It constrains the starting address of the segment -- for example, PARA will constrain the segment to commence exactly on a paragraph-address (ie in the case of a data segment, the starting address will have zero offset -- DS:0).

Back onto that "combine-spec" for a moment -- notice that one of the options I gave for it is **PUBLIC**. This is different from the PUBLIC directive described on the previous page, but has the same effect on segments -- makes them accessable by other modules. Here's an example:

253

```
progl   segment public  'code'
```

And as already meantioned, the 'code' qualifier on the end is the "class type".

More on SEGMENT >>>> *101*

EXTERNAL:

A symbol declared as "public" in module-B, can be accessed from module-A. The symbol in module-A must be declared as "external". Example;

```
extrn   var1:byte
```

Where VAR1 is a symbol, followed by a "**type**" specification of BYTE, WORD, DWORD, **FAR or NEAR**. So if you have a library of routines, declared PUBLIC at assemble-time, your main program can access them. PUBLIC and EXTRN work together, and the best way to show this is by example -- see the case study that follows.

99
99

More on EXTRN >>>> *327*

INCLUDE:

This is the odd one out. It's a diferent way of linking modules, that is done by the Assembler, not by the linker. The general syntax;

```
INCLUDE filespec
```

Putting this directive anywhere in your main program will cause the Assembler to insert the file designated by "filespec" at that point in the program. It is, effectively, a macro. Note that A86 ignores this directive.

LINKING .COM FILES

I haven't supplied sample code for .COM format, as it is sufficient to look at the more general case of .EXE format, for which a case study is given below.

Suffice to say that each module has only one segment, as per normal .COM format. It is important to note that to link modules, give segments in each module that you intend to be linked into one segment, the same name. Also don't forget to define them as public.

For example;

```
CODE SEGMENT PUBLIC
....
CODE ENDS
```

253

The simplest scheme is to label all code segments with the name CODE, and all data segments with the name DATA, though of course with .COM there is only the one segment, so this comment applies to .EXE -- for .COM give all segments a common name, like "commseg".

LINK will combine all segments with the same name and defined as PUBLIC, into one segment. If we had two modules, called MASTER.ASM and SLAVE.ASM, these are the steps required to **assemble and link**:

```
masm master
masm slave
link master+ slave
exe2bin master.exe master.com
del master.exe
```

111
111

Note that the same thing can be done with the **A86 assembler** on one line;

```
a86 master.asm slave.asm
```

A86 is particularly easy to link modules. Don't worry about GROUP, EXTRN, or PUBLIC declarations at all--- A86 is intelligent enough to work out what you want. The above example by default would treat the two modules as a single segment and would assemble directly to MASTER.COM.

A86 does understand the above declarations, if you insist on using them, and it doesn't have MASM's bug with GROUP -- refer to the Turbo Assembler Manual for a description of a "feature" of the

Microsoft GROUP that is an absolute pain -- it's good that GROUP is unlikely to be required for much of our linking work, but there are **exceptions**.

LINKING .EXE FILES

The appropriate files on your distribution disk are:

```
MASTREXE.ASM
SLAVEXE.ASM
SERF.ASM
```

This demonstrates linking of three modules, the MASTER, the library code module (SLAVE) and a data module (SERF).

The precise housekeeping will vary with different Assemblers, and this example may need some fine-tuning to work with them. It has been assembled using both A86 and MASM. A86's usage:

```
A86 mastrexe.asm slave.asm serf.asm finally.obj
link finally
```

Where MASTREXE.ASM, SLAVE.ASM and SERF.ASM are the source modules, and FINALLY.EXE is the end result.

MASM's usage:

```
masm mastrexe;
masm slave;
masm serf;
link mastrexe+ slave+ serf;
```

CALLING ASSEMBLY CODE FROM HIGH -LEVEL LANGUAGES

This very much depends on which language and compiler. Specific details can be found in a particular compiler's manual.

What we want to be able to do is write high-level code that can call an assembly routine, and be able to transfer parameters.

LINK is used to combine the object files produced by compiler and Assembler into a single executable file, and the mechanical process is described on the previous page.

The C language passes parameters to a function in a standardised manner, via the stack. Thus your assembly

```
; Skeleton Asm module, callable from C....
INCLUDELIB      SLIBCE
_TEXT   SEGMENT WORD PUBLIC 'CODE'            101
_TEXT   ENDS
_DATA   SEGMENT WORD PUBLIC 'DATA'
_DATA   ENDS
CONST   SEGMENT WORD PUBLIC 'CONST'
CONST   ENDS
_BSS    SEGMENT WORD PUBLIC 'BSS'
_BSS    ENDS
DGROUP  GROUP  CONST, _BSS, _DATA
   ASSUME DS: DGROUP, SS: DGROUP               102
;......................
EXTRN   __aNchkstk:NEAR
extrn _var1:word   ;added by me. see notes below.   254
;.................
_TEXT   SEGMENT
   ASSUME       CS: _TEXT
   PUBLIC       _add                           253
_add    PROC NEAR                              99
   push  bp
   mov   bp,sp
   mov   ax,2
   call  __aNchkstk     ;this is a compiler-
         ;csupplied routine, to check that the
         ;stack has enough room (no. bytes spec.
         ;by AX).                     continues...
```

routine just has to get them off the stack, and can return value/s -- usually C uses a particular register (AX) to return a value from a function.

The basic structure is in the listing -- but don't worry too much about some of thc detail -- focus on specific points as I discuss them.

```
; listing C2ASM.ASM continued from
; previous page.....
   mov    ax,WORD PTR [bp+6]      ;b
   add    ax,WORD PTR [bp+4]      ;a

adc ax,_var1  ;added by me. see notes
                    below.

   mov    sp,bp
   pop    bp
   ret
   nop
_add      ENDP
_TEXT     ENDS
   END
;.....................................
```

34

102

101

101

Basically, we call the code segment _TEXT and the data segment _DATA. Don't worry about CONST and _BSS -- when writing your own programs you can leave them out, though the compiler might expect you to leave in the GROUP directive, to name the dta segment as DGROUP.

Ditto leave in the ASSUME directive. You could also leave out "_aNchkstk".

Incidentally, the names _TEXT, _DATA and DGROUP are standards for the Microsoft and Borland products, but they also depend upon which model you're using (small, medium, etc), so double-check with the manual, or don't worry about the names at all and just use the **simplified directives**.

107

Anyway, this module is a function arbitrarily named "add" from C's point of view -- ie, C sees it as a function called "add". Look at the above listing and you'll see the main procedure, named "_add".

This example Asm module is named C2ASM.ASM on the Companion Disk, and I arrived at it in an interesting way --

To ensure that I got the directives, names and everything else right with the structure, I took advantage of C's capability of generating Asm output. All I did was write the "add" function in C, then compile it.

Note that I could have used a model directive in C to ensure full compatibility with the model I intend to use for all the modules, however the default is generally good enough.

The skeleton .ASM module below was created by compiling a skeleton C program of arbitrary name filename1.c, as follows;

```
add(a,b)
int a,b;
{ int x; x=a+b; return x; }
```

Then compiled with the /Fa switch to generate .ASM output, and the /c switch to suppress linking:
(Microsoft C v6.0. Refer to OOP.CPP on Companion Disk for info on doing this with Borland C++ v2.0).

```
CL /Fa /c filename1.C , , ,
```

You can see from the high-level listing what the function is supposed to do -- two parameters a and b passed to it, that it adds together, then returns answer x. Have a look at the Asm module to see how it does this.....

SOME C SYNTAX:

Notice that I named the procedure as "_add" in the Asm module, while it is "add" at C's end -- C expects all labels to commence with an underscore character.

A note about C -- since "add" is a function, it is capable of returning a value to C, and the standard with C compilers is that the AX register is used for returning word-size values. Well, check this out -- look at the above listing and you will see that the ADD instruction is leaving its result in AX.

THE STACK:

We haven't used BP much in this book, simply because it by default points to the stack segment, so requires a segment override with .EXE code if you want to use BP to address data or code. The above example routine uses BP to read a value from the stack.

Upon entry to the routine, SP will be pointing to the last entry on the stack, which will be the return address put on there by the calling program. The calling program will have pushed any parameters on prior to that.

```
SP ------------>   BP saved on top of stack.
                   Return address.
                   parameter a.
                   parameter b.
                   ...etc...
(higher
 addresses
  downward)
```

FIGURE 14.1

Since our routine also saves BP on the stack, our routine needs to look into the stack by four addresses. Remember that the stack grows down in memory, so our routine looks at higher address locations to get values inside the stack.

This example code is making an assumption; that this routine is NEAR. This depends on the model.

In such a case, only a single word return-address is saved on the stack, referring to the IP (offset) value of the host program.

If this routine was FAR, it would have a double-word return address on the stack, and would need to terminate with a far return (can define the **PROC** as **type** FAR, or can put a RETF instruction instead of **RET**).

-- check this out -- look at the listing and you'll see that the PROC is type NEAR.

The number of parameters passed by the calling program must be known by the Assembler routine, as must their size -- in this case the C program defined a and b as being 16-bit. Here is another C example, to explore possibilities:

```
..................................
extern int asmroutine(int *, int);
  ...
main()
{
  int I,J,m;
  ...
  m = asmroutine(&I,J);
  ...
}
..................................
```

101

31

C PARAMETER SYNTAX:

Those who know C will recognise this. This function, called "asmroutine()", passes two parameters, I and J.

"&I" means pass the address of parameter I, while "J" will pass the actual value if J is a variable, or will pass the address of J if it is a string.

Any value placed in AX by the routine, will return as the value of variable "m".

Another way to return a value to the C program is for the routine to place it in "I", since the actual address of I was passed to the routine.

A final comment on parameter passing via the stack -- if there are two parameters on the stack, the routine can get the second one by:

```
MOV AX,[BP+6]
```

You can deduce this from Figure 14.1, and you can see it actually done in the listing.

ACCESSING NAMED C DATA:

It is possible also for our assembly routine to access labeled data in the C program -- not just via the stack. Notice above (in the example Asm module) I defined an external integer variable "var1".

```
extern _var1:word
```

Assuming the default integer size to be a word. (16 bits). This does of course also assume DS to be set correctly in the Assembly routine.

Now some notes on Pascal --

PASCAL:

From within Pascal, an Assembly routine is accessed by declaring it external:

```
procedure asmroutine(I:integer;J:integer); external;
```

Note that parameter passing is via the stack, at least it is with Turbo Pascal, as for C, but you can also access I & J by name -- I & J must be declared as global by the Pascal program, and the Assembly routine must declare I & J as external, and can then access them by name.

In fact by global & external declarations, the asm routine can access any Pascal labels by name, including calling Pascal procedures.

There are some noteworthy differences between C & Pascal -- with Pascal the leftmost parameter is pushed on the stack first, but C does the reverse. Also C leaves the parameters on the stack and expects the C program to remove them, while Pascal expects the called routine to remove the parameters.

That's the basics of it, but check the manual of your particular compiler for specifics. Borland have a special directive to make linking with Turbo Pascal very easy -- also checkout the WINHULLO.ASM listing on the Companion Disk.

WRITING A C MODULE TO CALL THE ASM FUNCTION:

Have a look at the listing below. Note that z & y are defined as "int", which corresponds to MASM's "word", that is, 16 bits, so word-size values are passed on the stack to the .ASM routine. The "add" function returns a word-size value via AX, to variable x -- notice also that x is defined as 16-bit.

This C program will call the above .ASM "add" routine:

```
#include <stdio.h>
int var1=2;
main()
{ int x,y=3,z=5; x=add(y,z); printf("answer = %hu",x); }
```

It defines x,y and z as 16-bit, passes y and z on the stack to the .ASM routine, which returns a value to x via AX register. x,y and z are local variables, however I have also included a global variable, "var1" -- look back at the .ASM routine to see how it can access a C global variable.

If this C program is called filename2.c, and the .ASM program is filename1, this is the process of compiling & linking with MS C v6.0:

(OOP.CPP on Companion Disk for Borland C++ example).

```
MASM filename1;                 filename1.asm --> filename1.obj
CL /c filename2.c ,,,           filename2.c --> filename2.obj
LINK filename2+ filename1;      output is filename2.EXE
```

PASSING 32-BIT PARAMETERS:

what if you want to pass values other than 16-bit? C's "long int" is the same as MASM's "doubleword", that is, 32 bits. here is a C skeleton that you can compile to .ASM for passing long int's:

```
long int add(a,b)
long int a,b;
{ long int x; x=a+b; return x; }
```

As this must also return a long integer, Microsoft C does so in DX:AX.

A master C program that can call such a .ASM module --

C program to pass 32-bit parameters....

```
#include <stdio.h>
main()
{ long int x,y=3,z=5; x=add(y,z); printf("answer = %lu",x); }
```

note
that "%lu" is a format specifier for x, being "long unsigned integer".

LINKING WITH C++

If linking modules with conventional C, as per earlier discussion in this Chapter, which can be done in C++ -- as C++ allows mixed object-oriented and conventional-C code -- then no problem, but when dealing with objects you do need to have some understanding of what they are -- see Chapter 12.

C++ enhances the structure concept of C and gives it a new name -- OOP, however "a rose by any other name is still a rose". Digest the concept of **structures** and you're well on the way to understanding OOP.

233

Let's say that we wanted to write a function-member (method) of a C++ class, in Assembly language. When the C++ module calls the Asm module, it passes the parameters & return address, just as with C, but it also passes the address of the current object, as the top parameter on the stack (below the return address, ie at [BP+4]).

You can use this address to get at all the functions & data attached to that object, and you can use the same function-names as used in the C++ module, with one exception -- name-mangling.

NAME-MANGLING:

Due to C++'s ability to overload & "polymorphise", C++ converts functions of the same name into uniques names. The Assembler must refer to the functions by these "mangled" names. To find out what they are, you need to first compile the C++ module with the compiler switch set to generate .ASM output. This gives a .ASM file showing each line of C++ and its corresponding Asm -- also showing the mangled names. In fact, include a "stub" for your Asm function in the C++ module, and this will give you the skeleton .ASM file.

I've done all of this for you, and it's on the Companion Disk, as OOP.CPP and MEMBER.ASM, along with plenty of comments. It is written for Borland C++ and TASM.

A further note -- the .ASM module can access any public data & functions belonging to other objects in the C++ program. The demo file shows this. It is simply a matter of getting the address of that object, which is no problem. The simplest approach is to put all such code into the C++ stub, so you can see what it looks like in Assembly language. There is a problem with accessing member-data by name from the .ASM module, but by placing appropriate C++ code into the stub you will see how to do it -- OOP.CPP shows this. If you look in the Borland C++ manuals you will get the impression that this is a difficult topic, but it's not really.

IN-LINE ASSEMBLY:

Another option for both C and C++ is in-line Assembly code, and OOP.ASM contains an example -- inline Asm can access members by name very easily.

```
//example to show inline code....
  asm   {
        mov si,this      //addr of object
        mov [si].row,0//data-member,
                         //called "row".
        }
```

There are some limitations to inline Assembly -- for example you cannot have address labels -- so to perform a transfer-of-control to a labelled place-marker in the code, you have to go back to C, create a C label, then back to Asm inline. Messy. Basically you can use any registers, and C++ will automatically insert pushes & pops. The curly braces must open on the same line as the "asm" keyword, or are not required if only one instruction will be coded, on the same line as the "asm" keyword. In-line is handy for small amounts of Asm code, but larger jobs are better done as a separate module.

WORKSHEET: LINKING MODULES

1.
Study these 3 .ASM modules -- MASTREXE.ASM, SLAVEXE.ASM and SERF.ASM
Also refer back to the notes on how to **assemble & link these files.**
Have a close look at how the segments are declared in each module, and the use of **PUBLIC and EXTRN**.
You'll need to understand what's going on, because I want you to---
Rewrite the three modules so that they assemble and link to .COM format.
Try just MASTER and SLAVE to start with, then once that's working add on the third module, SERF.

2.
Now to consider linking between high level code and Assembler. There is a very simple method of developing the skeleton Assembler routine that a high level language can call -- many compilers have a switch that compiles to .ASM source. Here is a C program;

```
add(a,b)        //function name & parms
int a,b;        //declare parm types
{ int x;        //declare local var type
x = a+b;        //perform add operation
return x; }     //puts value into AX reg
```

Compile this to .ASM & analyse line by line*.

Now have a go at various refinements --
(i) Try writing a high level program that calls the Assembler module*.
(ii) Try passing parameters other than "int" (16 bit), such as "long int" (32 bit)*.
(iii) Try modifying your .ASM routine to directly access a global C variable*.

3.
If you've got Borland C++ & TASM, compile OOP.CPP and MEMBER.ASM -- instructions are in the files.
OR just perform a theoretical exercise: study the comments in the files and see if you can understand them.

*A lot of this is compiler-dependent, however for users of C, & Microsoft V6.0 in particular, I have included a help file in the \SOURCE directory of the companion disk -- C2ASM.ASM.

256

253

15
OVERLAYS

Memory management has become a major issue as programs get bigger, and the PC struggles with the 640K boundary. This lesson discusses one technique.

We have seen how a text file can be read from disk by using DOS functions, but how do we load another program from within a program, and transfer control to it?

Topics of this Chapter:

PARENT/CHILD PROCESSES

MSDOS's **EXEC function-4Bh** lets an executing program load another program, transfer control to it, and then regain control when the loaded program terminates. The first program is often referred to as the "parent" and the second the "child". This is the way many programs let you "drop into DOS"; they transfer control to the COMMAND.COM program via function-4Bh. In fact, EXEC is the mechanism by which MSDOS loads and executes programs.

357

EXEC:

357

Function-4Bh, load and execute a program, requires DS:DX to point to the filespec (ASCIIZ string) of the file to be loaded, AL to have a "method code", and ES:BX to point to a parameter block that contains control information for the load operation.

The required contents of the parameter block depends on the method-code.

For method-code = 0, a complete, independent program (child) is loaded and control transfers to it. Return to the parent is by **EXIT (function4Ch)**.

METHOD -CODE	DESCRIPTION
0	Child loaded, a PSP created, child executed.
3	Child loaded, no PSP created, not executed.

TABLE 15.1 EXEC Methods

357

For details of the parameter block refer to "Programmer's Guide to the IBM-PC & PS/2", by Peter Norton, Chapter 17.

For method-code = 3, the code is simply read into memory and control stays in the parent program. Refer to the same reference for details on the parameter block, but in the case-study to follow we will look at the simple case of loading a .COM-format child, in which case the parameter block is simply a two-byte value containing the segment-paragraph at which the child is to be loaded. In this case the parent needs to CALL the child to transfer control to it, and the child goes back to the parent by **RET**. *31*

THE "DAISY CHAIN"

Recall how you have been writing programs so far -- you always terminated them with **Function-4Ch**, which returns control to DOS. *357* HOWEVER more correctly, Function-4Ch returns control to the parent program.

Function-4Bh/method-code-0, is the technique for loading and executing a child, and such a child is terminated with Function-4Ch, EXIT, which deallocates the child-block (memory DOS has allocated to the child-program) and returns control to the parent. *357*

This is like a daisy-chain. For example, the parent program is in fact a child of **COMMAND.COM** (that was loaded at power-up), which is why applications terminate with Function-4Ch, to take control back to COMMAND.COM. *5*

In theory, the child program could have its own child -- which would be COMMAND.COM's great-grandchild!

Here is a picture -- look at Figure 15.1.

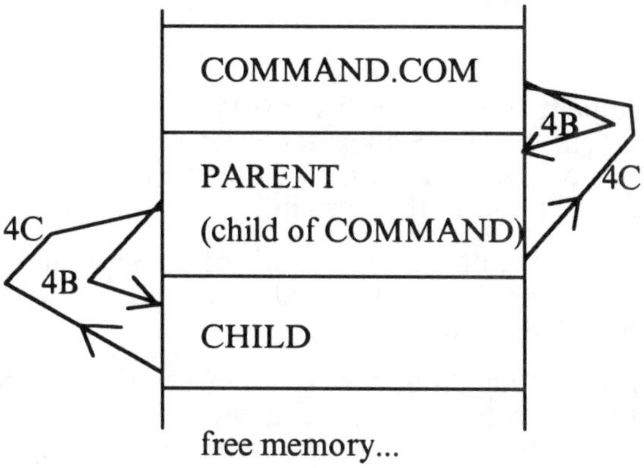

COMMAND.COM
4B
4C
PARENT
(child of COMMAND)
4C
4B
CHILD
free memory...

FIGURE 15.1 Daisy-Chaining.

It was mentioned above that an application can "drop into DOS", via Function-4Bh, however this would load a second copy of COMMAND.COM, which could be awkward if there isn't much RAM left.

OVERLAYS

Since .COM files are limited to 64K, overlays have been used to allow the program size to be larger, or simply to allow a modular approach with a number of small programs. That is, the program is kept as two or more files on the disk, the parent being a .COM file and the children with extension of .OVL to distinguish them.

Overlays are extremely handy for keeping a program's RAM occupation to a reasonable size, regardless of whether we are dealing with .COM or .EXE.

A wordprocessor for example needs to leave lots of free RAM for a document.

TSR's (resident programs) also can benefit from this technique. You can go to quite an extreme -- develop a 300K byte program, but split it up into a dozen overlays, then claim it only requires 30K of RAM!

The penalty you pay for going to this extreme is a time overhead for disk accesses.

SET_BLOCK:

Now, some revision-- When a .COM program is loaded, it resides in one segment, but DOS allocates 64Kbytes to it regardless of whether it is that big or not, and the stack pointer SP is initialised to FFFE, that is, right at the end of the segment.

This leaves a big hole in the middle of the segment with nothing in it, however the block-size allocated to the program can be reduced, using **SET_BLOCK**, function4Ah.

357

What I'm writing about here is not essential to overlays, but is a good housekeeping practice associated with efficient memory management -- what's the point of trying to save RAM by using overlays if your .COM parent program has a big hole in it, of wasted RAM?

The example program in the appropriate **Worksheet**, OVLPARNT.ASM, uses SET_BLOCK.

272

You may recall from way back in the course, when DOS **loads** a .COM program, DOS allocates the entire 64K segment to that program and initialises the stack pointer SP to FFFEh, even if the program itself is very small. So a technical detail here is that if you are going to use SET_BLOCK to reduce the allocation then don't forget to move SP closer to the end of the program -- the example program in the Worksheet shows this, and it is illustrated in Figure 15.2.

18

SP grows down in memory, toward the program, but only requires a small space (say about 128 bytes), so can be reinitialised closer to the program, then SET_BLOCK to free unused RAM.

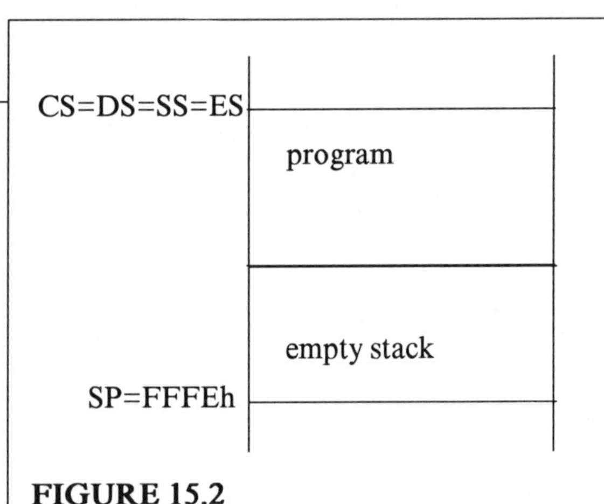

FIGURE 15.2

FREE_MEM:

After having loaded the child using **Function-4Bh**, and after control is returned to the parent, the child should be de-allocated -- ie DOS told to free the block the child occupied. *357*

If you had loaded the child usiing method-code-0, the child would terminate with **Function-4Ch**, which would return control to the parent and deallocate the block, so no problem. *357*

But, iif you used method-code-3, the child comes back to the parent by a RET instruction, so needs to be specifically deallocated, using FREE_MEM, **function49h** *357*

The Worksheet uses method-code-3, so by looking through it you should be able to clearly see how SET-BLOCK, FREE_MEM, EXEC, and EXIT are used.

TSR's (resident programs) are an interesting case. Ordinary programs terminate with Function-4C, which returns control to DOS and deallocates the block, but TSR's simply exit by a RETurn back to the host program (from which the TSR was popped up), leaving the TSR resident.

The TSR could be deallocated by popping it up, selecting a menu-item to uninstall, which would have to restore any altered interrupt vectors, then call Function-49 to deallocate the TSR, then exit back to the host in the normal way.

REFERENCE:

Look in "An Overview of Overlays", Byte magazine, Dec. 1988, pp 341-348 -- this is a general routine for .EXE files.

WORKSHEET: OVERLAYS

1.
OVLPARNT.ASM and DEMO.ASM are the sample files supplied on your distribution disk.
Study the source code, then assemble them. TASM prior to version 2.0 objects to ORG 0, so use TASM v2.0+, MASM or A86 for DEMO.

Note that you'll have to rename DEMO.BIN/COM to .OVL. Make sure OVLPARNT.COM works as expected.

2.
Finally, Modify OVLPARNT.ASM so that it loads and executes DEMO.OVL, goes back to the parent, then loads a different child program and executes it. Of course it will be necessary to create another slightly different version of DEMO.OVL.

This exercise will demonstrate how one block of RAM can be reused by many overlays, thus efficiently utilising limited RAM resources.
You will need to add additional code to OVLPARNT after CALL UNLOADOVL. Since the second child is to load at exactly the same place as the parent, the segment & offset previously calculated can be reused.
You will only need to write another procedure that references a different filespec and calls DOS Function-4Bh to load it -- the earlier steps of address calculation need not be repeated.

Of course your new parent program will have to change DS to the child prior to CALLing it, and restore DS upon RETurn to the parent.

INTRODUCTORY NOTES:

Remember that CS=DS=SS=ES = beginning of PSP, for .COM files.

The example here is very simple, though still quite useful. It simply loads a program, executes it, goes back to parent program, then quits. The only operations performed at each step are messages to the screen to show completion of each stage.

A small technical detail with the overlay file is that it must have **ORG** (origin) = 0, as Function-4B has used method-code-3, meaning that the child has no PSP.
Not having a PSP is an advantage as it saves some memory.
The child must also terminate with a far **RET** instruction, rather than use **Function-4C** like a normal program.

102

31
357

16
DEVICE DRIVERS

"Writing a device driver is a complex task that must be undertaken with considerable care; a great many caveats and "gotchas" lie in wait for the unsuspecting programmer."

Gordon Letwin, Inside OS/2, Microsoft press, 1988.

Device Drivers are mysterious to most people. They are difficult to write, and difficult to debug, but this Lesson should unravel some of the mystery.

SUBINDEX (DRIVER STRUCTURE):

INTRODUCTION:

The Device Driver is a concept almost universal to operating systems, however for the purposes of this lesson the particular implementation in PC-DOS is studied.

Standard DOS is set up to manage and control a set of standard PC devices, including the keyboard, screen, disks, and serial and parallel devices. Standard device drivers are normally part of the operating system's device management and are not visible to the user.

Prior to version 2.0, PC-DOS did not provide a uniform method for accessing external hardware -- instead, each device added to the PC required custom changes to DOS as well as changes to programs using the new device.

Beginning with 2.00, DOS allowed user-installable device drivers, to complement those available as part of DOS --- this has long been a feature of mainframe O.S.'s.

WHAT IS A DEVICE DRIVER?

Your computer's screen, keyboard, printer and drives are devices, and the software that interfaces between application programs and these devices are the device drivers. Examples of add-on devices, for which you will need to install special device drivers, are;

Image-digitiser,	CD-ROM,
Bar-code reader,	Mouse,
A/D,	Print-spooler,
Local Area Network,	Tape-drives,
Video-cassette,	RAM-disk,

CHARACTER & BLOCK DEVICES

Devices are classified as these two main types, based on how data is transferred to and from the PC. Character devices transfer one character at a time. EX: printer, modem, keyboard, mouse. Block devices transfer blocks of data, of say 512 or 1024 bytes. EX: tape, disk.

Generally, character device drivers are somewhat easier for the programmer to develop. Block devices drivers are used when higher transfer speed is required.

USING DOS's INBUILT DEVICE DRIVERS

There's no mystery here -- the BIOS and DOS services, called by the INT instruction or by external interrupt, are used to invoke the devices handlers.

These mechanisms you are already aware of.

Another important point is that DOS has certain **reserved device names**, that can be used on the DOS command-line or even within programs:

con:	Console (keyboard/screen)
aux:	Auxiliary port (same as com1)
com1:	Serial port no.1
com2:	Serial port no.2
prn:	Logical printer port (same as lpt1)
lpt1:	Printer port no.1
lpt2:	Printer port no.2
lpt3:	Printer port no.3
nul:	Null device
clock$	Software clock
A:	First disk drive
B:	Second disk drive
C:	Third disk drive, etc.

DOS' Reserved Device Names

226

Refer to the notes on disk file-handling for information about using **ASCIIZ** strings within programs, that can contain reserved names.

226

An example of using a reserved name on the DOS command-line:

```
TYPE DEMO.TXT >PRN
```

EXAMPLE OF AN INBUILT DEVICE DRIVER:

INT 21h, function 15h, is an example of one of DOS's early disk-access functions, using the File Control Block (**FCB**) concept. This operating system service will append the data contained in the DTA onto the end of the sequential data file on disk.

352
221

This is how the function appears from the programmer's point of view, however the DOS program called by INT 21 function 15 will have to in turn call the disk device driver. Thus there are three levels of program involved.

INT 21h/function-15h:

WRITE_SEQ/write sequential data to the file named by the opened FCB pointed to by DS:DX. One record is transferred from the DTA (Data Transfer Area) to the disk and the FCB CURRENT_RECORD field is updated.

Returns:

AL=0 if transfer successful,

AL=1 if access denied,

AL=2 if end of DTA.

The DOS function-15 will translate the program's request into what the device driver requires. Basically, the DOS function must ask the driver if there is space left on the disk, then send the data to the driver, then tell the driver to update the disk directory information. The driver in turn must translate these signals into those suitable for direct communication with the disk drive.

This shows the three levels:

APPLICATION PROGRAM

DOS FUNCTION 15

DISK DEVICE DRIVER

DRIVE

A couple of notes:

The application program, even if written in a high-level language, would be compiled into machine code, so ultimately it comes down to DOS function calls for all device handling. DOS's inbuilt device drivers themselves would call the BIOS services. Due to certain limitations in DOS, a driver is likely to hang up if it calls DOS functions, however when the Initialisation command (0) is sent to the driver, the initialisation processing part of the driver program can call INT-21h, **functions 01 to 0Ch and 30h**.

350

HOW DOS KEEPS TRACK OF DEVICE DRIVERS

You can reference a particular device driver by using its name (EX: PRN:), and new drivers you install will also have their identifying names. DOS keeps a list of all inbuilt and installed devices in a linked name-list (often called a "device-chain"), with NUL: first on the list. This needs clarification -- the linked list is actually in the "Device Header" of each driver -- the field labelled "**next_dev**" provides the link to the next (later) driver, with an entry of -1 meaning that this is the last driver to be loaded. 281

An interesting aspect of this list is that when a new device is installed, it is inserted into the linked list, and DOS looks for a particular driver by jumping back along this link -- therefore if you give the new custom driver the same name as an existing one, perhaps the name of one of DOS's inbuilt device drivers, DOS will only respond to the new one.

OVERVIEW OF A DRIVER'S STRUCTURE

DOS expects the driver to have a particular structure, consisting of these parts:

Device header, 281

data storage and local procedures, 282

the STRATEGY procedure, 282

the INTERRUPT procedure. 283

The header contains information about the driver itself, including the name for the driver and the link-address to the next driver. The STRATEGY and INTERRUPT procedures accept commands that DOS passes to the driver, and the last part is also the actual code routines that process the commands.

HOW DOS COMMUNICATES WITH THE DRIVER

Whenever DOS wants to tell the driver to do something, it automatically sets up what is called a "request header", pointed to by ES:BX. (it is setup in DOS's reserved memory space). The format of the Request Header:

Length of Request Header,	1 byte	
unit code of the device,	1	
" **command code**,	1	*279*
" **status upon completion**,	2	*284*
" reserved,	8	
data field.	varies	*277*

TABLE 16.1 Request Header

The unit code is used when the driver is controlling more than one device. An example would be a floppy disk controller, in which case the A: drive would be unit 0, B: drive unit 1, etc.

The command code is how DOS tells the driver what action to take.

The data field is information about and a pointer to the data that DOS is sending or receiving to/from the driver.

REQUEST-HEADER DATA FIELD

The portion of the Header prior to the data field is termed the static portion, while the data-field is the dynamic portion and has a format depending upon the command-code. Our little demo program (see later notes) will respond to only one command, the Initialise (0)

Number of units*,	1 byte
offset addr. for break,	2 "
segment addr. for break,	2 "
offset of ptr to BPB array*,	2 "
segment of ptr to BPB array*,	2 "
first available drive*	1 "

* signifies for block-drivers only.

TABLE 13.2 Initialise Data Field

command, and the corresponding format for the dynamic portion is shown in Table 13.2.

The only field of immediate concern to us is the break-address. What we must do here is return to DOS the address of the end of the driver program, so DOS will know where free memory starts.

code	CHARACTER-TYPE description	BLOCK-TYPE description
0	initialisation	initialisation
1	not applicable	media check
2	" "	BIOS params
3	IOCTL input	IOCTL input
4	input	input
5	nondestruct.I/P.	not applicable
6	input status	" "
7	input flush	" "
8	output	output
9	output w/verify	output with veri.
10	output status	not applicable
11	output flush	" "
12	IOCTL output	IOCTL output
13	device open	device open
14	device close	device close
15	not applicable	removble media
16	output til busy	not applicable
17-18	undefined	undefined
19	not applicable	generic IOCTL
20-22	undefined	undefined
23	get logical dev	get logical dev
24	set logical dev	set logical dev

TABLE 16.3 Driver Commands

TWO-STEP DRIVER CALLS

Each time that DOS asks the device driver to process a command, for example a read and write command, DOS will call the device driver twice, firstly calling the STRATEGY procedure, and secondly calling the INTERRUPT procedure. The former performs the setup and initialisation for the driver, while the latter accepts the actual command from DOS.

There is a sound reason for this two-step procedure. Although DOS is not multitasking, this technique has been brought down from mainframe operating systems that are --- and looking ahead maybe DOS will develop in that direction. When DOS first calls a driver, the driver's STRATEGY procedure puts the address of the **Request Header**, contained in ES:BX, into the driver's local-data-storage area. Thus the driver knows where the Request Header is, but doesn't have to do the actual work yet --- DOS can call the INTERRUPT procedure, to do the actual work, at a later time, as priority determines.

278

DEVICE DRIVER COMMANDS

The command-code is passed by DOS via the **Request Header**, and Microsoft has defined meanings for numbers 0 to 24. The codes differ for character and block drivers: see Table 16.3.

278

WRITING A DEVICE DRIVER PROGRAM

DOS requires that device drivers be in .COM format, so after invoking MASM and LINK, EXE2BIN will be required:

```
MASM demo;
LINK demo;
EXE2BIN demo.exe demo.sys
```

102

A86 recognises the **ORG** 0 directive in the source code and understands that this is to be a .BIN format. (.COM usually has ORG 100h).

If using the A86 assembler;

```
A86 demo.asm
REN demo.bin demo.sys
```

5

DOS will also require you to install the driver, in the **CONFIG.SYS** file:

```
DEVICE = demo.sys
```

Recall that the driver consists of these parts: Device Header, local data, STRATEGY procedure, and INTERRUPT procedure.

WRITING THE DEVICE HEADER

The device header is set up in a certain format. A value of -1 for next_dev indicates that no other drivers are to be loaded.

The attribute word tells DOS what type of driver this is:

```
;.................................
;DRIVER1.SYS    simple device driver
code_seg segment para public 'code'          101
main_proc proc    far                        102
 assume cs:code_seg,ds:code_s                102
 org 0    ;required for device drivers.      102
begin:
;this area is the DEVICE HEADER....
next_dev  dd -1  ;no other device driver     100
attribute dw 8000h   ;character device.      100
strategy  dw dev_str ;addr 1st DOS call.
interrupt dw dev_int ;addr 2nd DOS call.
dev_name  db "driver1$" ;name of driver.
;.................................
```

Dev_str and dev_int are the names that you give to the STRATEGY and INTERRUPT procedures, so DOS can look here and find where to go on first and second calls to the driver respectively.

Driver1$ is the device name that you choose for your driver. Using this name on the DOS command-line or within a program will cause DOS to call the driver. Note that this name must be specified as eight characters within the "..." delimiters. If less then it must be padded with blanks.

BIT	DESCRIPTION
0	standard input device
1	standard output device
2	null device
3	clock device
4	special
5-10	set these bits to zero
11	device supportsOPEN/CLOSE/ REMOVABLE-MEDIA
12	must be set to zero
13	non-IBM format
14	IOCTL
15	character device (0 if block dev).

TABLE 13.4 Attribute Word

WRITING THE LOCAL DATA STORAGE AREA

Recall that when DOS calls the driver the first time, it sets up a Request Header and places the address of the Header into ES:BX. Note that DOS will then pass control to the STRATEGY procedure, which puts the address into rh_off and rh_seg in the local workspace area. Don't worry about the "messages" a the moment --- they will be used by the demonstration driver processing-commands portion.

```
;.....................................
;this is the LOCAL WORKSPACE AREA....
rh_off    dw ? ;Request Header offset.        100
rh_seg    dw ? ;Request Header seg.           278
messages db 07h                                100
          db "Simple char device driver"
          db 0Dh,0Ah,07h,"$"
;.....................................
```

WRITING THE STRATEGY PROCEDURE

This is the routine that DOS calls on the first occasion. Since it is a CALL from DOS, it must be terminated by a RET instruction. Also the value of DS will be whatever it was while in DOS, so to point to the local workspace area will require CS override. The only task required of STRATEGY is to save the address in ES:BX to the workspace area, then return to DOS.

```
;.....................................
;this is the STRATEGY procedure area...
dev_str:
 push  ds         ;save DS.
 push  cs         ;to avoid segment
 pop   ds         ;      override.
 mov   rh_seg,es  ;save Req.Hdr seg.
 mov   rh_off,bx  ;save Req.Hdr offs.
 pop   ds         ;restore DS.
 ret                                           31
;.....................................
```

WRITING THE INTERRUPT PROCEDURE

HEX CODE	DESCRIPTION
0	write protect violation
1	unknown unit
2	drive not ready
3	unknown command
4	CRC error
5	bad drive request length
6	seek error
7	unknown media
8	sector not found
9	printer out of paper
A	write fault
B	read fault
C	general failure

TABLE 16.5 Error Code

The status word in the Request Header has this format:

BIT	DESCRIPTION
15	set to indicate an error.
9	Tells DOS driver busy.
8	set to indicate DONE.
0-7	error code (see above).

TABLE 16.6 Status Word

```
;this is the INTERRUPT procedure.....
dev_int:
 push  ds     ;save registers.
 push  es     ;    /
 push  ax     ;    /
 push  bx     ;    /
 push  cx     ;    /
 push  dx     ;    /
 push  di     ;    /
 push  si     ;    /
 push  cs     ;to avoid segment
 pop   ds     ;   override.
;I will not assume that the second call
;to the driver will still have the addr.
;of the Req. Hdr. in ES:BX. Loadit from
;workspace...
 mov   es,rh_seg
 mov   bx,rh_off
;perform branch based onthe command              279
;in the Request Header...                        278
 mov   al,es:[bx+2] ;get cmd code.
 cmp   al,0        ;check for zero.
 jne   errors
;perform required action...
 mov   dx,offset messages ;message               100
 mov   ah,9           ;to screen.                350
 int   21h            ;/
;must return the status via Req.Hdr....          284
 mov   es:word ptr [bx+3],0100h                  53
```

continued next page.....

This is the heart of the driver -- everything prior to this was just the skeleton. Since we are developing a demo program here, let's keep it very simple; we will only allow DOS to send it one command, of value zero. Looking in the table of **commands** for character-type device drivers, we see that this is the Initialise command. Our simple little driver will do only one thing; test that DOS has sent the correct Initialise command, display a short message, then go back to DOS.

STATUS CODE

The status code that we return to DOS via the **Request Header** needs some explanation: see Table 16.6.

You can see that moving 0100h into the status-code field of the Request Header will simply inform DOS that the job is DONE. Look at the code listing to see that this is coded just before exiting.

....continued from previous page....

```
;it seems that DOS will also require to
;know where the driver ends....
  mov ax,offset the_end ;end prog.                100
  mov es:[bx+14],ax ;break-addr forDOS.
  mov es:[bx+16],cs ;    /
  jmp finish                                      279
errors:
;again must return the status....                 284
mov es:word ptr [bx+3],8103h                      53
finish:
  pop si        ;restore all reg's.
  pop di
  pop dx
  pop cx
  pop bx
  pop ax
  pop es
  pop ds                                          278
  ret                                             55
the_end:
;.....................................
main_proc   endp                                  102
code_seg   ends                                   101
  end   begin                                     101
;*****end of device driver******
```

A final touch to this driver program will be to send an appropriate error message back to DOS if an incorrect command code was received by the driver. The procedure labeled "errors" puts 8103 into he status word. This notifies DOS that the driver has received an ınknown command.

Note that the program terminates with:

```
end    begin
```

This is only necessary from the assembler's point of view, but not for actual execution. The entry point for device drivers is determined by the address-labels placed in the device-header part of the program.

A CONSOLE DEVICE DRIVER

You can replace any of DOS's in-built device drivers, by adding your own and giving it the same name. As it will come earlier on the linked list, DOS will only recognise your driver.

The standard driver that controls the keyboard and screen for the PC is known as the con: device (console). DOS makes all keyboard/screen access through the con: device driver, and all DOS-functions called from within a program that involve standard input and standard output, also go via con: DOS will send commands via the third byte of the **Request Header**, to the driver. In the case of con: the main ones are;

(they are summarised in the **Table of Commands**)

* Initialisation.
* Input. Instructs con: to read data from the keyboard.
* Nondestructive Input.Instructs con: to see if the keyboard has any data.
* Input Flush. Tells con: to discard any data in the keyboard buffer.
* Output. Tells con: to write a specified amount of data to the screen.
* Output With Verify. con: will read the data after each write... not much use.

278

279

Looking back at the simple example, DRIVER1, there was an **attribute-byte** specified in the Device Header. For a con: replacement this would have to become 8003h. Bits 15, 1 and 0 are set. Refer to the Table showing the attribute bits:

280

0	Standard input device.
1	Standard output device.
15	Character device.

The Device_name field of the Device Header will have to contain the ASCII string "con ".

EXPANDING THE EXAMPLE DRIVER

What we'll do is expand the earlier example so that it recognises another **command** from DOS. The OUTPUT command, (8) is for transfering data to an output device. The dynamic portion of the **Request Header** will have this format;

Media description from DPB	1 byte
offs addr data transfer area	2 "
segm addr data transfer area	2 "
transfer count(bytes/sectors)	2 "
start sector number*	2 "
offs addr volume ID(DOS 3+)	2 "
segm addr volume ID(" ")	2 "

TABLE 16.7 Data-Field for Output

279

278

Thus the INTERRUPT procedure must recognise command-8, then read the characters from the data transfer area as pointed to by entries in the dynamic portion of the Request Header;

```
;.................................
;Processing the OUTPUT command...
;note that an offset of 13dec from the
;beginning of the Req Hdr is the start of
;the dynamic portion.
;first get the byte count....
  mov cx,es:[bx+18]
  ;now get the data address....
```

continued .....

278

```
...continues...
  mov di,es:[bx+14]
  mov es,es:[bx+16]
;now transfer the data....
  push bx         ;save BX.
  push es         ;save ES.
  mov bx,0
next_char:
  mov al,es:[di]
  inc di
  mov ah,0Eh        ;display char.
  int 10h           ;      /
  loop next_char
  pop es          ;restore ES.
  pop bx          ;restore BX.
;....................................
```

342

Want more detail? ....

This Chapter is only introductory and if you want to seriously write device drivers, you do need more information. A detailed guide to writing device drivers for DOS, with lots of practical examples, is:

"Writing MS-DOS Device Drivers", by Robert Lai, Addison Wesley, USA 1987.

I found Robert Lai's book to be superb when studying this topic.

To round off the introductory overview nature of this Chapter, I've finished with a quick look at direct control, and the mouse ....

DIRECT CONTROL OF THE DRIVER

Accessing a driver indirectly by calling standard DOS functions is restrictive if you want your driver to do something special. However we do have the option of sending any messages/commands we wish between an application program and a driver, by means of the IOCTL mechanism; DOS **INT-21h, function 44h**.

Operations 2 and 3 are particularly useful, as they enable us to send and receive any string of data. Also special commands can be sent to the driver.

DOS INT-21h

AH = 44h

AL = 0 Get device information.
- 1 Set device information.
- 2 Read.
- 3 Write.
- 4 Read from disk drive.
- 5 Write to disk drive.
- 6 Get input status.
- 7 Get output status.
- 8 Is device media removable?
- 9 Is drive local or remote?
- 10 Is file handle local or remote?
- 11 Changing the retry of a shareable entry.

BX = File handle returned from open-a-file-handle call.

CX = Count of the number of bytes to be transferred.

DX = With DS this is the address of the data transfer buffer.

356

MOUSE DRIVER

INDEX:

INTRODUCTION

Earlier notes described the concept of the device driver. The mouse driver as implemented by Microsoft has become the standard for IBM-PC's, and these notes discuss how to make use of the mouse in programs that you write.

These notes refer to DOS as the case-study.

REFERENCES:

1 Microsoft Mouse Programmer's Reference Guide (Part no. 000-099-066).

2 Advanced MS-DOS Programming (2nd Edition), Ray Duncan.

INTERRUPT 33h

Of course the driver must be installed using "DEVICE =" in the CONFIG.SYS file and once done, you can use **INT-33h** to access the mouse. *348*

Most reference literature shows this interrupt-function as being reserved by DOS, but Microsoft have dedicated it to mouse-usage. The Microsoft mouse driver can only be driven via INT-33h and cannot be opened by name and accessed via normal DOS INT-21h functions, as can many other drivers.

MOUSE CONTROL

348

A DOS program first calls **INT-33h**, function-00 (Reset Mouse Driver) to initialise the mouse driver for the current display mode and to check its status. At this point the mouse is "alive" and the application can obtain its state and position; the pointer does not become visible however, until the application calls INT-33h, function-01 (Show Mouse Pointer).

Note that function-02 does the opposite --- hides the mouse pointer.

The program can then call interrupt-33h, functions 03 (Get Mouse Position and Button Status), 05 (Get Button Press Information) and 06 (Get Button Release Information) to monitor the mouse position and the status of the mouse buttons.

The program can also control the mouse position with function-04 (Set Mouse Pointer Position) and change the mouse pointer shape with functions 09 and 0Ah (for graphics and text modes respectively).

MOUSE POLLING

A practical problem with writing an application using a mouse is the situation that arises with the keyboard --- we don't want the program to have to sit around waiting (polling) for a keypress --- rather we want the program to be doing something and have the keyboard interrupt the program when a key is pressed. This is what happens with the keyboard, and a similar mechanism can be used with the mouse.

In the case of the keyboard, the interrupt handler responds to a keypress by putting the character into a buffer, so when the program next reads the keyboard it in fact reads from the buffer, which is a FIFO queue of characters.

INT-33h function-0Ch enables the application to define an "event handler", a routine that is written by you and called by the mouse driver every time the mouse is moved or button-status changes.

MOUSE EVENT-HANDLER

This is the most interesting aspect of driving the mouse, so coding will be looked at.

The event handler must have an install portion and a runtime portion --- it could be a procedure that is called by the main program, which on the first call could have the effect of installing the handler.

To understand the installation process, have a look at function-0Ch. It requires the address of the runtime portion in ES:DX, an event-mask in CX, 0Ch in AX. Possible coding could look like this;

```
;MOUSE.ASM event handler.
data segment word public 'data'
...variables to be accessed by
calling program....
data ends
;...........................
code segment word public 'code'
  assume cs:main,ds:data
install proc near
  push cs
  pop  es
  mov  dx,offset mhandler
  mov  cx,1Fh
  mov  ax,0Ch
  int  33h
  ret
install endp
;...........................
mhandler proc far
  push ds       ;save DS.
  mov  di,data  ;to addr. data
  mov  ds,di    ; /
...driver provides mouse-data in
the registers.  Move this data
into the variables...
  pop ds
  ret
mhandler endp
code ends
  end
```

348

289

There would also need to be another portion of this program, so that the main program could call it, read the variables, and return the mouse-data.

The install portion uses function-0Ch, which tells the mouse driver the address of the runtime portion (mhandler) of the event handler.

Thus every time the mouse changes status it will call the runtime portion of the event handler, which will in turn read the appropriate registers into a data area.

The exact configuration of the handler is up to you --- refer to the **References** for detailed programming examples.

WORKSHEET: DEVICE DRIVER

WARNING
Do this exercise on a bootable floppy disk, not the hard disk. Chapter Five explains how to make a bootable disk, and of course you will need to assemble DRIVER1.ASM to produce DRIVER1.SYS.

Put DRIVER1.SYS in the **CONFIG.SYS** file, then reset the computer. When DOS loads the driver, it sends it an **initialisation** command, so the driver should go ahead and cause a beep and a message on the screen.
This is also an exercise in producing a .SYS program, since only the source code is supplied on disk.

Note that you can open your driver from within an application program by using the name "PRN" as an ASCIIZ-string, used in conjunction with DOS's file-handling functions that use the file-handle method.
Also reference to "PRN" on the DOS command-line will access your driver.
Try this ----

(make sure the printer has plenty of paper!)

COPY CONFIG.SYS PRN

Examine the printout carefully and determine the sequence of commands that DOS sends.

WORKSHEET: DRIVER ANALYSIS

Before doing this Workshop you should have done the evaluation of a **simple device driver** (alongside)

For this Worksheet the following programs are required. They are available on disk, in source-form, to avoid having to type them in. 5
They are ---

279

DRIVER2.ASM
DRIVER2.SYS
NOTHING.ASM
NOTHING.COM

1.
Create or modify the **CONFIG.SYS** file in the root directory of a **bootable disk**. 5 4
It is preferred if you use a bootable floppy disk rather than the hard disk.
The file should contain the entry ---

DEVICE = DRIVER2.SYS

Also make sure a parallel printer is connected to your computer, turned on with paper inserted and ready to go.

Typing CTRL-ALT-DEL with bootable disk inserted will reload DOS along with the driver.

2.
When the driver is loaded, or installed, by DOS, you should see a message on the screen and something will also appear on paper.

Your first exercise is to examine the source listing of DRIVER2.ASM and explain how the code generates the display message and printout, and the meaning of the messages.

3.
The printout is very useful for understanding how DOS interacts with your driver.

17
ADVANCED OPERATING SYSTEMS

INTRODUCTION

DOS is a single-tasking operating system, though we have seen how this limitation has been partially overcome by such techniques as TSR's. DOS's memory management is minimal, but we have seen how techniques like overlays can enable large programs to better utilise limited memory.

DOS does not make use of the virtual-mode features of the **'286 and '386**, and it cannot address beyond 1M byte. This chapter describes one operating system designed from the ground-up to utilise these advanced CPU's; OS/2, and a "DOS shell" -- Windows -- that takes DOS into the virtual machine and Graphical User Interface environment.

188

We are concerned here with principles, but often it is necessary to see practical implementations for the concepts to sink in. Hence I have shown actual Asm and/or C code.

OS/2

INTRODUCTION:

OS/2 is an operating system designed to take advantage of the protected modes of the '286 and '386. Although similar at the prompt command-level to DOS, and able to run many DOS applications, OS/2 is a complete rewrite and a very different beast underneath.

The well known alternative to OS/2, Microsoft Windows, is conceptually different as it is a shell built on top of DOS, not a replacement for DOS. This approach does make it difficult for the designers of Windows to get around many of DOS's limitations, but with Windows 3.0 they have done a surprisingly good job.

OS/2 is a very complex operating system, and here I am only introducing it. There are a number of reference books, including some excellent ones printed by Microsoft Press. I particularly recommend "Advanced OS/2 Programming", by Ray Duncan, 1989, for an in-depth treatment of the O.S. kernel.

For information on programming the graphical interface Presentation Manager, Microsoft have another book, "Programming the OS/2 Presentation Manager", by Charles Petzold.

Two separate books, one for the character-based kernel, and another for the graphical Presentation Manager. OS/2 has these two independent components. OS/2 on its own is a conventional character-based operating system, much like DOS, with a set of about 250 system services -- programmers can write character-based applications using these services.

FIGURE 17.1
OS/2 memory map.

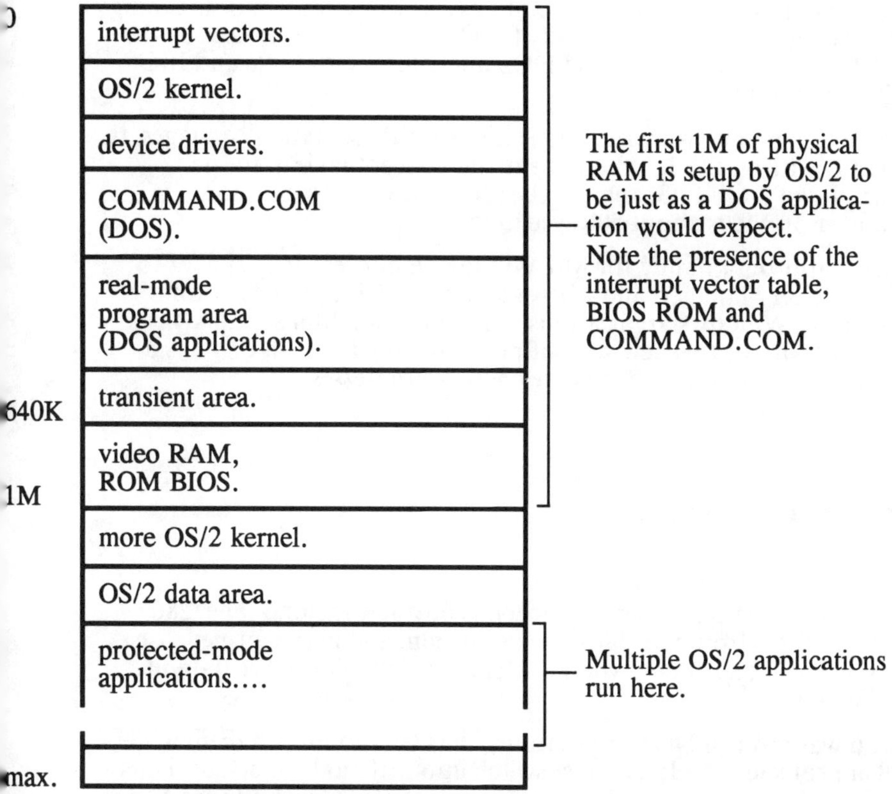

0	interrupt vectors.
	OS/2 kernel.
	device drivers.
	COMMAND.COM (DOS).
	real-mode program area (DOS applications).
640K	transient area.
1M	video RAM, ROM BIOS.
	more OS/2 kernel.
	OS/2 data area.
	protected-mode applications....
max.	

The first 1M of physical RAM is setup by OS/2 to be just as a DOS application would expect. Note the presence of the interrupt vector table, BIOS ROM and COMMAND.COM.

Multiple OS/2 applications run here.

Note that a '386 - specific version of OS/2 would have a somewhat different layout to this. The conventional memory area would not have to be setup as per a real DOS machine, since the '386 can run multiple DOS applications anywhere in memory -- conventional or extended. The '286 is basically limited to running one DOS application at a time, in the conventional memory area -- with the CPU switched into real-mode. The '386 can also map OS/2 applications into the conventional area. These comments also apply to Windows.

Note that these services are invoked by far CALL's, not by **INT** *62* instuctions as with DOS. Of course OS/2 is supposed to be compatible with DOS applications, so it can provide the BIOS/DOS services as well, though be clear that this is not OS/2's normal way of doing things -- applications written specifically for OS/2 invoke the services by the CALL instruction, and the old DOS interrupt vector table and BIOS ROM are not used.

Programmers can also write applications for Presentation Manager, to be really with-it, though there is a major conceptual leap to the principles of a GUI (Graphical User Interface) -- Presentation Manager provides about 500 system services.

Note that programming for MS-Windows is conceptually similar to Presentation Manager, and Microsoft also provide guidelines for converting Windows applications to Presentation Manager. A popular term for this new style of programming is "event driven", a term that will become clear as the chapter progresses.

MEMORY MAP:

How OS/2 sets up the memory depends on a few factors. The '286 version differs from the '386-specific version, and in the former case the setup will depend on whether OS/2 is required to run real -mode applications.

If you want to run DOS applications, the '286 cannot run them while still in protected mode, so must switch into real mode to do so. Thus the first 1M of memory must be setup permanently with a **layout that** *9* **DOS applications expect**.

The '386's virtual-86 mode doesn't have this limitation, allowing DOS applications to run in protected mode, with true multitasking of them -- and they can occupy any place in the entire address space.

The '286 can only run one DOS application at a time.

Current versions of OS/2 are designed for the '286, though a '386-specific version is promised.

The diagram, Figure 17.1, shows how the '286 version of OS/2 sets up memory with the capability of running a DOS application.

Of course the OS/2 applications can occupy any of the area indicated, and can be swapped in and out as segments.

FIGURE 17.2 Segment & register initialisation.

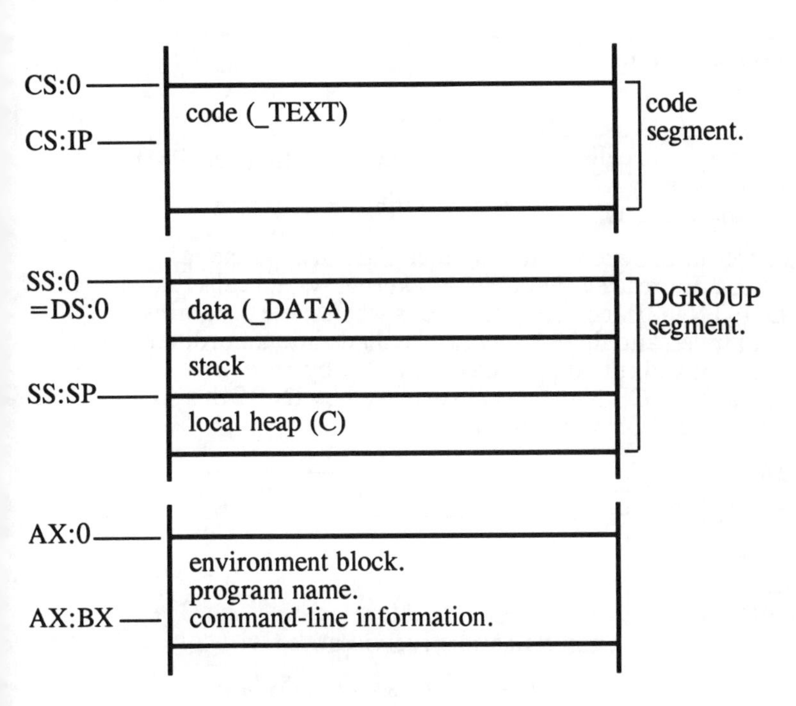

Note that this picture depends upon the memory model. I touched upon this in Chapter Five when introducing the simplified segment directives. The directives allow a model specification, that determines the number of segments in the final program. Basically this is set by the size of your program. The smallest model is TINY, which is a .COM program, which OS/2 doesn't support. The above map is for the SMALL model -- for Assembly language programs this is okay, since your code size is unlikely to exceed 64K. Other models allow for multiple code or data segments. When writing Windows applications in C, the MEDIUM model is usually used -- it has a single data/stack segment as above, but allows multiple code segments.

DEVELOPING OS/2 APPLICATIONS

An OS/2 application can have system calls at three levels of complexity:

1. Kernel
2. Family
3. Presentation Manager (PM).

Kernel-based applications use only the 250-odd kernel system calls. This is okay for developing character-based applications.

Family-based applications are written in much the same manner as kernel applications, but restrict themselves to kernel system calls that have a direct DOS INT-21h counterpart. Thus when these programs are assembled/compiled and linked they can be made into an ordinary OS/2 application that will run in protected mode, or by an extra conversion step have the OS/2 system calls replaced by INT-21h's so can run as a real-mode DOS application.

Although it can be argued that family-based applications do not fully exploit the OS/2 kernel, a lot of current development is taking this practical route.

ASSEMBLY LANGUAGE:

How do Assembly language programs differ in their basic structure, from those we have been writing for DOS? For a start, they must be in .EXE format:

```
;................................
.286
...
;since all system services are far
;calls, OS/2 expects you to declare
;them here...
  extrn DosExit:far                                254
;
DGROUP group _DATA ;req'd byOS/2.                  252
                  ;refer DGROUP notes.             299
;.........
_DATA segment public 'data'                        101
... ;the usual data declarations.
_DATA ends
;........
_TEXT segment public 'code'
  ....continued....
```

Note that there is no stack defined here. Certain parameters such as the stack size are defined in what is called a "Module Definition File". You can recognise these as they have the extension .DEF.

KERNEL SYSTEM CALLS:

"DosExit" has already been introduced. It has also been mentioned that many calls correspond exactly with DOS functions. For example "DosGetVersion" will return the OS/2 version number.

What about the passing of parameters? This is done via the stack.

"DosWrite" is one of the basic output calls, using the method of handles. Here is some code:

Note that it is extremely easy to call the system services from a high-level language such as C or Pascal, as long as the parameters are passed via the stack.

If you refer back to the chapter on **linking modules**, there is a description of this.

Note also my use of the name DGROUP for the data segment. OS/2 expects:

```
.....continued.....
  assume cs:_TEXT,ds:DGROUP                      102
;
main proc far                                    102
...
...
  push 1  ;DosExit requires parameters
  push 0  ; on the stack.
  call DosExit   ;back to parent.
main endp                                        102
;
;other procedures....
...
_TEXT ends
  end main    ;specifies program entry           101
              ;point.
```

```
extrn DosWrite:far
...
;within data segment....
stdout equ 1   ;standard output device
               ;(screen).
outlen dw  ?   ;actual bytes written.            100
msg    db  "hi there"                            100
msglen equ 8                                     251
...
;within code segment...
 push stdout        ;handle
; continues next page .....
```

DGROUP group _DATA

as **unlike DOS** the data segment register DS is initialised to DGROUP when the program is loaded. To be sure that OS/2's assembler and link programs work properly, note that DGROUP seg. override may be required with MASM if data addressing is to be correct with multiple data segments.

```
; ..... continued from previous page
  push ds            ;far address of messag
push offset msg        ; "   "    " "*
push msglen        ;length of message
push ds          ;far address of actual
push offset outlen      ; bytes written.*
call DosWrite
cmp  ax,0          ;AX=0 if an error.
jnz  error
;..................................
* see note about DGROUP override
```

18

REGISTER INITIALISATION:

This logically leads us to another question -- to what values are the registers initialised when an OS/2 application is loaded?

Although OS/2 applications are in .EXE format, it is somewhat different from **DOS's .EXE format**, and this is reflected in how the registers are initialised:

REG.	CONTENT
CS	Segment selector for code.
CS:IP	Initial entry point, within code.
SS:SP	Base of the stack.
DS	Segment selector for DGROUP.
ES	Zero.
AX	Segment selector of environment.
BX	Offset of command-line information
CX	Initial size of DGROUP.
DX	Initial size of stack.
SI	Initial size of local heap.
DI	Module handle for the process.
BP	Zero.

TABLE 17.1

18

We cannot really draw a memory map, for the simple reason that the data and code segments can be located anywhere in memory, determined by the Local Descriptor Table (LDT) for the task. The arrangement in memory also depends on the size of the program.

For what Intel & Microsoft refer to as the "small model", there are three segments in memory, looking like this-- refer to Figure 17.2.

ASSEMBLING & LINKING A PROGRAM:

MASM is used in the normal way, but with LINK there is more to think about:

111

```
MASM  DEMO:
LINK  DEMO , , DEMO , OS2 , DEMO
```

The generalised format for LINK's command-tail is as follows --

```
LINK [options] objectfiles, [exefile], [mapfile], [libraries], [deffile]
```

The example specifies an object file DEMO.OBJ, the name of the output .EXE file is not specified so defaults to DEMO.EXE, the output mapfile is DEMO.MAP and two other input files are specified; OS2.LIB, a library file required for system calls, and DEMO.**DEF**, the definition file that you must produce (with a text editor) to set certain parameters for the program.

307

Note that there is a utility program called BIND.EXE, that converts a family-based OS/2 program to run as a DOS program.

IMPLICATIONS OF MULTITASKING

Obviously direct I/O is a problem, and all hardware access must be via the operating system, that arbitrates all requests.

(note: there are mechanisms for **direct I/O to ports** and to video and **device drivers**).

306

For example, should a task running in the background request keyboard input, it is blocked, as only the foreground task is using the keyboard and screen.

OS/2 is of course a multitasking operating system, making use of the virtual mode of the '286 and '386 to isolate tasks. We can make a number of key statements about this capability --

1. PREEMPTIVE SCHEDULING:

The task scheduler uses "preemptive scheduling", meaning that a higher priority task can take control away from another task, as opposed to a scheduler that allows a task to run to completion before executing another. Note that in practice the operating system appears to be executing all tasks simultaneously even though it is actually executing one at a time. See also point-6 below.

2. LEAST RECENTLY USED:

The memory manager uses a "least recently used" (LRU) algorithm for decidng which segments should remain in memory. Since any one task can consist of many segments (data, code, TSS, LDT), it may not be necessary for them all to be in memory at the same time. This is an interesting aspect of virtual memory management -- unlike DOS applications, that usually load themselves in their entirety (except for overlays). OS/2 can load as much of the program as it wants, and also place them wherever it wants in physical memory. Whenever a program addresses a segment that is not physically resident in memory, a certain bit is set in the appropriate **descriptor** in the LDT, so OS/2 knows to load it. Once loaded, OS/2 can update the descriptor, and the task can continue.

204

3. RING PROTECTION:

Ring protection. **Privilege levels** are an inbuilt feature of the '286. The levels are from 0 to 3, with 0 being most privileged. An application program would usually run at level 3, set by certain bits in the descriptor for each segment, and cannot normallv access more privileged levels. There are however mechanisms for getting around this, called "**gates**", most notably system calls and direct I/O.

210

4. THREADS:

"Tasks" are separate programs, operating in their own "virtual machines" and normally isolated from each other. An interesting aspect of OS/2 is that even an individual task can become concurrent, in that it can create its own tasks, called "threads". This is rather like the DOS **EXEC** function, that loads a child program and executes it.

267

FIGURE 17.3 Mechanism for the device monitor.

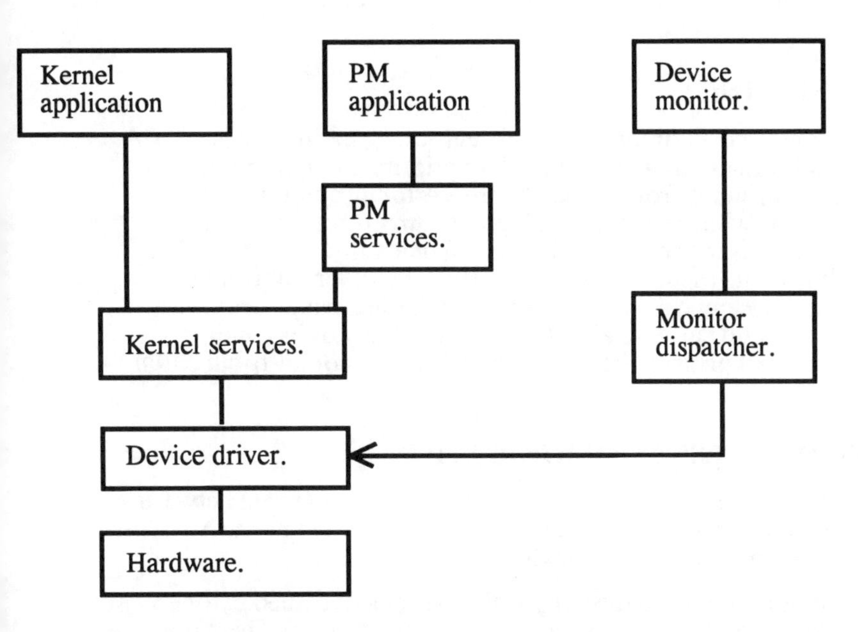

The monitor is method to allow a program to watch the raw flow of data to and from a device driver. This can allow some preprocessing of data, before it goes into the operating system. In the case of the console driver, a monitor can pickup keypresses and either pass them on to the operating system (see page 311) or act upon them in some way. Thus a monitor, which can be created as a thread of an application, can behave just like a DOS resident program that has modified the interupt - 16h or 9 vector.

However with DOS the parent is dead while the child executes. OS/2's "DosExecPgm" system call can work in the same way as DOS, for upward compatibility reasons, but also has an "asynchronous mode", in which the parent continues to execute after calling the child. The parent and child are referred to as threads of the task.

5. SCHEDULING:

A thread is classed as "interactive", "foreground", or "background". A background thread has a low scheduling priority and doesn't output to the screen or input from the keyboard. A foreground thread has higher priority, while interactive is highest. Any thread involving keyboard input is in the latter category. When a thread is created, it by default inherits the parent's priority level, however this can be changed by a system call. A program can alter its own priority with "DosSetPrty", and can also alter the priority of any of its children. Threads of equal priority are treated by OS/2 on a round-robin basis.

6. INTERPROCESS COMMUNICATION:

Despite tasks being isolated, they may need to communicate between each other, and there are mechanisms for this -- Shared memory, Semaphores, Pipes, Queues, Signals.

Shared memory is a mechanism by which a segment owned by one task can be given away or made available to other tasks. There is a system call for this.

Semaphores are of two types: System and RAM, the latter being for communication between threads of a task.

Semaphores are a mechanism for ensuring mutual exclusion when executing critical sections of code.

Pipes work like DOS or Unix pipes and involve redirection of the standard system read and write calls.

Queues are a method of sending messages, via shared memory.

Signals are a kind of software interrupt, that send a single number and a word of information only.

FIGURE 17.4 Mechanism for a Call-Gate.

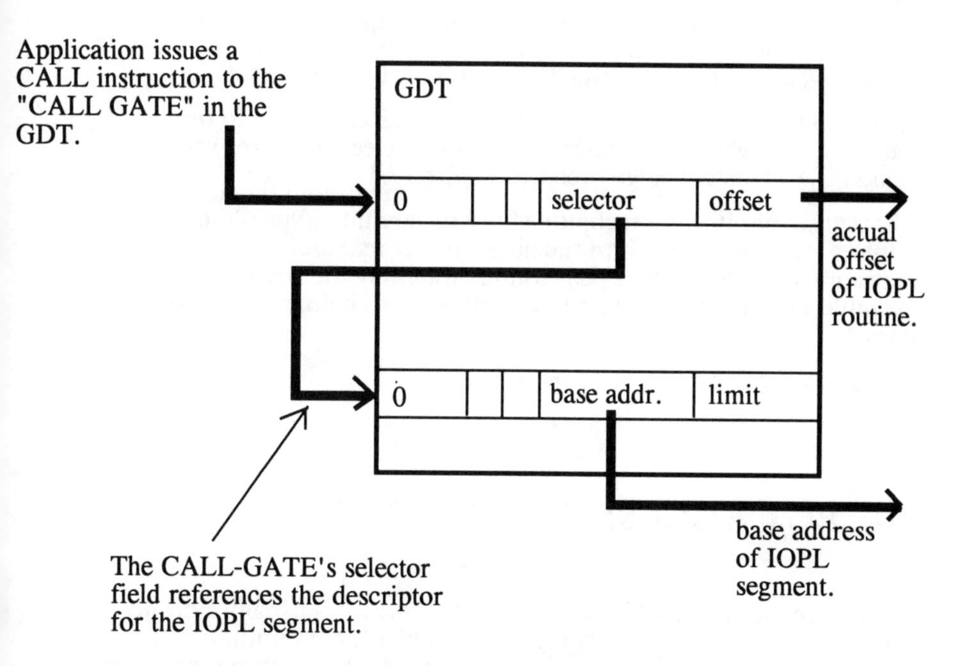

A call-gate cannot be created dynamically when your program executes -- it is created by the operating system when the program loads from disk. When the program is written, you designate a segment as being the IOPL segment, by means of naming it in the .DEF file. The LINK program stores the .DEF information into a special area of the .EXE file, so when OS/2 loads the program it sees that there is an IOPL segment in the file, so creates the call-gate. Any transfer of control to that segment will be transparently via the call-gate -- see pages 307 and 308.

DEVICE DRIVERS & MONITORS:

Philosophically the device driver is **structured** much the same as in DOS, with a "strategy" routine and an "interrupt" routine. This two-part structure is excellent for a multitasking environment. Also OS/2 drivers can be **character**-type or **block**-type, as with DOS. *277* *274*

Reviewing the basic concept, the driver interfaces directly to the hardware, allowing application programs to access the hardware by using general system calls -- refer to Figure 17.3.

The device monitor is a technique for a program to bypass the system services and get directly into the device driver and look at its data flow. A program written as a device monitor watching the keyboard for example, could detect certain key-combinations before they go to the kernel.

There is some **example code >>>** *311*

DIRECT ACCESS TO I/O PORTS:

The device monitor is effectively doing this, which is usually a no-no for a multitasking/user operating system. OS/2 is not multiuser however, so there can be some leniency. Beside device monitors, there are other mechanisms for an application to get straight to the hardware.

Remember that the CPU is operating in protected mode, so each task is encased in a virtual machine. Every access to memory is redirected via the LDT's and/or page tables, to wherever the operating system decides to put that task. The OS will sound an alarm if a task tries to address somewhere outside its boundaries.

The '286 has a couple of flags in the **flags-register**, called the I/O-Privilege-Level (IOPL) field. The operating system sets this field to the privilege level required by code if it is entitled to execute direct I/O instructions, such as **IN and OUT**, or to control the **interrupt-flag** with CLI and STI. *367* *136* *139*

Usually this field is set to two, while an application's code is set to three. Thus, an application cannot perform direct I/O.

IOPL SEGMENT & THE CALL-GATE:

The code to talk directly to I/O must be created in a separate segment, called an IOPL segment, that has privilege-level two. The application can execute this more privileged segment by a mechanism called a "call gate".

When the program is first loaded from disk, OS/2 sees that it has an IOPL segment, and creates two descriptors in the **GDT**, a call-gate, and an actual descriptor -- refer to Figure 17.4.

SO, HOW DO WE WRITE AN IOPL-SEGMENT?

Fairly simple. Isolate all code that uses the direct I/O instructions, and put it into its own segment:

```
; IOPL segment ....
.286
IO_TEXT segment public 'code'          101
assume cs:IO_TEXT                      102
public mainio                          253
;....
mainio proc far                        102
... ;save reg's.                       202
... ;get parameters off stack.
...
  in al,25 ;25 is arbitrary port num.
  mov ah,0
...
... ;restore reg's.
  ret ;returns port-data in AX.        31
;................................
```

This IOPL segment (listed alongside) could be written as a separate program, assembled, then linked with the main body.

The main program would look like the listing on the next page.

The **.DEF file** contains all sorts of useful information about your program, including which segment/s is/are IOPL segments. A section of the .DEF file would be setup like this --

"EXPORTS" defines the number of parameters to be passed on the stack and also identifies MAINIO as callable from outside the IOPL segment.

```
.DEF file ....                         301
SEGMENTS
IO_TEXT IOPL
EXPORTS
MAINIO 1
```

```
; Main program, to access IOPL......
extrn DosPortAccess:far ;kernel service
extrn mainio:far
;.....
DGROUP group _DATA                                         252
_DATA  segment public 'data'                               101
...
_DATA  ends                                                101
;....
_TEXT  segment public 'code'
assume cs:_TEXT,ds:DGROUP                                  102
main proc far   ;entry point from OS/2                     102
...
... ;push parameters on stack.
  call DosPortAccess ;request access to
                     ;a range of ports.
...
... ;push parameters on stack.
  call mainio ;actual port access.
... ;get returned value/s.
...
... ;push parameters on stack.
  call DosPortAccess ;close access right
...
... ;push parameters on stack.
  call DosExit
_TEXT ends                                                 101
  end  main                                                102
;.................................
```

DIRECT VIDEO ACCESS

With DOS applications we are accustomed to getting at the video in two ways; via system services, or by writing directly to the **video-RAM**.

77

OS/2 also has system calls, but what about direct access to the video RAM? Notes above describe mechanisms for getting into the device drivers, and for reading & writing the I/O ports directly, but OS/2 also has mechansims for directly accessing actual memory addresses.

DosWrite is an example of a system service, analogous to DOS's Int-21h, **function 40h**. There are also a range of services called the "Vio" services, that are similar to DOS's BIOS video services.

355

There are two types of direct access to video-RAM:

Logical Video Buffer (LVB),

physical video buffer.

A task can have a logical video buffer, whose selector it obtains by a certain system call, and this is a buffer somewhere in memory, but not the actual physical buffer residing on the video adaptor card.

Each task or "screen group" can have its own logical buffer, to which it can write directly. The currently active foreground task will have its logical buffer automatically copied to the physical buffer, so you will see it on the screen.

Thus any number of tasks can be outputing to logical buffers, and by a simple keypress you can flick between tasks to view the output.

Again, we have another conventional no-no here. An application can, via a certain system call, "lock" the screen's physical buffer onto that task, and the service will return a selector enabling direct communication with the screen.

Another service unlocks the screen.

(With device monitors, IOPL-segments and direct physical video buffer access, I do see a lot of potential for poorly behaved programs -- and for viruses!).

```
;  Code to produce a window....
;data area....
PopFlags   dw 1  ;flag controls
           ; action if window not avail.
;1=wait, 0=no wait.
msg        db "this is a tsr window"
msg_len    equ $-msg
;................................
;code area....
...
;put up pop-up window...
push ds       ;address of pop-up flags.
push offset PopFlags ;  /
push 0        ;VIO handle (reserved).
call VIOPOPUP ;pops up TSR
                    ;window.
or   ax,ax    ;test if succeeded.
jnz  error
...
;now write a message to window...
push ds       ;address of message.
push offset msg ;   /
push msg_len  ;length of message.
push 12       ;y-coordinate.
push (80-msg_len)/2 ;x-coordinate.
push 0        ;VIO handle (reserved).
call VIOWRTCHARSTR
;displays string.
or   ax,ax    ;test if succeeded.
jnz  error
...
;remove pop-up window from scrn...
push 0        ;VIO handle (reserved).
call VIOENDPOPUP ;remove wind.
or   ax,ax    ;test if succeeded.
jnz  error
```

TSR's

The above notes mention the "Vio" services -- these are very convenient for screen output and typical usage is shown below, in example TSR code. But what have TSR's got to do with OS/2?

What we now have is a multitasking operating system, in which a program can most naturally reside alongside another. Since this book has been using the term TSR I am retaining it here, and showing how the TSR concept can be implemented with OS/2.

Firstly, how to produce a window... listed on the next page.

This code should be quite readable. VIOPOPUP is fascinating -- it saves the current content of the screen, regardless of what mode it is in, places the current foreground task into the background, and changes the screen to 80x25 text mode, then clears the screen before returning to our program.

VIOENDPOPUP does exactly the opposite, restoring the screen to what it was and reinstating the previous program to the foreground.

Very nice -- these two services remove some headaches associated with TSR's.

But what about getting the TSR to pop-up and go away? One method is to pick up the keyboard characters right at the device driver, before the rest of the system gets hold of them -- for this we need a **device monitor**.

Part of our TSR can declare itself to be a monitor, and watch the character stream, looking for the "hot-key".

The sample code alongside originated from Microsoft's "Advanced OS/2 Programming" by Ray Duncan, a reference that I have found particularly helpful for my own recent project of porting a DOS-based TSR over to OS/2:

```
; Device monitor code....
data area...
KbdName   db "\DEV\KBD$",0
  ;keyboard logical device name.
KbdHandle dw ?
  ;handle from  DOSMONOPEN.
KbdMonIn  dw 128,64 dup(0)
  ;monitor input buffer.
KbdMonOut dw 128,64 dup(0)
  ;monitor output buffer.
KbdPacket db 128 dup(0)
  ;holds keyboard data packet.
KbdPktLen dw ?
  ;length of data in KbdPacket
ScrGroup  dw ?
  ;current screen group number
;..................................
;code area...
...
  ;open monitor connection...
  push ds    ;address of \DEV\KBD$
  push offset KbdName ; /
  push ds    ;address to receive handle.
  push offset KbdHandle ; /
  call DOSMONOPEN       ;open monitor.
  or   ax,ax            ;test if error.
  jnz  error
...
  ;register keyboard monitor...
  push KbdHandle
  ;handle fromDOSMONOPEN.
  push ds   ;addr of monitor input buffer
  push offset KbdMonin ;  /
  push ds   ;addr of output buffer.
  push offset KbdMonOut ; /
; continues next page.....
```

306

```
; Device monitor continued.....
  push 1   ;request front of list.
  push ScrGroup
  ;push screen group number
  call DOSMONREG
  ;register keyboard mon.
  or  ax,ax     ;test if error.
  jnz error
  ...
  ;now for the actual keyboard monitor...
nextchar:
mov KbdPktLen,KbdPktLen-KbdPacket
  ;set maximum length for read.
  push ds  ;address of input buffer.
  push offset KbdMonIn ; /
  push 0   ;wait until data available.
  push ds  ;address to receive packet.
  push offset KbdPacket ; /
  push ds  ;address of length variable.
  push offset KbdPktLen ; /
  call DOSMONREAD
  or  ax,ax        ;test if error.
  jnz error
  ...
  ;test if character is the hot-key...
  cmp byte ptr KbdPacket+3,HotKey
  jz  ProcessKey ;jump if it is.
  ;not the hot-key, so pass char on...
  push ds  ;addr of output buffer.
  push offset KbdMonOut ; /
  push ds  ;addr of keyboard packet.
  push offset KbdPacket ; /
  push KbdPktLen
  ;length of data packet.
  call DOSMONWRITE
; continues ......
```

DOSMONOPEN returned a monitor handle. DOSMONREG is also required to set the program up for reading data from the keyboard and passing it along, using two local data buffers.

DOSMONREAD reads the data, in the form of a "packet".

Of course this code is in a loop, and has a high priority, so as not to holdup the keyboard input. The above monitor could be implemented as a "thread" of our program.

```
; Device monitor continued....
  or  ax,ax
  jnz error
  jmp nextchar  ;wait for another
                ;key.
...
  ;prgram should close monitor
                ;when
  ; done..
  push KbdHandle  ;handle for
                ;monitor.
  call DOSMONCLOSE
  or  ax,ax
  jnz error
...
;..................................
```

MICROSOFT WINDOWS

Index...

INRODUCTION

Windows is a GUI for DOS, much like Presentation Manager (PM) is for OS/2.

As the concepts of the two GUI's are similar, applications developed for the former are readily transported to the latter, and as the current interest is concentrated on the former, I have described the Windows GUI here.

For hands-on work, Windows is required, plus the Microsoft Windows Software Development Kit (SDK), plus Microsoft MASM & C.... at least that was the situation until quite recently -- now we have the superb Borland Turbo Pascal and C++ for Windows, that do not require the SDK.

Windows development is complex, but there are various tools designed to ease the task. One example is C_Talk_Views, a set of object-oriented C routines. Another is Actor, a language in its own right, that tends to shield the developer from the complex details of normal programming languages and from the messy details of Windows itself.

This Chapter gives an overview, then dives in at a fundamental level, which is excellent for learning -- a complete application is shown, written entirely in Assembly language. Firstly, the basic concepts....

Very basically, how do Windows programs differ from those we write for DOS?

There are a number of additional features that will add to the complexity of our program --

1. A GUI featuring windows, menus, dialog boxes and controls for applications.
2. Queued input.
3. Device-independent graphics.
4. Multitasking.
5. Data interchange between applications.

1.

WINDOWS:

Since it is a multitasking environment, every task has its own window on the screen. Your program must start by creating this window, and the operating system will then look after it (resizing, moving, etc) in response to the operator.

Windows makes sure that all your program's screen output goes into its window, and not elsewhere on the screen.

2.

QUEUED INPUT:

You are familiar with DOS's **keyboard-queue**. However with Windows there are system queues for keyboard, mouse, etc, and separate queues for each application. The input information provided to the application's queue is more comprehensive than with DOS, and is referred to as an "input message".

137

3.

DEVICE-INDEPENDENT GRAPHICS:

These are routines built-in to Windows for drawing graphics, such as lines, boxes and circles. You can use these standard routines without having to be too concerned about the specific printer, plotter or monitor connected -- this is taken care of by loading the appropriate

FIGURE 17.5
Steps to develop a Windows application.

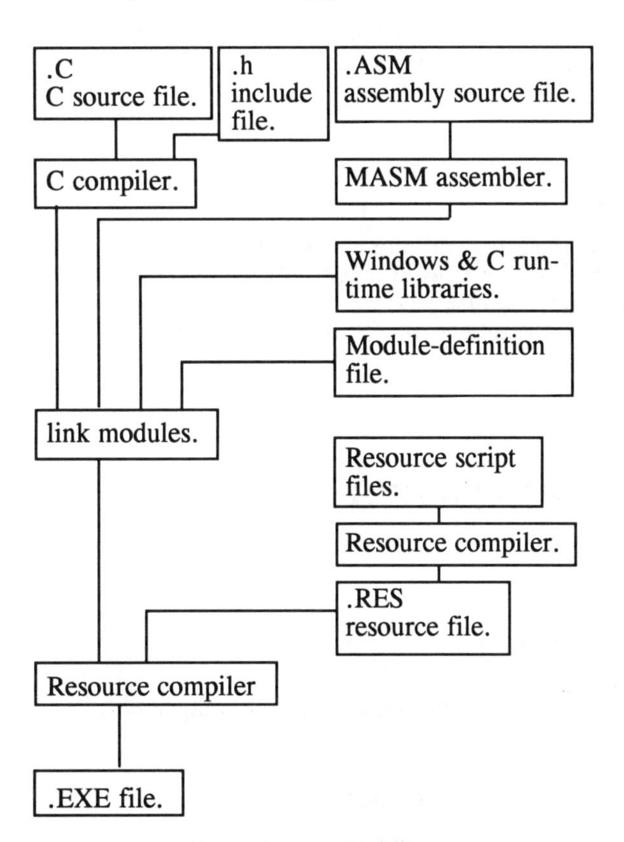

This may at first glance seem formidable, but in practice the steps are automated and fairly painless. The key to the automation is a MAKE file -- if working from the DOS command-line that is (or the RUN command-line from within Windows' File Manager). Integrated development environments perform all of the steps without requiring you to know anything about MAKE files, but I always find such environments to be too limiting, and end up back on the command-line. Some products will generate the MAKE file for you automatically -- see page 338.

device driver. Windows provides a large selection of device drivers, and suppliers of specialist peripherals usually supply a device driver for it.

Of course your program is not going to be totally device independent, due to the constraints imposed by the particular device.

4. MULTITASKING:

Windows will manage the memory, moving and swapping segments/pages as required, so your program cannot assume that it will permanently sit at some absolute address. Ditto for the video-RAM. Applications cannot (normally) write directly to the screen RAM.

BUILDING A WINDOWS APPLICATION

The Windows routines operate like C functions, (though stack handling follows the **Pascal** convention). The library of functions can be split into three types:

1. User:

Provides window management.

261

2. Kernel:

System services, such as multitasking, memory & resource management.

3. GDI:

Graphics Device Interface.

We have to generate many different files to obtain a final Windows .EXE file (note that the format is "**new .EXE**")

300

The overall process is shown in Figure 17.5.

Note that the C compiler, Assembler, Linker and Resource Compiler must all be Windows-compatible, and of course the various libraries and resource editors & compiler are supplied with the SDK.

The Module Definition File defines various program parameters that the linker needs -- this is basically the same as **.DEF files in OS/2**.

307

FIGURE 17.6
Windows application message-passing.

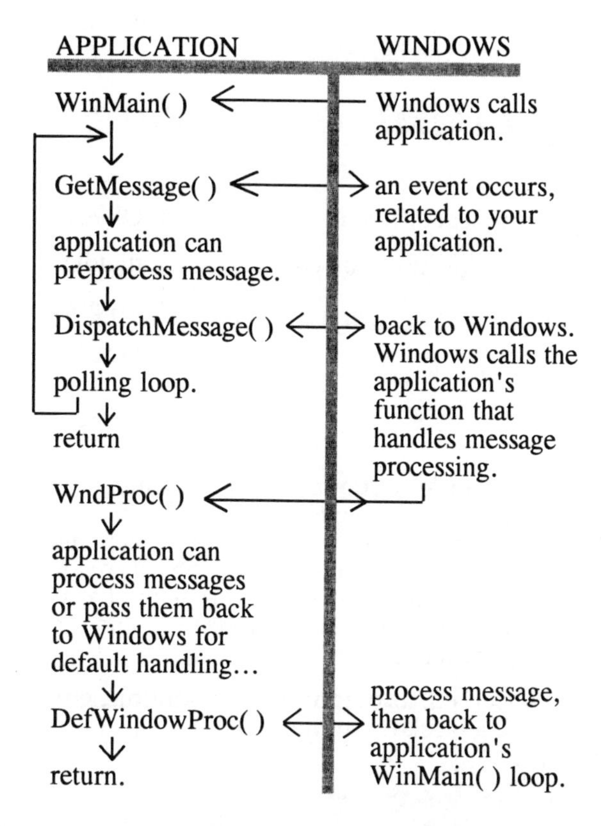

The above flow of control backwards and forwards between Windows and the application looks devious, but there is some logic to it. A major problem is that it steepens the learning curve, and makes even trivial programs quite large. See my listing of an Assembly language program that says "Hullo World" on page 327 -- it occupies ten pages! Two major reasons for its size are firstly the necessity of creating and displaying a window, plus associated paraphenalia such as menu-bar and mmessage-boxes, and secondly the processing of messages. The above diagram shows that Windows sends messages to WndProc( ) -- lots of them -- and many need to explicitly handled by the program, rather than the option with many of sending them back to Windows for default handling. Updating the window client-area is an example. All of this builds into a sizable skeleton program, but the basic skeleton can be built upon for much more substantial programs.

The resource file defines parameters connected with the windows, icons, menus, dialog boxes & **segments**.

324

WINDOWS PROGRAMMING CONCEPTS:

There are some major philosophical differences from conventional DOS-based programming. It is useful to start off with some appreciation of some new terms intrinsic to Windows:

Object,
handle,
instance,
message.

OBJECTS:

These days we are finding the term "object oriented programming" popping up in the literature and as an "enhancement" to popular compilers. Windows treats an application's window as an object, and the parts of the window (menu items, scroll bar, etc) are objects related to the main object (the window). You can reference this main object as a single entity, and perhaps resize or move it on the screen, and the related objects will also change or move.

As far as your program is concerned, its output is to the window, not to the screen, and all positioning is relative to the window's coordinates, not the screen's.

HANDLES:

The **concept of the handle** has already been introduced in relation to file access, but Windows takes it a step further. Just as you obtained a handle to reference a disk file, so in Wiindows you can obtain a handle to reference an object. For example, a particular window will have a handle.

226

Handles are an important aspect of object-oriented programming. Somewhere near the start of your Windows application, you would need to create a window and display it on the screen -- this doesn't happen automatically -- your program must call appropriate Windows functions:

CreateWindow()
ShowWindow()

These are functions that you would call from your C program.

Both have parameters that you pass to the function. With CreateWindow(), you pass such information as the type of window, its size, and the handle of your current application.

With Windows, think of everything as having handles. This includes every program currently loaded. Your program's handle is given to it when Windows started your program executing. In fact Windows treats your program just like a function, calling it and passing parameters to it on the stack -- your handle included.

CreateWindow() returns a handle for the new window, and from now on your program can use that handle to reference that window. It follows from this that an application can have more than one window.

INSTANCE:

Windows documentation will confuse you with sentences like this -- "...the current instance of the application...". Think of the word "instance" as meaning a particular "handle", and you're on the right track. Windows uses all sorts of names for handles, each name clarifying what the handle is.

Your program will have its own handle -- this is because multiple copies of your program can be running concurrently in the computer, and each copy will need to have its own handle. Thus we refer to each "instance" of the program.

I use the word "copies" very loosely here, since although many "instances" of the program may be running or loaded concurrently, the actual code is not necessarily duplicated -- this is an interesting aspect of Windows programming, to conserve memory.

MESSAGES:

There is a fascinating difference in how we write programs for Windows, apart from all of the above. The program has to kind of "wait around" for Windows to tell it what to do next. Instead of our program explicitly interrogating the keyboard for example, to learn its status or to read a key, our Windows program sits there waiting for a "message" from Windows.

While waiting, it is in an idle state and other tasks can be executing.

Windows is always busy, watching what is going on -- should Windows see that something has happened to your application's window, say the mouse-button pressed while the pointer was somewhere over your window, it sends a message to your program to tell you. Your program doesn't have to keep on asking the mouse directly what it's doing -- Windows does that, and will only send a message to your application if something has happened in your window.

Don't forget that everything is referenced by handles. Just as your window has a handle, so do the components of your window -- each component is an "object" related to the window. Say that the mouse pulls down a menu and selects an item -- this has happened in your window, so affects your program -- Windows sends a message, with the appropriate handle, to your program.

The main part of your program, the top level, always given the function-name WinMain(), is usually in a waiting loop, hoping that Windows will be so kind as to send it a message:

GetMessage() is the Windows function that your program calls to obtain a message.

TranslateMessage() is specifically for converting keyboard messages into a more usable form.

```
/*..................................*/
int PASCAL FAR WinMain(hInstance,
        hPrevInstance,lpCmdLine,nCmdShow)
HANDLE hInstance;   /*current instance*/
HANDLE hPrevInstance; /*previous inst.*/
LPSTR  lpCmdLine;   /*command line ptr*/
int    nCmdShow     /*show-type*/
...
/*...initialisation...*/
/*...previous instance handling...*/
/*...create & display a window...*/
...
while (GetMessage(&msg,NULL,NULL,NULL))
{
TranslateMessage(&msg);
DispatchMessage(&msg);
}
/*..................................*/
```

ANSI C:
Note that I've written this example code in "traditional" C syntax rather than "ANSI" C, as this is how it is given in many books and what many people will be most familiar with. ANSI C compilers will still compile traditional C okay. Looking at the listing on the previous page, the ANSI C type declarations would be inside the function brackets.

Now here is the twist -- having just got the message, your program now sends it straight back to Windows, via DispatchMessage()!

Note that your program does have the option of doing something with the message before sending it on.

Having sent the message, and execution, back to Windows, Windows then calls the other major function of your program -- WndProc() -- sending it the message.

Before we consider WndProc(), a few more notes on the above sample code.

```
long FAR PASCAL WndProc(hWnd,message,
                        wParam,lParam)
HWND    hWnd;   /*window handle*/
unsigned message; /*type of message*/
WORD    wParam;  /*more information*/
LONG    lParam;  /*more information*/
{
...
/*...case-logic to analyse message,..*/
/*...send control to a routine.......*/
...
/*...user-written message-handling...*/
/*...functions...*/
...
/*...default message-handling........*/
DefWindowProc(hWnd,message,wParam,
                        lParam)
...
}
```

Windows expands considerably on standard C, with many functions and data-types. The "h" preceding a name signifies type of "handle", while "lp" signifies "long pointer". "&msg" is a far address supplied to GetMessage(), for the message.

Although this example code is C, Windows uses Pascal conventions for passing parameters to functions, hence the "PASCAL" declaration above. (Pascal passes parameters on the stack in the **opposite order to C**, and also expects the function to remove the parameters. C leaves the parameters on the stack and expects the calling program to remove them).

Now for WndProc() -- I stuck the listing on the previous page.

Some input "events", such as a mouse movement to resize your application's window, has to be done by Windows itself, so for such messages the WndProc( ) function just returns control back to Windows by calling "DefWindowProc()".

Figure 17.6 puts it all together, diagrammatically.

This messaging mechanism may seem devious to those familiar with DOS programming.

You'll find my notes on OS/2 to be relevant, as Windows has many similarities, though not so refined -- task scheduling for example is only a shadow compared with OS/2.

Turn the page to look at Windows from the most basic level.....

WINDOWS ASSEMBLY LANGUAGE PROGRAMMING

Yes it's quite feasible to write entire applications for Windows in Assembly language, though it is more usual to restrict Asm to just critical sections of the program. Looking at how to write the entire program at the Asm level is most useful for learning purposes and gives us useful insights into how Windows works.

I have organised this section by example -- our universal "Hullo World" introductory program. Here we go through step by step and put together the complete application. I have written the program at the most fundamental level, for instructional purposes, however since a lot of pushing onto the stack is involved, it is better in practice to make use of macros -- the Microsoft Windows SDK provides an include file for this purpose; CMACROS.INC -- this is a refinement that you could look at later.

So what do you need? I used various tools from the SDK, though Borland's Windows development tools will have equivalent functions -- the WINHULLO files on the Companion Disk clarify this. In the case of the SDK, what you need is:

MASM.EXE	(mine is v5.10)
LINK.EXE	(mine came from C v6.00)
NMAKE.EXE	(mine came from C v6.00)
RC.EXE	(resource compiler, from the SDK)
RCPP.EXE	(from the SDK)
RCPP.ERR	(from the SDK)
LIBW.LIB	(from the SDK)
SLIBCEW.LIB	(from the SDK)
WINSTUB.EXE	(from the SDK)

If you don't have the SDK installed on your computer, you could just acquire these files and put them all into the one directory, and you're ready to go. The next step is to write the application, which of course you use a text editor to do, but it is no longer a case of producing a single .ASM source file -- let's call it WINHULLO.ASM. The application files we will need are:

WINHULLO.ASM	(program source)
WINHULLO.RC	(resource script)
WINHULLO.MAK	(make file)
WINHULLO.DEF	(definition file)
include files	

RESOURCE & DEFINITION FILES:

Resource (.RC) and definition (.DEF) files are produced by a text editor, though you can get some help with special paint programs to generate the resource scripts. Resource scripts describe the appearance of what is seen on the screen -- dialog boxes, menus, etc, plus can store other information. I wrote WINHULLO.RC directly using a text editor, since it is a simple example. The **definition file** defines the name, segments, memory requirements and exported (including callback) functions of the application, and is straightforward enough to write with a text editor.

316

I have listed the .RC and .DEF files here for reference -- examine them in detail with the help of a book on Windows programming.

```
# WINHULLO.RC
//these (arbitrary) equates could have been in an include file...
#define IDM_QUIT     100
#define IDM_ABOUT  101
winhullo   MENU
  BEGIN
   POPUP "File"
    BEGIN
          MENUITEM "Quit",  IDM_QUIT
          MENUITEM "About...",  IDM_ABOUT
    END
  END
```

You will be able to figure out what this .RC file does by observing the execution of the program -- a menu-bar with only one selection: "File", which drops down two menu-items: "Quit" and "About...".

The equates are identifiers that we assign -- Windows will pass the identifier as a parameter (wParam) to the WM_COMMAND message, to the application, to enable the latter to identify which selection has been made.

MESSAGE FORMAT:

Ah, now you'll be wondering what wParam and WM_COMMAND are.... the latter is one of many messages that Windows sends via the application's GetMessage( ) call. wParam, along with lParam, are extra values attached to every message. A message incidentally, is just a 16-bit number, but we use equates such as WM_COMMAND for readability.

wParam is 16-bits also, hence the "w" (word) prefix. Every message has two parameters attached to it, wParam and also lParam, the latter being 32-bit (hence the "l" prefix, meaning "long"). What these parameters contain depends upon the message.

message-type
wParam
lParam

Before we delve further in this direction, here is the .DEF file:

WINHULLO.DEF...

```
NAME          winhullo
DESCRIPTION   'Demo ASM hullo program'
EXETYPE       WINDOWS
STUB          'WINSTUB.EXE'
CODE          PRELOAD MOVEABLE
DATA          PRELOAD MOVEABLE MULTIPLE
HEAPSIZE      1024
STACKSIZE     4096
EXPORTS       winhulloproc
```

Winhulloproc() is the "callback" function, referred to as WndProc( ) in earlier notes. This is where Windows sends messages to be processed. An application can have a separate callback function for each window, dialogbox or control.

DOS COMPATIBILITY:

WINSTUB.EXE is interesting -- since Windows uses the "**new .EXE**" format for files, they won't execute straight from DOS. DOS normally expects the code to commence from **CS:0**, so the STUB command places a jump there, to a short section of code. WINSTUB.EXE is just such a short section of code -- it is a standard DOS program that Windows appends to the application, with the afforementioned jump. WINSTUB just displays a message that the application is a Windows program, then exits back to DOS. It uses the standard INT-21h function-9, and INT-21h function 4Ch (exit). It is very easy to customise the stub.

316
18

MAKE FILE:

```
# WINHULLO.MAK...
all:winhullo.exe
winhullo.obj : winhullo.asm
    masm winhullo;
winhullo.res : winhullo.rc
    rc -r winhullo.rc
winhullo.exe : winhullo.obj winhullo.def winhullo.res
    link winhullo /NOD, , , libw slibcew , winhullo.def
    rc winhullo.res
```

Before we go ahead with the application itself, let's consider the Make file. This determines the assemble, compile, and link steps.

Note that there are four steps. The first is to assemble WINHULLO.ASM to produce WINHULLO.OBJ. MASM has various directives to aid with creating Windows applications, however by writing the program at the most fundamental level I have avoided these, which means that just about any Assembler should work. The resource script, WINHULLO.RC, has to be compiled, which produces WINHULLO.RES. Note that the "-r" switch is used, as RC.EXE serves double purpose -- later on it is reused to append the .RES file onto WINHULLO.EXE, in which case no switch is required. LINK converts the .OBJ to .EXE and attaches the called functions from the libraries LIBW.LIB and SLIBCEW.LIB. Note also that LINK refers to the .DEF file (see Companion Disk. for Borland notes).

DEVELOPMENT CYCLE WITHIN WINDOWS:

The Workshop will require you to play around with the program -- you can run the Make file from the DOS prompt, but I recommend doing it from within Windows. What you should do is open the File Manager and go to the directory containing the application. Then iconise the File Manager and open the Notepad. Use the Notepad to view and edit WINHULLO.ASM, and iconise when finished. It is a simple matter to flip between the Notepad and File Manager. When in the File Manager, and the directory containing the application is open (and the directory must contain all software tools if the SDK is not installed properly on the PC), select "Run..." from the "File" menu. In the box type "NMAKE WINHULLO.MAK", just as you would on the DOS command line. After running the Makefile, all you need to do to test your program is double-click on WINHULLO.EXE in the File Manager.

STRUCTURE OF AN APPLICATION:

The presentation I have chosen here is to list the entire application and attach notes here and there as appropriate. You should be able to follow it through. Do bear in mind that "Hullo World" is a whole new ball game!

You will also be able to view this using the Notepad, as it is on the Companion Disk.:

```
;.................................................................................
;WINHULLO.ASM --> WINHULLO.EXE  Windows demo program.
;........
IDI_APPLICATION  EQU    32512
                 ;identifier for icon type.
IDC_ARROW        EQU    32512
                 ;identifier for cursor type.
OEM_FIXED_FONT   EQU    10
                 ;identifier for font type.
COLOR_BACKGROUND EQU 1
              ;identifier for background colour.
WM_CREATE        EQU    1
```

These equates could have been placed in a separate include file.... note that I got these from WINDOWS.H which is part of the Microsoft SDK (& also supplied with the Borland compilers).

```
                                ;these are messages from Windows.
WM_DESTROY       EQU  2      ;      /
WM_PAINT         EQU  15     ;      /
WM_COMMAND       EQU  273    ;      /
WM_LBUTTONDOWN EQU  513    ;      /
WM_CHAR          EQU  258    ;      /
IDM_QUIT     EQU          100
                   ;menu-identifiers from Windows -- must
IDM_ABOUT    EQU          101
                   ;be same as defined in .RC file.
MB_OK        EQU          0        ;a messagebox type.
```

These are just some of the messages that the call-back function WinHulloProc() receives from Windows, via GetMessage() and DispatchMessage().

```
;.................
;_TEXT SEGMENT  WORD PUBLIC 'CODE'
_TEXT  ENDS
_DATA SEGMENT  WORD PUBLIC 'DATA'
_DATA  ENDS
DGROUP        GROUP  _DATA
  ASSUME DS: DGROUP, SS: DGROUP
```

Convenient spot to declare our segments. Standard naming is used for linking compatibility with high level languages.

```
;............
EXTRN  __acrtused:ABS
EXTRN UPDATEWINDOW:FAR
EXTRN BEGINPAINT:FAR
EXTRN ENDPAINT:FAR
EXTRN DEFWINDOWPROC:FAR
EXTRN POSTQUITMESSAGE:FAR
EXTRN REGISTERCLASS:FAR
EXTRN GETSTOCKOBJECT:FAR
EXTRN CREATEWINDOW:FAR
EXTRN SHOWWINDOW:FAR
EXTRN GETMESSAGE:FAR
EXTRN LOADCURSOR:FAR
EXTRN TRANSLATEMESSAGE:FAR
EXTRN DISPATCHMESSAGE:FAR
EXTRN LOADICON:FAR
EXTRN TEXTOUT:FAR
EXTRN INVALIDATERECT:FAR
EXTRN MESSAGEBOX:FAR
EXTRN SELECTOBJECT:FAR
```

These are Windows library functions that our program calls. All Windows and I/O operations are done via these functions -- our use of the BIOS & DOS services needs to be severely curtailed, due to possible conflicts with Windows and other applications.

These functions are attached to the program at link time, which is why they are declared external here. They are FAR, which means that they can reside in a segment other than _TEXT.

```
;..............................................................................
_DATA    SEGMENT
wintitle         DB          'HULLO DEMO PROGRAM',0
winhulloname     DB          'WINHULLO',0
hOemFont         DW          0         ;handle to OEM font.
_hInst           DW          0
outstring        DB          'Hullo World'
aboutstr         DB  'Assembly Language Windows Demo',0
                                       ;messagebox
```

This is data that we are using in our program.

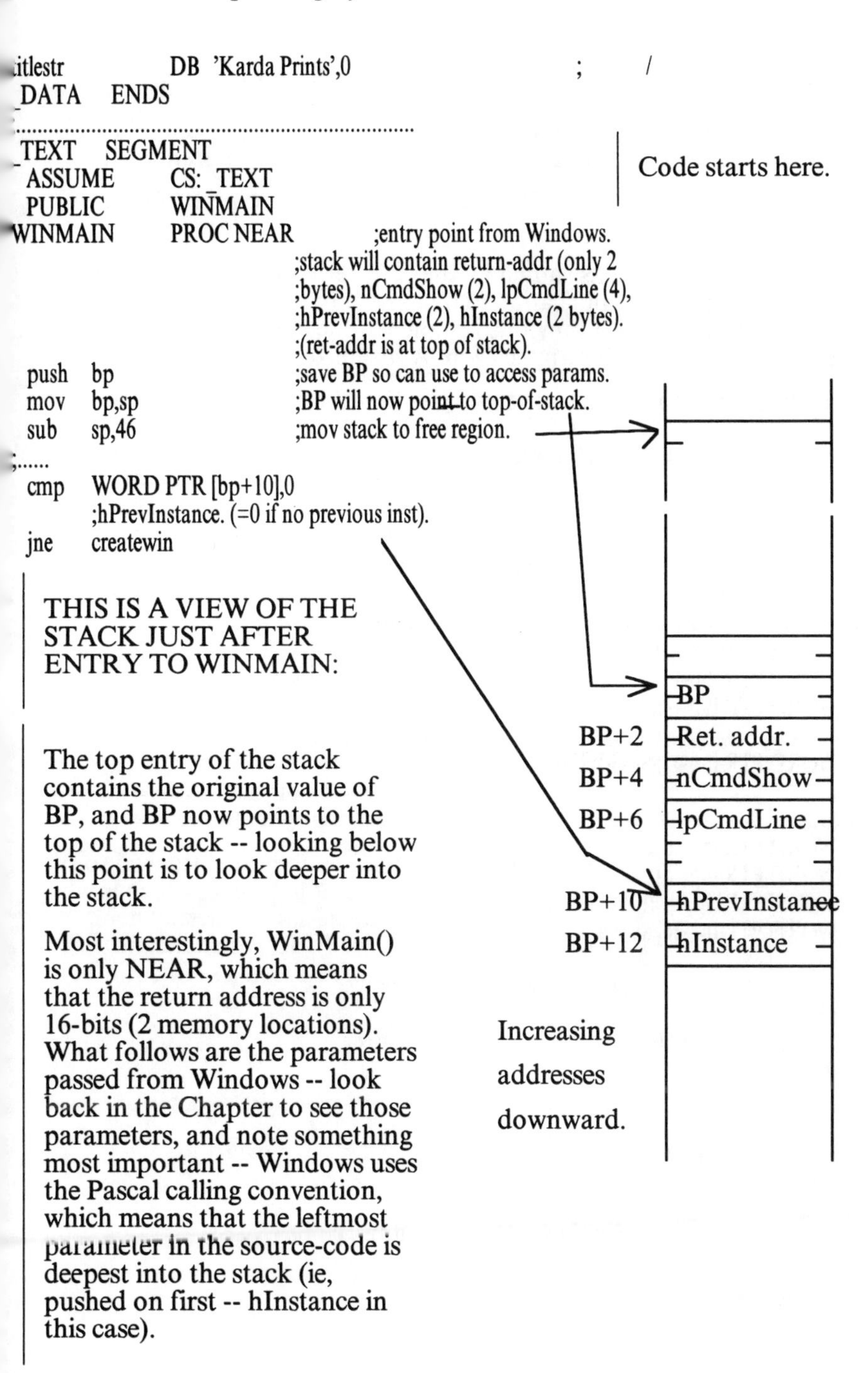

titlestr DB 'Karda Prints',0 ; /
_DATA ENDS
_TEXT SEGMENT
ASSUME CS: _TEXT
PUBLIC WINMAIN
WINMAIN PROC NEAR ;entry point from Windows.
;stack will contain return-addr (only 2
;bytes), nCmdShow (2), lpCmdLine (4),
;hPrevInstance (2), hInstance (2 bytes).
;(ret-addr is at top of stack).
push bp ;save BP so can use to access params.
mov bp,sp ;BP will now point to top-of-stack.
sub sp,46 ;mov stack to free region.
;......
cmp WORD PTR [bp+10],0
;hPrevInstance. (=0 if no previous inst).
jne createwin
Code starts here.
THIS IS A VIEW OF THE STACK JUST AFTER ENTRY TO WINMAIN:
BP
BP+2
Ret. addr.
BP+4
nCmdShow
BP+6
lpCmdLine
BP+10
hPrevInstance
BP+12
hInstance
Increasing addresses downward.
The top entry of the stack contains the original value of BP, and BP now points to the top of the stack -- looking below this point is to look deeper into the stack.
Most interestingly, WinMain() is only NEAR, which means that the return address is only 16-bits (2 memory locations). What follows are the parameters passed from Windows -- look back in the Chapter to see those parameters, and note something most important -- Windows uses the Pascal calling convention, which means that the leftmost parameter in the source-code is deepest into the stack (ie, pushed on first -- hInstance in this case).

"lpCmdLine" is a long-pointer (hence the "lp" prefix), which means that it is a FAR address. See how it looks on the stack -- 4 bytes, and most importantly, the segment-address is pushed on first, followed by the offset -- thus storing the offset at a lower address as per the Intel standard).

Handles are all 16-bit, as are C's INT and BOOL data types. C's LONG INT is 32-bit.

"hInstance" is a handle, as shown by the "h" prefix. Windows assigns a handle-number to the application and passes it to the application as hInstance. If there was a previous instance of the application already loaded, Windows tells this application by means of hPrevInstance.

If it is the first instance, the window-class has to be registered, hence all the code just prior to CREATEWIN: Basically, this code sets up a data-structure then calls RegisterClass( ).

```
;..........
;we only come this way if this is the first instance of the application.
;The first instance needs to create certain resources, and all following
;instances can use them....
;The code below is creating a window-class data-structure, as required
;by RegisterClass() further down....
  mov   WORD PTR [bp-46],3                          ;wndclass
  mov   WORD PTR [bp-44],OFFSET WINHULLOPROC
                                    ;addr of callback
  mov   WORD PTR [bp-42],SEG WINHULLOPROC
                                    ;function for window.
  sub   ax,ax
  mov   WORD PTR [bp-40],ax
  mov   WORD PTR [bp-38],ax
  mov   ax,WORD PTR [bp+12]         ;hInstance
  mov   WORD PTR [bp-36],ax
  sub   ax,ax
                              ;null -- use Windows default icons.
  push  ax                          ;       /
  mov   cx,IDI_APPLICATION          ;Default application icon.
  sub   dx,dx                       ;       /
  push  dx                          ;       /
  push  cx                          ;       /
  call  FAR PTR LOADICON
  mov   WORD PTR [bp-34],ax
  sub   ax,ax
                              ;null -- use Windows default cursor.
  push  ax                          ;       /
  mov   ax,IDC_ARROW                ;Standard arrow cursor.
  cwd                               ;       /
  push  dx                          ;       /
```

```
  push   ax                               ;          /
  call   FAR PTR LOADCURSOR
  mov    WORD PTR [bp-32],ax
  mov    ax,COLOR_BACKGROUND
  mov    WORD PTR [bp-30],ax
  mov    ax,OFFSET DGROUP                 :winhulloname
  mov    WORD PTR [bp-28],ax
  mov    WORD PTR [bp-26],ds
  mov    WORD PTR [bp-24],ax
  mov    WORD PTR [bp-22],ds
  lea    ax,WORD PTR [bp-46]              ;wndclass
  push   ss
                              ;this is address of above data
  push   ax                               ;structure.
  call   FAR PTR REGISTERCLASS
                              ;registers this class of window.
  or     ax,ax                            ;
  je     quitwinmain
;............
createwin:
;CreateWindow() requires the following params on the stack --
;long pointer to window class name, lp to window title, type of window,
;x coord, y coord, width, height, parent-handle, menu-handle, instance-
;handle, lp to params to pass-on.
  mov    ax,OFFSET DGROUP:winhulloname    ;see _DATA segment.
  push   ds                               ;long-pointer (far address) of
  push   ax                               ;class-name.
  mov    ax,OFFSET DGROUP:wintitle ;see _DATA segment.
  push   ds                               ;far address of window-title.
  push   ax                               ;          /
  sub    ax,ax                            ;type of window (32-bit value).
  mov    dx,207                           ;          /
  push   dx                               ;          /
  push   ax                               ;          /
  mov    ax,150                           ;x-coord (16-bit).
  push   ax                               ;          /
  sub    ax,ax                            ;y-coord (16-bit).
  push   ax                               ;          /
  mov    ax,400                           ;width (16-bit).
  push   ax                                       ;          /
  mov    ax,300                                   ;height (16-bit).
  push   ax                                       ;          /
  sub    ax,ax
  push   ax                                       ;0=no parent for this window.
  push   ax                                       ;0=use the class menu.
  mov    ax,WORD PTR [bp+12]                      ;hInstance -- handle for this
```

The code immediately alongside creates the main window and displays it.

```
 mov   WORD PTR _hInst,ax              ;application's instance.
 push  ax                         ;(passed to applic from Windows).
 sub   ax,ax
 push  ax                              ;0=no params to pass-on.
 push  ax                              ;(32-bit long-pointer).
 call  FAR PTR CREATEWINDOW
 mov   WORD PTR [bp-2],ax              ;returns hWnd in AX
                                       ;(handle to the window).
                                       ;Here we save it temporarily.
 push ax                               ;ShowWindow() requires hWnd and
 push  WORD PTR [bp+4]   ;nCmdShow     ;nCmdShow on the stack.
 call  FAR PTR SHOWWINDOW              ;Tells Windows to display window.
 push  WORD PTR [bp-2]                 ;hWnd
 call  FAR PTR UPDATEWINDOW            ;tells Windows to redraw now.
 jmp   SHORT messageloop               ;go to the main message-loop.
;..............................................................................................................
............................
;This is the main message loop, in which Windows waits for messages
;by calling GetMessage(), then translates keypresses with
;TranslateMessage() then passes them back to Windows with
;DispatchMessage()....
mainloop:
 lea   ax,WORD PTR [bp-20]        ;far-addr of message.
 push  ss                         ;        /
 push  ax                         ;        /
 call  FAR PTR TRANSLATEMESSAGE
;.......
 lea   ax,WORD PTR [bp-20]        ;far-addr of message.
 push  ss                         ;        /
 push  ax                         ;        /
 call  FAR PTR DISPATCHMESSAGE
;........
messageloop:
 lea   ax,WORD PTR [bp-20]        ;long-pointer (far addr) of
 push  ss                         ;message. (we use the stack
 push  ax                         ;region for convenience).
 sub   ax,ax
 push  ax                         ;null
 push  ax                         ;null
 push  ax                         ;null
 call  FAR PTR GETMESSAGE
 or    ax,ax
 jne   mainloop
;........
;GetMessage() returns FALSE (AX=0) if a "quit" message...
;so here we are quiting....
 mov   ax,WORD PTR [bp-16]        ;return wParam to Windows.
quitwinmain:
```

The text earlier in the Chapter describes the message-loop. Windows applications are often described as "event-driven", referring to their having to wait until Windows sends a message. The application calls GetMessage( ) to pass control to Windows, and control will only come back when Windows is sending a message. Execution enters the message-loop at MESSAGELOOP:

```
  mov   sp,bp
  pop   bp
  ret   10
        ;Causes RET to add 10 to SP prior to
        ;popping ret-address, effectively
        ;dumping all params (as for PASCAL
        ;convention).
WINMAIN       ENDP
;..................................................................
;..........................................................
;What follows is the "callback" function, that
;Windows calls after the message has been given
;back to it via DispatchMessage(). This function
;employs CASE logic to direct execution to
;specific routines to handle each message.  In
;many cases the message ;cannot be handled by
;the application, so it is sent back to Windows
;(again!) for default handling....
;......
  PUBLIC        WINHULLOPROC
WINHULLOPROC    PROC FAR
;The function is entered with far-return-addr (4 bytes), lParam (4),
;wParam (2), message-type (2), and window-handle (2 bytes) on the stack
;(ret-addr on top).
;.....
```

GetMessage( ) returns the message, at an address passed to GetMessage( ) as a parameter (BP-20):

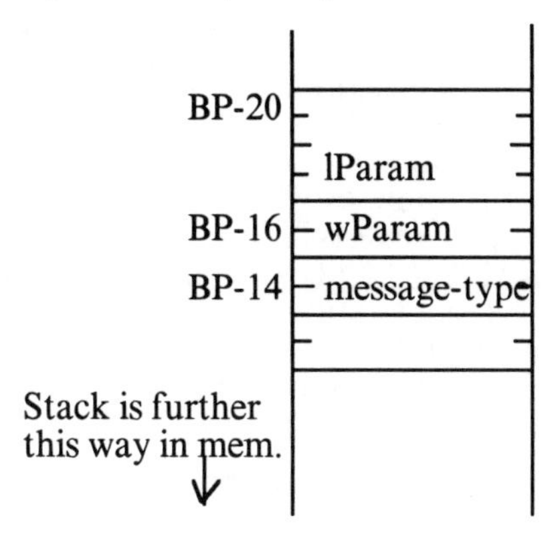

Callback functions (other than WinMain( )) must be FAR, hence the return address is 4 bytes. Callback functions have some "prolog" code, that may look a bit weird -- notice that DS is saved temporarily in AX, and BP is incremented before being pushed. After the prolog, the stack looks as follows:

DS
BP — old BP+1
ret. addr.
BP+6 — lParam
BP+10 — wParam
BP+12 — message-type
BP+14 — hWnd

Deeper into stack.

```
  push  ds        ;This is some standard preliminary
  pop   ax        ;shuffling of the registers.
  nop             ;          /
  inc   bp        ;          / (it is called the prolog code)
  push  bp        ;          /
  mov   bp,sp     ;          /
  push  ds        ;          /
  mov   ds,ax     ;          /
```

You might find it instructive to look ahead to the matching "epilog" code, at the end of the function.

WinHulloProc( ) grabs the message-type from the stack then implements a CASE statement to direct control to the appropriate routines. Here we are only dealing with some of the dozens of possible messages, and any message that "falls through" the CASE statement goes back to Windows for default handling, by calling DefWindowProc( ) -- note that in most cases this is quite okay.

Windows sends a message when it does anything at all related to the application, or when anything happens to a relevant I/O device. When we called CreateWindow( ) earlier in the program, Windows generates a WM_CREATE message, which it puts into the message-queue. When the program continues on to the message-loop it will receive WM_CREATE and can then perform any other window-initialisations required. I decided to get a handle to the PC OEM (Terminal) font, for possible use later in the program, though for a skeleton program this was unnecessary.

Have a look at another message -- WM_PAINT. Whenever any change occurs to the window, such as the operator resizing or moving it with the mouse, Windows will perform the operation and will then send WM_PAINT to the application to tell it that the window has changed -- this gives the aplication the opportunity to redraw any information within the windows "client area". In this case I have put the TextOut() function to display "Hullo World". Note that BeginPaint() and EndPaint() are required at each end of the routine.

I implemented the WM_CHAR case to show that there can be output to the screen from anywhere else in the program, by use of GetDC() and ReleaseDC().

```
  ASSUME DS: NOTHING              ;         / (enters function with DS=_DATA)
;.......
  sub   sp,146                    ;move the stack to a free region
                                  ;(so as not to mess-up the params).
  mov   ax,WORD PTR [bp+12]       ;get message-type.
  cmp   ax,WM_CREATE              ;message received after CreateWindow()
  je    xcreate                   ;function is called.
  cmp   ax,WM_DESTROY             ;message received if a window is closed.
  je    xquitmessage
  cmp   ax,WM_PAINT               ;message received if Windows has (already)
                                  ;redrawn any part of the window (due to
                                  ;a size-change for example).
  je    xpaint
  cmp   ax,WM_COMMAND             ;any selection of the menu will produce
  jne   notwmcommand
  jmp   xmenu                     ;this message.
notwmcommand:
  cmp   ax,WM_LBUTTONDOWN         ;one of many mouse messages.
  jne   notwmlbutton
```

```
  jmp    xbreak
notwmlbutton:
  cmp    ax,WM_CHAR                  ;message that a key pressed.
  je     xchar
;.......
;Default handling of messages....
  push   WORD PTR [bp+14]            ;hWnd
  push   WORD PTR [bp+12]            ;Message-type
  push   WORD PTR [bp+10]            ;wParam
  push   WORD PTR [bp+8]             ;hi-half of lParam
  push   WORD PTR [bp+6]             ;low-half of lParam
  call   FAR PTR DEFWINDOWPROC
  jmp    xreturn                     ;Back to Windows, which will in turn
                                     ;return to after DispatchMessage().
;.................................
xcreate:
 mov ax,OEM_FIXED_FONT
 push ax
 call FAR PTR GETSTOCKOBJECT
 mov WORD PTR hOemFont,ax            ;handle to font.
  jmp    SHORT xbreak
;.......
xquitmessage:
  sub    ax,ax
  push   ax
  call   FAR PTR POSTQUITMESSAGE
  jmp    SHORT xbreak
;.......
xchar:
;If I wanted this program to display "Hullo World" only when any key is
;pressed, TextOut() would have been placed here.
;note below that BeginPaint() returned a "display context", a handle
;required for drawing, but we don't normally use BeginPaint() outside
;of WM_PAINT cases -- instead we use GetDC()....
;here is what the code would look like if placed here (in C)....
;  hDC = GetDC(hWnd);
;  TextOut(hDC,10,20,"Hullo World",11);
;  ReleaseDC(hWnd,hDC);
;If we want the string to be redrawn everytime the window is redrawn,
;it is better to put TextOut() within the WM_PAINT case... this will
;also mean that "Hullo World" will appear when the window is first drawn.
  jmp    SHORT xbreak
;........
xpaint:
  push   WORD PTR [bp+14]            ;hWnd -- handle of current window.
  lea    ax,WORD PTR [bp-42]         ;ps -- far-addr of paint-structure.
  push   ss                          ;(BeginPaint() will fill the structure).
```

```
  push  ax                        ;          /
  call  FAR PTR BEGINPAINT        ;BeginPaint() returns handle hDC.
  mov   WORD PTR [bp-146],ax      ;hDC -- display-context, required
                                  ;before can output to screen.
;For this simple demo, any redraw of the Window will cause output of our
;"hullo world" string....
        ;Windows by default uses the System font, but I
        ;am changing it. I need to attach the new font to the
        ;display....
        push  ax                              ;hDC
        push  hOemFont
        call  FAR PTR SELECTOBJECT
                          ;attaches hOemFont to hDC.
  push  WORD PTR [bp-146]    ;hDC
  mov   ax,10                ;16-bit x-coord
  push  ax                   ;          /
  mov   ax,20                ;16-bit y-coord
  push  ax                   ;          /
  mov   ax,offset outstring  ;far-address of string to o/p
  push  ds                   ;          /
  push  ax                   ;          / (note low half pushed 2nd)
  mov   ax,11                ;number of chars in string.
  push  ax
  call  FAR PTR TEXTOUT
  push  WORD PTR [bp+14]     ;hWnd
  lea   ax,WORD PTR [bp-42]  ;ps -- far-addr of paint-structure.
  push  ss                   ;(filled by BeginPaint()).
  push  ax                   ;          /
  call  FAR PTR ENDPAINT
  jmp   SHORT xbreak
;
;........................
xmenu:
;comes here if WM_COMMAND message.
;let's stick with menus... the .RC file assigns the number for each
;menu-item, and this is what we look for in wParam...
  cmp   WORD PTR [bp+6],0              ;low-half of lParam
  jne   xbreak                         ;test if a menu-message.
  cmp   WORD PTR [bp+10],IDM_QUIT      ;wParam.
  jne   notquit
  jmp   xquitmessage
notquit:
  cmp   WORD PTR [bp+10],IDM_ABOUT
  jne   xbreak                    ;no other menu items.
                                  ;let's put up a message about this program...
        push  WORD PTR [bp+14]    ;hWnd -- handle of parent window.
        mov   ax,OFFSET aboutstr  ;far-addr of string to display.
        push  ds                  ;          /
```

If anything is selected on the window, such as a menu-item, a WM_COMMAND message is generated.

The two parameters associated with the message, lParam & wParam, tell us more.... low-order word of lParam=0 if message is a menu-selection. hi-order word of lParam=1 if message is an accelerator-key. If low/lParam<>0, message is from a "control" (such as a scrollbar), and low/lParam=handle of control, hi/lParam=notification code. wParam contains the menu-item, the control-ID or the accelerator-key-ID.

You will need to refer to WINHULLO.RC to understand this code. I assigned arbitrary names and equivalent type-codes for each menu-item, that the code alongside looks at in a CASE statement.

IDM_ABOUT is interesting -- here I have implemented a MessageBox to display information about the program, as all Windows programs do.

Finally we have the "epilog" code. Refer back to the diagram at function-entry, on page 230. BP is pointing to the saved "old BP+1" -- now we decr BP twice so it points to the saved DS, which we make the top of stack and then pop to restore the original DS, followed by the "old BP+1", which we decr to restore to its original value.

RET 10 causes RET to add 10 to SP prior to popping the ret. address, effectively dumping all parameters, as required for the Pascal convention.

```
        push    ax                      ;       /
        mov     ax,OFFSET titlestr      ;far-addr of title of dialog-box.
        push    ds                              ;       /
        push    ax                              ;       /
        mov     ax,MB_OK                        ;type of message-box.
        push    ax                              ; / (displays single "ok" button)
        call    FAR PTR MESSAGEBOX
;........................
xbreak:
  sub   ax,ax                           ;returns 0 in DX:AX. (callback functions
  cwd                                   ;return a 32-bit (long) value).
xreturn:
  dec   bp                              ;final standard manipulation of regs.
  dec   bp                              ;       /
  mov   sp,bp                           ;       / (it is called the epilog code).
  pop   ds                              ;       /
  pop   bp                              ;       /
  dec   bp                              ;       /
  ret   10                              ;removes parameters.
WINHULLOPROC    ENDP
;..............................................................
_TEXT ENDS
END
```

ENHANCING THE DEVELOPMENT CYCLE

3-IN-1:

There are all kinds of tools available to help us with Windows programming. Possibly you could write the user-interface and some other aspects of a program in C or Pascal, then flesh-out the critical sections in Assembly. For designing the user-interface skeleton, I use an excellent and inexpensive product: "3-in-1" by GUI Computer Inc., of 6604 Fernshaw Drive, Dallas, Texas 75248, USA. This product consists of two programs: a screen designer and a code generator. The designer enables you to design the windows and dialog boxes, thus producing the required resource files. Then the code generator produces a skeleton program complete with all .C, .H, .RC and .MAK files (note that I usually give Make files and extension of .MAK, but it is more common to give them no extension at all). You could then take this skeleton and flesh it out as necessary, including Assembly modules or even in-line Assembly. There are two versions of 3-in-1: for C and for C++.

MASM/TASM NOTES:

Writing Windows programs at the Assembly level is not so difficult, but one tedious aspect of it is the amount of stack manipulation, especially when putting parameters onto the stack prior to a function call. The WINHULLO.ASM file on the Companion Disk contains some examples of how this tedium can be relieved. Recent versions of TASM & MASM allow calling of functions without having to explicitly manipulate the stack. Although the SDK contains a macros file CMACRO.INC, I don't use it, as the latest Assemblers (especially TASM v2.5) have superb high-level constructs. The tedium of prolog/epilog code need not be explicitly coded either.

As a general rule, do not use the BIOS services, and refer to your SDK or similar documentation for information about restrictions on the DOS services.

As the CPU will most likely be operating in protected mode, take extreme care with modification of the interrupt flag and the segment registers. One technique Asm programmers use with the flags is to save them using PUSHF and later restore them using POPF, but the interrupt flag will not necessarily be restored -- CLI and STI are the only instructions that will change the interrupt flag.

Callback functions should never begin with "MOV AX,xxxx" as this confuses Windows -- instead put a NOP before it.

Generally speaking, you should not access video-RAM directly -- you cannot simply load B800h or whatever into ES and expect it to be addressing the video-RAM. All screen output should be via the library functions. There are some "backdoor" ways around this. I have written a Windows program that switches the screen into text-mode & directly addresses the video-RAM, and successfully exits back to Windows -- maybe the fourth edition will have a chapter on this. A safe rule is to leave the segment registers alone.

WORKSHEET: WINDOWS

It will be logical for this Worksheet to tie-in with the example program developed in this Chapter. As some readers will not have the Microsoft SDK or equivalent development tools, I have divided this Worksheet into two sections: theoretical and hands-on -- you may be in a position to do the theoretical part only, which is still very instructive.

THEORETICAL:

1.

Basically what I want you to do is examine each of the supporting modules, and describe what each does:

i WINHULLO.RC

ii WINHULLO.DEF

iii WINHULLO.MAK

2.

Now I want you to write a description, of about one page, describing how the application WINHULLO.ASM interacts with Windows. You should describe the flow of execution -- you could illustrate by explaining the flow after a key is pressed at the keyboard.

3.

Describe the epilog and prolog code -- what does it "do", at each end of the callback function?

4.

Describe, in about half a page, how we are able to design pull-down menus using resource scripts, and then access the menu-items within the application.

5.

Using TextOut( ) as an example, explain how the parameters are passed to the function. In particular explain how the different data types are pushed onto the stack -- handles, long integers, far pointers, integers.

HANDS-ON:

1.

You should have the satisfaction of assembling and linking the complete application, but first make a copy of all the WINHULLO files onto a floppy, or into a temporary place on the hard disk. Then use a text editor to view WINHULLO.ASM and resave it -- the reason for this is that NMAKE looks at file dates to decide whether to reassemble the file. Then follow the instructions given on page 226 to assemble and link. Finally test the program and see if it works as expected.

NOTE: The files on the Companion Disk have been modified for Borland compatibility -- use the listings of this Chapter to convert back to Microsoft compatibility if required.

2.

Now to modify the program, but make sure that you modify only your copy, not the original.

Modify the .RC and .ASM files so that there is another menu-item under "File", called "extra", which when selected brings up a messagebox with a short message. Test it.

A

BIOS & DOS SERVICES

INT Type (hex)	AH Subfunction (hex)	Description
	N	DIVIDE_BY_0 Automatically taken upon division overflow
	N	SINGLE_STEP taken after every instruction when CPU Trap flag indicates single-step mode (bit 8 of FLAGS is 1)
	N	NON_MASKABLE (nmi) :vector not disabled via CLI. Taken when hard memory error (or some other error *****) occurs. Displays message, halts system.
	N	BREAKPOINT taken when CPU executes the breakpoint opcode (0CCH)
4	N	OVERFLOW taken when OF=1 and INTO opcode is executed
5	N	PRINT_SCREEN service dumps the screen to the printer Invoked by KBD_INT for shifted key 55 (PrtSc)
6 -7	N	reserved
8	N	**TIME_INT** (irq0) 55ms timer "tick" taken 18.2 times per second. Updates BIOS clock and turns off diskette drive motors after 2 seconds of inactivity

INT Type (hex)	AH Subfunction (hex)	Description
9	N	**KBD_INT** (irq1) taken whenever a key is pressed or released Stores characters and scan-codes in buffer at 0040:001E Updates shift key status 0040:0017,18
A	N	Hardware interrupt (irq2) Cascade for ir8-irq15** Vertical retrace interrupt*
B	N	COM2 hardware interr. (irq3)
C	N	COM1 hardware interr. (irq4)
D	N	Alternate printer LPT2#### (irq5) 80287 initial interrupt##
E	N	DISKETTE_INT (irq6) indicates that a seek is in progress (sets bit 0 of 0040P003F)
F	N	Parallel printer LPT1 (irq7)
10		**VIDEO_IO** services handle video output
	0	SET_MODE :set video mode. AL=0: 40x25 BW text =1: 40x25 colour text =2: 80x25 colour text =3: 80x25 colour text =4: 320x200 colourgraphics =5: 320x200 BW graphics =6: 640x200 BW graphics =7: 80x25 mono ...etc.. (see text) Note that if bit-7 of AL is clear, this service clears the screen. If bit-7 set, leaves video RAM alone.
	1	SET_CUR_TYPE :set the size of the cursor or turn it off CH=start line (bit 5=no cursor), CL=end line
	2	SET_CUR_POS :set the coordinates of the cursor DH=row (0-24), DL=coloum (0-79 or 0-39), BH=video page. Note: usually can assume page is zero.
	3	READ_CUR_POS :return the position of the cursor BH=video page returns: DH=row, DL=column, CX=cursor size NOTE: Also mucks up AL
	4	READ_LIGHT_PEN :fetch light pen information returns: AH=0: light pen not triggered. AH=1: DH, DL=character row, column CH, CL=graphics row, column ****
	5	SELECT_ACTIVE_PAGE :set page number for services 6 and 7 AL=new page (0-7 for modes 0 and 1. 0-3 for modes 2 and 3).
	6	SCROLL_PAGE_UP :scroll up or clear a display window AL= number of lines to scroll (0=blank entire window) CH, CL=row, column of top left corner of windeow DH, DL= row, column of lowest right corner of window BH=video attribute for blanked lines
	7	SCROLL_PAGE_DOWN :scroll down or clear a display "window" (see subfunction 6 for parameters).

INT Type (hex)
AH Subfunction (hex)
Description

8 READ_CHAR_ATTR :fetch a character from the cursor position BH=page returns: AL=character, AH=attribute

9 WRITE_CHAR_ATTR :display character(s) and attribute at cursor BH=display page, CX=repeat count, AL=character to display BL=attribute (graphics modes: BL= color (add 80H for XOR).

A WRITE_CHAR :display character(s) only (use current attributes. See subfunction 9 for parameters).

B SET_COLOR_PALETTE :set palette for graphics or border for text BH=0: select border (text mode) BL=colour (0-31 [16-31 is high intensity]) BH=1: select graphics palette BL=palette code (0=green/red/yellow, 1=cyan/magenta/white)

C WRITE_DOT :plot 1 graphics pixel DX=row, CX=column, AL=colour (bit 7 to XOR the dot).

D READ_DOT :determine the color of 1 graphics pixel DX=row, CX=column, returns: AL=color of dot

E WHITE_TTY :write one character and update cursor. Also handles CH (0DH), beep (07H0, and scrolls screen if needed. AL=char to write, BH=page, BL=foreground (in graphics mode).

F VIDEO_STATE :fetch the mode and width (columns) of the screen. returns: AL=mode (see subfunction 0), AH=width, BH=page

INT Type (hex)
AH Subfunction (hex)
Description

10 Set_Palette_ Registers*

11 Character_Generator*

12 Alternate_Select*

13 Write_String**

1A AL=00 Read_Display_Codes*** AL=01 Write_Display_ Codes***

1B Return_State***

1C AL=00 Return_Save/ Restore*** AL=01 Save_State*** AL=02 Restore_State***

11 N EQUIPMENT_CHECK fetch a code describing active peripherals. returns: AX=equipment code bits: PP-JSSS-DDVVRRNI. PP = number of printers J = joystick (--XT only) SSS = serial devices (RS-232 ports) DD = number of disk drives (00=1, 01=2,10=3, 11=4) VV = video (11=BW card, 01 and 10=color/graphics card) RR = RAM in mother-board (00=16K...11=64K --XT only) N = numeric coprocessor I = disk-existence (0=no drives in system)

12 N MEMORY_SIZE fetch AX=count of contiguous 1K RAM blocks

13 DISKETTE_IO access the diskette drives.

0 RESET/reset the disk controller chip

INT Type (hex)
AH Subfunction (hex)
Description

1 GET_STATUS :fetch AL=status of most recent operation

2 READ_SECTORS :read one or more sectors from diskette DH=head DL=drive(0=A,1=B,etc CH=track CL=sector (1-8,1-9 for DOS 2.0) AL=sectors to read ES:BX = address to store /fetch data [0000:0078] = doubleword pointer to disk parameters returns: Carry Flag=NC (0) successful Carry Flag=CY (1) failure AH=disk status(error reason) 80H=timeout: disk failed to respond. 40H=seek operation failure 20H=NEC disk drive control- ler failed. 10H=bad cyclical redundancy check (CRC error). 09H=attempted access across 64K boundary 08H=DMA overrun 04H=record not found 03H=write protect error 02H=sector ID error (can't find address mark) 01H=unknown command

3 WRITE_SECTORS/write from memory to disk (parameters as with subfunction 2)

4 VERIFY/verify that a write operation was successful (parameters as with subfunction 2, but ES:BX not needed)

5 FORMAT_TRACK :write sector -ID bytes for one track ES:BX points to 8 (or 9) 4-byte sector ID marks: byte 0=track number byte 1=head number byte 2=sector number byte 3=bytes in sector (0=128, 1=256, 2=512, 3=1024)

6 Format_Track_Set_ Bad_Sector_Flags@

INT Type (hex)
AH Subfunction (hex)
Description

7 Format_Drive_Starting _At_Cylinder@

8 Read_Drive_Parameters

9 Init_Drive_Pair_Character

C Seek

D Alternate_Disk_Reset

10 Test_Drive_Ready

11 Recalibrate_Drive

13 Read_DASD_Type**

16 Disk_Change_Line_ Status*

17 Set_DASD_Type_For_Format*

18 Set_Media_Type_For_ Format****

19 Park_Heads

1A Format_Unit***

14 **RS232_IO**
initialize and access serial communication port

0 INIT_COM/initialize port named by DX (0 or 1) AL has initialization bit pattern: BBBPPSLL BBB=baud rate: 110,150,300,600,1200,2400 4800,9600 PP =partity:00=none,01=odd, 11=even S =stop bits: 0=1, 1=2 LL =word length: 10=7 bits, 11=8 bits 1 SEND_CHAR/send character to comm port DX (0 or 1) AL=character. returns: bi 7 of AH=1 if error.

2 AWAIT_COMM_CHAR/wait for character from comm port DX returns: AL=character AH=error code (o= no error)

3 COMM_STATUS/fetch the status of comm port DX (0 or 1) returns: comm-line status in AH, modem statu

INT Type (hex)
AH Subfunction (hex)
Description

in AL AH bit 7=timeout bit 6 = empty transmit shift register bit 5 = empty transmit holding register bit 4 = break detected ("long space") bit 3 = framing error bit 2 = parity error bit 1 = overrun error bit 0 = data ready AL bit 7 = received line signal detect bit 6 = ring indicator bit 5 = data set ready bit 4 = clear to send bit 3 = delta receive line signal detect bit 2 = trailing edge ring detector bit 1 = delta data set ready bit 0 = delta clear to send 4 Extended_Init***

5 AL=0 Read_Modem_Control_Register***
AL=1 Write_Modem_Control_Register***

15 CASSETTE_IO
access cassette tape drive (NOP for IBM-XT)

0 CASS_ON/start the motor

1 CASS_OFF/turn the motor off

2 CASS_READ/read CX bytes into buffer at ES:BX

3 CASS_WRITE/write CX bytes to tape from buffer at ES:BX

F Format_Periodic_Interrupt***

4F Keyboard_Intercept**

80 Open_Device**

81 Close_Device**

82 Program_Terminate**

83 Event_Wait**

84 Joystick_Support**

85 System_Request_Key_Pressed**

86 Wait**

INT Type (hex)
AH Subfunction (hex)
Description

87 Move_Block**

88 Get_Extended_Memory_Size**

89 Switch_To_Protected_Mode**

90 Device_Busy**

91 Interrupt_Complete**

C0 Return_System_Config. parameters****

C1 Return_Ext_BIOS_Segment_Address***

C2 ***

C3 ***

C4 ***

16 KBD_IO
access the keyboard buffer.

0 AWAIT_CHAR/read the next character in keyboard buffer If no key is ready, wait for one. returns: AL=ASCII character, AH = scan code

1 PREVIEW_KEY :see if key is ready. returns: ZF = 1 if no key is ready ZF = 0 if char ready, and AX = character and scan code

2 SHIFT_STATUS :fetch bit flags indicating shift status. returns: AL = bit codes (same as 0000:0417) bit 6 = CapsLock state bit 5 = NumLock state bit 4 = ScrollLock state bit 3 = Alt key down bit 2 = Ctrl key down bit 1 = left caps-shift key bit 0 = right caps-shift key Other codes found at 0000:0418 -- bit 7 = Ins key pressed bit 6 = CapsLock key pressed bit 5 = NumLock key pressed bit 4 = ScrollLock key pressed bit

INT Type (hex)	AH Subfunction (hex)	Description
		3 = Ctrl-NumLock is in effect
	5	Keyboard_Write**** places keycode into keyboard buffer. Requires: CH=scancode, CL=ASCII code. Returns: Status in AL.
	10	Extended_Keyboard_Read****
	11	Extended_Key_Status****
	12	Extended_Shift_Status****
17		**PRINTER_IO** access the parallel printer(s)
	0	PRINT_CHAR :send AL to printer DX(0, 1 or 2). returns: AH = 1 if unable to print, else AH = status (as below)
	1	INT_PRINTER/set init line low, send 0CH to printer DX. returns: status as below
	2	PRINTER_STATUS/read status of printer DX into AH. returns: bit flags: bit 7 = printer is busy bit 6 = acknowledge line state bit 5 = out-of-paper line state bit 4 = printer selected line state bit 3 = I/O error bit 2 = unused bit 1 = unused bit 0 = timeout error
18 N		ROM_BASIC execute nondisk BASIC at F600:0000
19 N		BOOT_STRAP read track 0, sector 1 into 0000:7C00, then transfer control to that address. If no diskette drive available, take INT 18H
1A		**TIME_OF_DAY** acces the PC internal clock
	0	READ_CLOCK :fetch count o 55ms "ticks" since power up (on recent machines loads timer from real-tim clock at power-up). returns: CX = high word o count DX = low word of count AL = 0 when no 24-hour overflow since power up
	1	SET_CLOCK :set number of 55ms in clock variable CX =high word of timer ticks DX = low word of timer ticks note: the clock ticks are incremented by TIMER_INT at about 18.2 times per second. Therefore: counts/second 18(12H) counts/minute = 1,092 (444H) counts/hour 65,543(10011H) counts/day=1,573,040 (180080H)
	2	Read_Real_Time_ Clock_Time****,** returns CH=hours, CL=minutes, DH=seconds (in BCD). If RTC is defective, returns with carry flag set.
	3	Set_Real_Time_Clock_ Time****,**
	4	Read_Real_Time_ Clock_Date** returns: CH=century, CL=year, DH=month,DL=day (BCD). If RTC defective, returns carry set.
	5	Set_Real_Time_Clock_Date*
	6	Set_Real_Time_Clock_ Alarm**

INT Type (hex)

AH Subfunction (hex)

Description

INT Type	AH	Description
	7	Turn_Off_Real_Time_ Clock_Alarm**
	9	Read_Real_Time_ Clock_Alarm*****
	A	****,*****
	B	****,*****
1B	N	KEY_BREAK routine taken when KBD_INT senses Ctrl-Break
1C	N	USER_TIME_INT taken 18.2 times per second; invoked by the TIMER_INT; normally vectors to dummy IRET
1D	N	VIDEO_PARMS_PTR vector of video initialization parameters: This doubleword address points to three sets of 16 bytes containing data used to initialize for video modes. Parameter table format corresponds to the Motorola 6845 CRT controller registers: R0 = horizontal total (horizontal sync. in chars) R1 = horizontal displayed (characters per line) R2 = horizontal sync. pos- ition (move display left or right) R3 = sync. width (vertical & horiz.pulse:4 bits each) R4 = vertical total (total character lines) R5 = vertical adjust (adjust for 50 to 60 Hz refresh) R6 = vertical displayed (lines of chars displayed) 'R7 = vertical sync. position (lines shifted up or down) R8 = interlace (bits 4 and 5) and skew (bits 6 and 7) R9 = max scan line address (scan lines per char row) R10 = cursor start (starting scan line of cursor) R11 = cursor stop (ending scan line of cursor) R12 = display memory start address high byte (6 bits) R13 = display memory start address low byte (8 bits) R14 = cursor address high byte (6 bits) R15 = cursor address low byte (8 bits)
1E	N	DISKETTE_PARMS_PTR vector of diskette controller parameters: This doubleword address points to a data table used by DISKETTE_IO (INT 13H). 11-byte table format: byte 0 = 4 bit step rate, 4-bit head unload time byte 1 = 7-bit head load time, 1-bit DMA flag byte 2 = 55ms counts--delay until motor off byte 3 = sector size (0 = 128,1=256,2=512,3= 1024) byte 4 =last sector on track byte 5 = gap between sectors byte 6 = data length for DMA transfers byte 7=gap length for format byte 8 =fill byte for format byte 9 = head settle time (in milliseconds) byte 10 = motor start time (in 1/8th second intervals)
1F	N	GRAPHICS_TBL_PTR vector of data used by VIDEO_10 to display characters above ASCII 127 in graphics modes. This doubleword address points to a 1K table composed of 128 8-byte character

INT Type (hex)	AH Subfunction (hex)	Description
		definition bit patterns. The first byte of each entry is top row, last byte is bottom row.
20 N		TERMINATE exit from the DOS program that has a PSP located at CS:0000 DOS 2.0 EXIT :(INT 21H, service 4CH) is similar but provides a means to leave an exit code and does not require CS to point to the PSP.
21		DOS_FUNCTIONS invoke DOS service named by AH note: see PC-DOS function summary page 350.
22		DOS_TERMINATE_ADD vector points to address of parent process. Jumped to by TERMINATE (INT 20H)
23		DOS_BREAK_ADDR vector points to address of Ctrl-Break handling routine for currently executing program
24		DOS_ERROR_ADDR vector points to address of critical error handling routine for currently executing program
25		DOS_DISK_READ transfers control to DOS disk driver logic. Expects: AL=drive number(0=a,1=B,etc) CX = count of sectors DX=beginning logical sector# DS:BX=address of data buffer Returns: Carry Flag = CY (1) if error and AH = error code warning: leaves 1 word (old flags) on stack
26		DOS_DISK_WRITE transfers control to DOS disk driver logic (see DOS_DISK_READ, INT 25H, for parameters)
27 N		FIX_IN_MEMORY exit to DOS, but leave program and/or data resident. Expects CS:DX to point to first byte available for subsequent programs. DOS 2.0 KEEP(service 31H) is similar, but provides a means to leave an exit code.
28 -29		Reserved by DOS
2A		NETBIOS
2B -2E		Reserved by DOS
2F		Multiplex## NETBIOS
33		MOUSE_FUNCTIONS
	0	Mouse_Installed_Flag
	1	Show_Cursor
	2	Hide_Cursor
	3	Get_Position_&_ Button_Status

INT Type (hex)	AH Subfunction (hex)	Description
	4	Set_Mouse_Cursor_Position
	5	Get_Button_Press_ Information
	6	Get_Button_Release_ Informat.
	7	Set_Min_&_Max_Horiz_Pos.
	8	Set_Min_&_Max_Vert_Pos.
	9	Set_Graphics_Cursor_Block
	A	Set_Text_Cursor
	B	Read_Mouse_Motion_Counters
	C	Set_User_Defined_ Subroutine_Input_Mask
	D	Set_Light_Pen_Emulation_On
	E	Set_Light_Pen_ Emulation_Off
	F	Set_Mickey_To_Pixel_Ratio
	10	Conditional_Off
	13	Set_Double_Speed_Threshold
34 -3F		Reserved by DOS
40		Reserved: XT fixed disk BIOS
41 -5F		Reserved
41 -66		Not used, avaiilable
67		EXPANDED_MEMORY
	40	Get_Status
	41	Get Page_Frame_Address
	42	Get_Page_Count
	43	Allocate_Pages
	44	Map_Memory
	45	Deallocate_Pages
	46	Get_Version
	47	Save_Page_Map
	48	Restore_Page_Map
	4B	Get_Handle_Count
	4C	Get_Page_Count_For_Handle
	4D	Get_Page_Cnts_All_Handles
	4E	Map_Services
60 -6A		EEMS management.
68 -7F		Note used, available for applications
80 -F0		Reserved by BASIC
F1 -FF		Not used, available for applications

PC-DOS FUNCTION SUMMARY

The following functions are selected by a value in AH, and executed by INT 21h.

AH Subfunction (hex)
Description

0 TERMINATE
terminate the program that has a PSP at CS:0000. Works exactly like INT 20H.

1 KEYBOARD_INPUT
read (wait for) a character from the standard input and echo that character to the standard output. returns: AL = character read

2 DISPLAY_OUTPUT
send a character to the standard output device. expects: DL = character to output

3 AUX_INPUT
read (wait for) a character from the asynchronous comms adapter (COMn or AUX). returns: AL = character read

4 AUX_OUTPUT
send a character to the asynchronous communications adaptor (COMn or AUX). expects: DL = character to output

5 PRINTER_OUTPUT
send a character to the printer (LPTn or PRN). expects: DL = character to output

6 CONSOLE_IO
receive a character from standard input or send a character to the Standard Output. expects: DL = FFh to fetch waiting input character from input. returns: ZF = ZR (1) if not ready, else AL = character if DL is not FFH, then the character in DL is output.

7 CONSOLE_INPUT
read (wait for) a character from the standard input. The character is not displayed. returns: AL is input character.

8 NO_ECHO_INPUT
identical to function-1 but the character is not output.

9 PRINT_STRING
send a string of characters to the standard output. expects: DS:DX points to the string to print. The string must be terminated by dollar sign ('$' = ASCII 24H)

AH Subfunction (hex)
Description

A BUFFERED_INPUT
read a string of characters from the standard input. expects: DS:DX points to input buffer. first byte is maximum number of characters desired. returns: second byte (DS:DX+1) is actual length of input--less the terminating carriage return (ASCII 0DH) -- the rest of the buffer contains the characters read.

B INPUT_STATUS
see if the standard input has a character ready. returns: AL = FFH if a character ready. AL = 00 if no character

Note: Dos 1.0 and DOS 1.1: the standard input device is always the keyboard and standard output device is always the screen.

C CLEAR_AND_INPUT
clear the standard input device buffer of any pretyped keys and then invoke an input function. expects: AL = input function 1,6,7,8 or 0AH

D RESET_DISK
flush all file buffers.

E SELECT_DISK
select new default disk drive, query valid drives. expects: DL = new default drive (0 = A, 1 = b, etc) returns: AL = total number of drives (floppy and fixed disk drives)

F OPEN_FILE
open a file with unopened FCB pointed to by DS:DX. returns: AL = FFH if file not found. AL = 00 if file found.

10 CLOSE_FILE
close file with opened pointed to by DS:DX.

11 SEARCH_FIRST
search the current directory for first file that matches the name in the unopended FCB pointed to by DS:DX. returns: AL = FFH if no match AL = 0 if match found, and DTA is filled with a 32-byte directory entry

12 SEARCH_NEXT
after calling function-11h, this will search for other files that match the specified wildcard (global) filename. returns: same as SEARCH_FIRST (function 11H)

13 DELETE_FILE
delete file named by the FCB pointed to by DS:DX.

14 READ_SEQ
read sequential data from the file named by the opened FCB pointed to by DS:DX. Count of bytes is in FCB RECORD_SIZE field. returns: one record is

AH Subfunction (hex)
Description

read into DTA (see DOS function 1AH) sets FCB CURRENT_RECORD field for the next read operation AL = 0 if transfer was successful AL = 1 if end of file & record empty AL = 2 if DTA segment was overrun (can't cross 64-K boundary) AL = 3 if end of file and partial record is read.

15 WRITE_SEQ
write sequential data to the file named by the opened FCB pointed to by DS:DX. One record is transferred from the DTA to the disk and the FCB CURRENT_RECORD field is updated. returns: AL = 0 if transfer was successful AL = 1 if diskette is full or access denied (read-only file) AL = 2 if end of DTA segment was encountered (overrun error)

16 CREATE_FILE
like OPEN_FILE, except the file is truncated to length 0.

17 RENAME_FILE
special FCB format is used to change the name of a file returns: AL = FFH if file not found or new name already exists AL = 0 if no error

18 Used internally by DOS

19 CURRENT_DISK
return the current default disk in AL (0 = A, 1 = B, etc.)

1A SET_DTA
establish a Disk Transfer Address. In DOS 1.0 and 1.1, all diskette data transfers pass through this area. expects: DS:DX points to the new buffer for diskette transfers (DTA).

1B FAT_DATA
in DOS 1.0 and 1.1; returns DS:DX = address of the file allocation table of the default disk. DOS 2.0 returns address of the FAT identification byte for the default disk.

1C DISKETTE_FAT_DATA
like FAT_DATA (function-1Bh), but will return information about a specific diskette drive. (DOS 2.xx only.) expects: DL = the number of the drive (0 = default, 1 = A, 2 = B, etc)

1D
-20 Used internally by DOS

21 READ_RANDOM
read one disk record into the DTA. expects: RANDOM_RECORD field of the FCB to identify the record. DS:DX points to FCB of an opened file.

AH Subfunction (hex)	Description
22	WRITE_RANDOM like subfunction 21H, but writes a record.
23	FILE_SIZE search the directory for file named in FCB pointed to by DS:DX, then set the FCB RANDOM_RECORD field to the number of records in the file; i.e., total bytes/(bytes per record field). returns: AL = FFH if file not found, AL = 0 if file found
24	SET_RANDOM_FIELD sets the RANDOM_RECORD field of the FCB pointed to by DS:DX to agree with the CURRENT_BLOCK and CURRENT_RECORD fields.
25	SET_INT_VECTOR change doubleword address in the interrupt vector table. expects: AL = interrupt type DS:DX = new address to place in vector table.
26	CREATE_PROG_SEGMENT build a PSP at the paragraph named by DX.
27	READ_BLOCK read one or more records from an open FCB (at DS:DX) into the DTA. expects: CX = count of blocks to read.
28	WRITE_BLOCK write one or more records from the DTA to the open FCB pointed to by DS:DX. expects: CX = count of blocks to read.
29	PARSE_FILENAME scan a command line and create an unopened FCB. Note: this call is not useful for command lines with path names. expects: DS:SI points to the command line to parse, ES:DI points to an area to build an unopened FCB AL = bit flags for special options
2A	GET_DATE fetch the date according to the DOS internal clock. returns: CS = year (1980-2099) DH = month (1-12), DL = day (1-31)
2B	SET_DATE set the date for the DOS internal clock. expects: parameters as GET_DATE (function 2AH) returns: AL = FFH if invalid date, AL = 0 if operation successful
2C	GET_TIME fetch the time of day according to the DOS internal clock. returns: CH = hours (0-23), CL = minutes (0-59) DH = seconds (0-59), DL = hundredths of a second
2D	SET_TIME set the time of day for the DOS internal clock. expects: parameters as GET_TIME (function 2CH). returns: AL = FFH if

AH Subfunction (hex)
Description

invalid date, AL = 0 if operation successful

2E VERIFY_SWITCH
sets or resets the flag that DOS checks to see if a diskette write operation should be followed by a verify operation. expects: DL = 0, AL = 1 (turn verify on) DL = 0, AL = 0 (turn verify off)

NOTE:
The Functions above were originally developed prior to version 2.0, and those below developed from 2.0.

2F GET_DATA
fetch the current DTA into ES:BX

30 GET_VERSION#
fetch AL = DOS Version number, AH = subrelease.

31 KEEP_PROCESS#
terminate a program, leaving its code and data resident. expects: DX = number of paragraphs to remain resident (starting at the paragraph of the PSP) AL = exit code (may be interrogated via ERRORLEVEL)

32 Used internally by DOS.

33 BREAK_CHECK#
set or query the level of DOS Ctrl-Break checking. expects: AL = subfunction 0 = fetch switch into DL (0 = OFF, 1 = ON). 1 = set switch to DL (0 = OFF, 1 = ON)

34 Used internally by DOS.

35 GET_INT_VECTOR#
fetch the doubleword value of an entry in the interrupt table. Vector of the interrupt type in AL is returned in ES:BX. Note: returns original values of vectors changed via SET_VECTOR (function 25H).

36 GET_FREE_SPACE#
determine the amount of free space on a disk. expects: DL = drive number (0 = default, 1 = A, 1 = B, etc). returns: AX = FFFFH if invalid drive number; otherwise AX = sector per cluster BX = free clusters CX = bytes per sector Note:total free bytes =BX = AX = CX

37 SWITCHAR#
set or query the current command-line parameter delimiter (usually slash ('/') ASCII 2FH) if AH = 0, then set the switch character to the value of DL if AH = 1, then return the current switch character in DL note: This is an undocumented DOS service

38 COUNTRY_INFO#
AL=0: fetch

AH Subfunction (hex)

Description

country-dependent data (currency symbol, etc) AL not 0: Set_Country_Info##

39 MKDIR#
create a subdirectory. expects: DS:DX points to ASCIIZ string with path name of directory. returns: error code in AX if CF = CY (codes: 3 or 5)

3A RMDIR#
remove a sub-directory. expects: DS:DX points to ASCIIZ string with path name of directory. returns: error code in AX if CF = CY (codes: 3 or 5)

3B CHDIR#
change current directory to that named by ASCIZ string. expects: DS:DX points to ASCIIZ string with path name of directory. returns: error code in AX if CF = CY (code: 3)

3C CREATE#
create a file (supersedes CREATE_FILE, function 16H). Open the file, truncating it to length 0. expects: DS:DX points to ASCIIZ string with drive, path, and name. CX = file attribute: 01H = read-only 02H = hidden 04H = system 08H = entry contains VOLUME label 10H = entry is sub-directory 20H = archive bit (used by BACKUP utility). returns: AX = error code if CF = CY (codes: 3,4 or 5); otherwise, AX = file handle

AH Subfunction (hex)

Description

3D OPEN#
open a file (supersedes OPEN_FILE, function 0FH). expects: DS:DX points to ASCIIZ string of path a filespec. AL = access code: 0 = open for reading 1 = open for writing 2 = open for reading and writing. returns: AX = error code if CF = CY (codes: 3,4 or 12); otherwise AX = file handle

3E CLOSE_HANDLE#
close a file. (supersedes CLOSE_FILE, funct. 10H) expects: BX is 16-bit file handle returned by OPEN or CREATE. returns: AX = error code if CF = CY (code: 6)

3F READ_HANDLE#
read bytes from a file or device. expects: BX = 16-bit file handle, CX = count of bytes to read DS:DX points to buffer to receive data. returns: AX = error code if CF = CY (codes: 5 or 6); otherwise AX = actual number of bytes read note: AX = 0 means end of file reached

40 WRITE_HANDLE#
write bytes to a file or device. expects: BX = 16-bit file handle CX = count of bytes to write DS:DX points to buffer containing data to write. returns: AX = error code if CF = CY (codes: 5 or 6); otherwise AX = actual number of bytes written note: error occurred if AX not equal to CX after call

AH	Subfunction (hex) Description
41	UNLINK# delete a file from a specified directory. expects: DS:DX points to ASCIIZ string of path and filespec. returns: AX = error code if CF = CY (codes: 2 or 5)
42	LSEEK# move file read/write pointer according to method and offset. expects: AL = method code: 0 = pointer is moved to offset from start of file (offset unsigned) 1 = pointer is increased by offset (offset is 2's compl number) 2 = pointer is moved to end of file + offset (offset is 2's compl) CX:DX = offset value BX = 16-bit file handle. returns: AX = error code if CF = CY (codes: 1 or 6); otherwise DX:AX = new value of file point (DX is most significant)
43	CHMOD# change or query file mode (alter the attributes of a file). expects: DS:DX points to ASCIIZ string of drive, path, and filename AL = subfunction code: 0 = return file attribute in CX 1 = set file attribute to that named by CX. returns: AX = error code if CF = CY (codes: 3 or 5)
44	IOCTL#,## input and output device control. Writes control information to or reads status from devices that support IOCTL requests.
45	DUP_HANDLE# duplicates a file or device handle. This funct. creates a new handle that may be used to refer to an existing file or device. expects: BX = handle of device or file to duplicate. returns: AX = error code if CF = CY (codes: 4 or 6); otherwise AX = new handle for same device.
46	REDIRECT# force an existing file or device to refer to the data stream. defined by another file or device. expects: CX = handle of current file/devide BX = handle of file/device that will take over the I/O. returns: AX = error code if CF = CY (code: 6)
47	GET_DIR# fetch the pathspec of the current default directory. expects: DS:SI points to buffer to receive ASCIIZ string pathspec DL = drive number (0 = default, 1 = A, etc). returns: AX = error code if CF = CY (code: 15)
48	ALLOCATE_MEM# request DOS to reserve bytes for a process. expects: BX = number of paragraphs requested returns: AX = error code if CF = CY (codes: 7 and 8) and BX is number of free paragraphs; otherwise AX:0000 is address of allocated block

AH Subfunction (hex)
Description

49 FREE_MEM#
return an allocated block of memory back to the common pool expects: ES is the segment of a block allocated by ALLOCATE_MEM. returns: AX = error code if CF = CY (codes: 7 or 9)

4A SETBLOCK#
change the size of an allocated block of memory. expects: ES is the segment of the block to change. BX = the desired new size of the block (in paragr's). returns: AX = error code if CF =CY (codes: 7,8 or 9) and BX is number of available paragraphs

4B EXEC#
load and execute a program. Create a "child" process. expects: DS:DX points to ASCIIZ string of path and filename EX:BX points to a parameter block (see below) AI = method code 0 = create a PSP, load, and execute a program ES:BX points to parameter block: WORD segment address of environment, DWORD points to command line for program, DWORD points to first FCB to be passed,DWORD points to second FCB to be passed. 3 = load only; ES:BX points to parameter block: WORD segment address to load file, WORD relocation factor. returns: AX = error code if CF = CY (codes: 1,2,5,8,10 or 11)

4C EXIT#
terminate the current process, transferring control to the parent process. Supersedes TERMINATE (function 0). CS need not point to the base segment of the terminating process. expects: AL = exit code (may be interrogated by WAIT (function 4DH) or by ERRORLEVEL batch commands).

4D WAIT#
fetch the exit code returned by a terminated process returns: AX = return code of most recently exited process AH = 0 normal termination 1=terminated by Ctrl-Break 2=terminatd by critical error handlr 3=terminated by KEEP (function 31H) AL=1-byte return (ERRORLEVEL) code note: this works only once per termination.

4E FIND_FIRST#
find a file that matches a path and filespec. Supersedes SEARCH_FIRST (function 11H expects: DS:DX points to ASCIIZ string of drive, path, and filespec CS is the attribute to be used to find the match. (see function 3CH) returns: AX = error code if CF = CY (codes: 2 or 18); otherwise DTA (set via function 1AH) is filled with 43 bytes; 21 bytes - used for subseq. searches 1 byte - attribute found 2 bytes - time stamp of file 2 bytes - date stamp of file 2 bytes - low word of file size 2 bytes - high

AH Subfunction (hex)
Description

word of file size 13 bytes - ASCIIZ string

4F FIND_NEXT#
after a call to FIND_FIRST, this function returns other directory entries that also match a global filespec. Supersedes SEARCH_NEXT (function 11H) expects: must be called after FIND_FIRST (parameters are the same). returns: AX = error code 18 and CF = CY when no match is found.

50
-53 Used internally by DOS.

54 GET_VERIFY_STATE#
find whether the write-verify switch is OFF or ON. returns: AL = 0 if verify is OFF; AL = 1 if verify is ON

55 Used internally by DOS.

56 RENAME#
change a directory entry to give a file a new name and optionally, move a file to a different sub-directory (same drive). expects: DS:DX points to ASCIIZ string of existing path and file ES:DI points to ASCIIZ string with new path and filename returns: AX = error code if CF = CY (codes: 3,5, or 17)

AH Subfunction (hex)
Description

57 TIME_STAMP#
fetch or change the date and time stamp of a file. expects: BX = the file handle AL = subfunction code: 0 = change date to DX, time to CX 1 = fetch date into DX and get time into CX. returns: AX = error code if CF = CY (codes: 1 or 6)

58 Allocation_ Strategy####

59 Get_Extended_Error##

5A Create_Temporary_File##

5B Create_New_File##

5C Lock/Unlock_File##

5E Get_Machine_Name###, Printer_Str###

5F Assignment_List_ Entry###

62 Get_Program_Segment_ Prefix##

63 Get_Lead_Byte_ Table*****

65 Get_Extended_ Country_Info#####

66 Global_code_Page#####

67 Set_Handle_Count#####

68 Commit_File#####

LEGEND:

#	XT only,
##	AT only,
###	AT & XT/2 only,
####	PS/2 only,
*	EGA systems only,
**	AT & PS/2 (incl.'386) only,
***	PS/2's only, ('386-comp?)
****	Not available early BIOS's (typically XT's pre '87, AT's pre '86)
*****	Not recommended.
@	Systems with hard disks only.
N	Nothing.

ERROR CODES:

From DOS 2.0, error codes were returned from the functions:

ERROR CODE (hex)	MEANING
1	Invalid function number
2	File not found
3	Path not found
4	Too many open files
5	Access denied
6	Invalid handle
7	Memory control blocks destroyed
8	Insufficient memory
9	Invalid memory block address
A	Invalid environment
B	Invalid format
C	Invalid access code
D	Invalid data
E	(not used)
F	Invalid drive specified
10	Attempted to remove the current directory
11	Not same device
12	No more files

B

80x86 INSTRUCTION SET SUMMARY

INSTR.	FUNCTION	FLAGS Affected	86/286/386
AAA	ASCII adjust AL after add	AF, CF	X X X
AAD	ASCII adjust before divide	SF, ZF, PF	X X X
AAM	ASCII adjust AFter multipiy	SF, ZF, PF	X X X
AAS	ASCII adjust AFter subtract	AF, CF	X X X
ADC accum,imm	Add with CF	OF,SF,ZF,AF,PF,CF	X X X
ADC mem,imm	Add with CF	OF,SF,ZF,AF,PF,CF	X X X
ADC mem,reg	Add with CF	OF,SF,ZF,AF,PF,CF	X X X
ADC reg,imm	Add with CF	OF,SF,ZF,AF,PF,CF	X X X
ADC reg,mem	Add with CF	OF,SF,ZF,AF,PF,CF	X X X
ADC reg, reg	Add with CF	OF,SF,ZF,AF,PF,CF	X X X
ADD accum, imm	Add	OF,SF,ZF,AF,PF,CF	X X X
ADD mem,imm	Add	OF,SF,ZF,AF,PF,CF	X X X
ADD mem,reg	Add	OF,SF,ZF,AF,PF,CF	X X X
ADD reg,imm	Add	OF,SF,ZF,AF,PF,CF	X X X
ADD reg,mem	Add	OF,SF,ZF,AF,PF,CF	X X X
ADD reg,reg	Add	OF,SF,ZF,AF,PF,CF	X X X
AND accum, imm	Logical AND	OF=0,SF,ZF,PF,CF=0	X XX
AND mem, imm	Logical AND	OF=0,SF,ZF,PF,CF=0	X XX
AND mem, reg	Logical AND	OF=0,SF,ZF,PF,CF=0	X XX
AND reg, imm	Logical AND	OF=0,SF,ZF,PF,CF=0	X XX
AND reg, reg	Logical AND	OF=0,SF,ZF,PF,CF=0	X XX
AND reg, mem	Logical AND	OF=0,SF,ZF,PF,CF=0	X XX
ARPL	Adjust requested privilege level	ZF	X X
BOUND reg, source	Detect array index out of range	None	X X
BSF reg,mem or reg,reg	Bit scan forward	ZF	X

INSTR.	FUNCTION	FLAGS Affected	86/286/386		
BSR reg,mem or reg,reg	Bit scan reverse	ZF			X
BT	Test bit	CF			X
BTC	Test bit and complement	CF			X
BTR	Test bit and reset	CF			X
BTS	Test bit and scan	CF			X
CALL 16 memptr	Call (control transfer)	None @	X	X	X
CALL 16 regptr	Call (control transfer)	None @	X	X	X
CALL 32 memptr	Call (control transfer)	None @	X	X	X
CALL farproc	Call (control transfer)	None @	X	X	X
CALL nearproc	Call (control transfer)	None @	X	X	X
CBW/CWDE	Convert byte to wd/wd to dbl wd	None	X	X	X
CLC	Clear CF	CF = 0	X	X	X
CLD	Clear DF	DF = 0	X	X	X
CLI	Clear IF	IF = 0	X	X	X
CLTS	Clear task switched flag	TS = 0 in CRO reg.			X
CMC	Complement CF	CF	X	X	X
CMP accum, imm	compare	OF,SF,ZF,AF,PF,CF	X	X	X
CMP mem, imm	compare	OF,SF,ZF,AF,PF,CF	X	X	X
CMP mem, reg	compare	OF,SF,ZF,AF,PF,CF	X	X	X
CMP reg, imm	compare	OF,SF,ZF,AF,PF,CF	X	X	X
CMP reg, mem	compare	OF,SF,ZF,AF,PF,CF	X	X	X
CMP reg, reg	compare	OF,SF,ZF,AF,PF,CF	X	X	X
CMPS (rep)deststr,sourc	compare byte,wd,dblwd str	OF,SF,ZF,AF,PF,CF	X	X	X
CMPS deststr,sourcestr	compare byte, wd or dbl wd	OF,SF,ZF,AF,PF,CF	X	X	X
CWD/CDQ	Convert wd to dbl wd /dw to qw	None	X	X	X
DAA/DAS	Decimal adjust after add/subtract	SF, ZF, AF, PF, CF	X	X	X
DEC mem	Decrement	OF, SF, ZF, AF, PF	X	X	X
DEC reg	Decrement	OF, SF, ZF, AF, PF	X	X	X
DIV 16 mem	Divide	None	X	X	X
DIV 16 reg	Divide	None	X	X	X
DIV 8 mem	Divide	None	X	X	X
DIV 8 reg	Divide	None	X	X	X
ENTER 16 imm, 0	Enter procedure	None		X	X
ENTER 16 imm, 1	Enter procedure	None		X	X
ENTER 16 imm, level	Enter procedure	None		X	X
ESC imm, mem	Escape to external device	None	X	X	X
ESC imm, reg	Escape to external device	None	X	X	X
HLT	Halt	None	X	X	X
IDIV 16 mem	signed integer divide	None	X	X	X
IDIV 16 reg	signed integer divide	None	X	X	X
IDIV 8 mem	signed integer divide	None	X	X	X
IDIV 8 reg	signed integer divide	None	X	X	X
IMUL 16 mem	signed integer multiply	OF, CF	X	X	X
IMUL 16 reg	signed integer multiply	OF, CF	X	X	X
IMUL 8 mem	signed integer multiply	OF, CF	X	X	X
IMUL 8 reg	signed integer multiply	OF, CF	X	X	X
IMUL destreg,16,reg,imm	signed integer multiply	OF, CF		X	X
IMUL destreg, mem, imm	signed integer multipl	OF, CF		X	X

INSTR.	FUNCTION	FLAGS Affected	86/286/386
IN accum, 8 imm	Input from port	None	X X X
IN Accum, DX	Input from DX port	None	X X X
INC mem	Increment	OF, SF, ZF, AF, PF	X X X
INC reg	Increment	OF, SF, ZF, AF, PF	X X X
INS (rep) deststr, DX	Input string	None	X X
INS deststr, DX	Input string	None	X X
INT 8 imm	Interrupt	IF = 0, trap = 0	X X X
INTO	Interrupt on overflow	IF = 0, trap = 0	X X X
IRET	Interrupt return	All	X X X
JMP 16 memptr	Unconditional jump	None	X X X
JMP 16 regptr	Unconditional jump	None	X X X
JMP 32 memptr	Unconditional jump	None	X X X
JMP far	Unconditional jump	None	X X X
JMP near	Unconditional jump	None	X X X
JMP short	Unconditional jump	None	X X X
Jxxx short	Conditional jump	None	X X X
LAHF	Load AH with flags(LO byte flags)	None	X X X
LAR	Load access rghts byte	ZF	X X
LDS 16 reg, 32 mem	Load pointer to DS	None	X X X
LEA 16 reg, 16 mem	Load effective address to registr	None	X X X
LEAVE	Leave procedure	None	X X
LES 16 reg, 32 mem	Load pointer to ES	None	X X X
LFS	Load pointer to FS	None	X
LGDT	Load global descriptor table	None	X X
LGS	Load pointer to GS	None	X
LIDT	Load IF descriptor table	None	X X
LLDT	Load local descriptor table	None	X X
LMSW	Load machine status wd	None	X X
LOCK	Bus lock prefix	None	X X X
LODS (rep) sourcestr	Repeat load byte/wd/dwd	None	X X X
LODS sourcestr	Load byte/wd/dwd	None	X X X
LOOP short	Loop	None	X X X
LOOPE/LOOPZ short	Loop equal/zoom	None	X X X
LOOPNE/LOOPNZ short	Loop while not equal/not zero	None	X X X
LSL	Load segment limit	ZF	X X
LSS	Load pointer to SS	None	X
LTR	Load task register	None	X X
MOV 16 reg, segreg	Move	None	X X X
MOV accum,mem	Move	None	X X X
MOV mem,accum	Move	None	X X X
MOV mem, imm	Move	None	X X X
MOV mem, reg	Move	None	X X X
MOV mem, segreg	Move	None	X X X
MOV reg, imm	Move	None	X X X
MOV reg, mem	Move	None	X X X
MOV reg, reg	Move	None	X X X
MOV segreg, 16 mem	Move	None	X X X
MOV segreg, 16 reg	Move	None	X X X

INSTR.	FUNCTION	FLAGS Affected	86/286/386
MOVS(repeat)desstr,sourcstr	Move string	None	X X X
MOVS deststr,sourcestr	Move string	None	X X X
MOVSX	Move with sign extension	None	X
MOVZX	Move with zero extension	None	X
MUL 16 mem	Multiply	OF, CF	X X X
MUL 16 reg	Multiply	OF, CF	X X X
MUL 8 mem	Multiply	OF, CF	X X X
MUL 8 reg	Multiply	OF, CF	X X X
NEG mem	Change sign	OF,SF,ZF,AF,PF,CF	X X X
NEG reg	Change sign	OF,SF,ZF,AF,PF,CF	X X X
NOP	No operation	None	X X X
NOT mem	Invert	None	X X X
NOT reg	Invert	None	X X X
OR accum, imm	Logical OR	OF=0,SF,ZF,PF,CF=0	X X X
OR mem, imm	Logical OR	OF=0,SF,ZF,PF,CF=0	X X X
OR mem, reg	Logical OR	OF=0,SF,ZF,PF,CF=0	X X X
OR reg, imm	Logical OR	OF=0,SF,ZF,PF,CF=0	X X X
OR reg, mem	Logical OR	OF=0,SF,ZF,PF,CF=0	X X X
OR reg, reg	Logical OR	OF=0,SF,ZF,PF,CF=0	X X X
OUT 8 immed, accum	Output to port	None	X X X
OUT DX, accum	Output to DX port	None	X X X
OUTS (rep) DX,sourcestr	Output string	None	X X X
OUTS DX, sourcestr	Output string	None	X X
POP mem	Restore from stack	None	X X X
POP reg	Restore from stack	None	X X X
XPOPA	Restore general reg's from stack	All	X X X
PUSH imm	Save to stack	None	X X
PUSH mem	Save to stack	None	X X X
PUSH reg	Save to stack	None	X X X
PUSHA	Save all to stack	None	X X
PUSHF	Save flags to stack	None	X X X
RCL/RCR/ROL/ROR mem,1	rot thru CF lft/CF rght/rot. lft/rght	OF, CF	X X X
RCL/RCR/ROL/ROR mem,CL	rot thru CF lft/CF rght/rot. lft/rght	CF	X X X
RCL/RCR/ROL/ROR mem,cnt	rot thru CF lft/CF rght/rot. lft/rght	CF	X X
RCL/RCR/ROL/ROR reg, 1	rot thru CF lft/CF rght/rot. lft/rght	OF, CF	X X X
RCL/RCR/ROL/ROR reg,CL	rot thru CF lft/CF rght/rot. lft/rght	CF	X X X
RCL/RCR/ROL/ROR reg,cnt	rot thru CF lft/CF rght/rot. lft/rght	CF	X X
REP	Repeat	None	X X X
REPE/REPZ	Repeat equal/zero	None	X X X
REPNE/REPNZ	Repeat not equal/not zero	None	X X X
RET (far with pop)	Return	None	X X X
RET (far, no pop)	Return	None	X X X
RET (near with pop)	Return	None	X X X
RET (near, no pop)	Return	None	X X X
SAHF	Store AH into flags	SF, ZF, AF, PF, CF	X X X
SAL/SHL/SAR/SHR mem,1	Shft arith-lft/lft/shift arith.-rght/rght	OF=0,SF,ZF,PF,CF	X X X
SAL/SHL/SAR/SHR mem,CL	Shft arith-lft/lft/shift arith.-rght/rght	SF(SHR=0),ZF,PF,CF	X X X
SAL/SHL/SAR/SHR mem,cnt	Shft arith-lft/lft/shift arith.-rght/rght	SF(SHR=0),ZF,PF,CF	X X X

INSTR.	FUNCTION	FLAGS Affected	86/286/386		
SAL/SHL/SAR/SHR reg,1	Shft arith-lft/lft/shift arith.-rght/rght	OF=0,SF,ZF,PF,CF	X	X	X
SAL/SHL/SAR/SHR reg,CL	Shft arith-lft/lft/shift arith.-rght/rght	SF, ZF, PF, CF	X	X	X
SAL/SHL/SAR/SHR reg,cnt	Shft arith-lft/lft/shift arith.-rght/rght	SF,(SHR=0)ZF,PF,CF		X	X
SBB accum, imm	Subtract with borrow	OF,SF,ZF,AF,PF,CF	X	X	X
SBB mem, imm	Subtract with borrow	OF,SF,ZF,AF,PF,CF	X	X	X
SBB mem, reg	Subtract with borrow	OF,SF,ZF,AF,PF,CF	X	X	X
SBB reg, imm	Subtract with borrow	OF,SF,ZF,AF,PF,CF	X	X	X
SBB reg, mem	Subtract with borrow	OF,SF,ZF,AF,PF,CF	X	X	X
SBB reg, reg	Subtract with borrow	OF,SF,ZF,AF,PF,CF	X	X	X
SCAS (repeat) deststr	Scan byte/wd	OF,SF,ZF,AF,PF,CF	X	X	X
SCAS deststr	Scan byte/wd	OF,SF,ZF,AF,PF,CF	X	X	X
SETxxx	Conditional byte set	None			X
SGDT	Store global descriptor table	None		X	X
SIDT	Store Int. descriptor table	None		X	X
SLDT	Store local descriptor table	None		X	X
SMSW	Store machine status wd	None		X	X
STC/STD/STI	Set CF/DF/IF	CF = 1/DF = 1/IF = 1	X	X	X
STOS (repeat) deststr	Store byte/wd	None	X	X	X
STOS deststr	Store byte/wd	None	X	X	X
STR	Store task register	None		X	X
SUB accum, imm	Subtract	OF,SF,ZF,AF,PF,CF	X	X	X
SUB mem, imm	Subtract	OF,SF,ZF,AF,PF,CF	X	X	X
SUB mem, reg	Subtract	OF,SF,ZF,AF,PF,CF	X	X	X
SUB reg, imm	Subtract	OF,SF,ZF,AF,PF,CF	X	X	X
SUB reg, mem	Subtract	OF,SF,ZF,AF,PF,CF	X	X	X
SUB reg, reg	Subtract	OF,SF,ZF,AF,PF,CF	X	X	X
TEST accum,imm	AND function to flags	OF=0,SF,ZF,PF,CF=0	X	X	X
TEST mem, imm	AND function to flags	OF=0,SF,ZF,PF,CF=0	X	X	X
TEST reg, imm	AND function to flags	OF=0,SF,ZF,PF,CF=0	X	X	X
TEST reg, mem	AND function to flags	OF=0,SF,ZF,PF,CF=0	X	X	X
TEST reg, reg	AND function to flags	OF=0,SF,ZF,PF,CF=0	X	X	X
VERR	Verify read access	ZF		X	X
VERW	Verify write access	ZF		X	X
WAIT	Wait for 80X87	None	X	X	X
XCHG accum, 16 reg	Exchange	None	X	X	X
XCHG mem, reg	Exchange	None	X	X	X
XCHG reg, reg	Exchange	None	X	X	X
XLAT sourcetable	Translate byte	None	X	X	X
XOR accum, imm	Exclusive OR	OF=0,SF,ZF,PF,CF=0	X	X	X
XOR mem, imm	Exclusive OR	OF=0,SF,ZF,PF,CF=0	X	X	X
XOR mem, reg	Exclusive OR	OF=0,SF,ZF,PF,CF=0	X	X	X
XOR mem, reg	Exclusive OR	OF=0,SF,ZF,PF,CF=0	X	X	X
XOR reg, imm	Exclusive OR	OF=0,SF,ZF,PF,CF=0	X	X	X
XOR reg, mem	Exclusive OR	OF=0,SF,ZF,PF,CF=0	X	X	X
XOR reg, reg	Exclusive OR	OF=0,SF,ZF,PF,CF=0	X	X	X

INSTR.	FUNCTION	FLAGS Affected	87/287/387
F2XM1	2^X-1	UE,PE	X X X
FABS	Absolute value	IE	X X X
FADD dest,source	Add real	IE,DE,OE,UE,PE	X X X
FADDP dest,source	Add real & pop	IE,DE,OE,UE,PE	X X X
FBLD source	Packed decimal (BCD) load	IE	X X X
FBSTP	Packed decimal (BCD) store & pop	IE	X X X
FCHS	Change sign	IE	X X X
FCLEX/FNCLEX	Clear exceptions	None	X X X
FCOM source	compare real	IE,DE	X X X
FCOMP source	compare real & pop	IE,DE	X X X
FCOMPP	compare real & pop twice	IE,DE	X X X
FCOS	Cosine		X
FDECSTP	Decrement stack pointer	None	X X X
FDISI/FNDISI	Disable interrupts	None	X $ $
FDIV dest,source	Divide real	IE,DE,ZE,OE,UE,PE	X X X
FDIVP dest,source	Divide real & pop	IE,DE,ZE,OE,UE,PE	X X X
FDIVR dest,source	Divide real reversed	IE,DE,ZE,OE,UE,PE	X X X
FDIVRP dest,source	Divide real reversed & pop	IE,DE,ZE,OE,UE,PE	X X X
FENI/FNENI	Enable interrupts	None	X $ $
FFREE dest	Free register	None	X X X
FIADD source	Integer add	IE,DE,OE,PE	X X X
FICOM source	Integer compare	IE,DE	X X X
FICOMP source	Integer compare & pop	IE,DE	X X X
FIDIV source	Integer divide	IE,DE,ZE,OE,UE,PE	X X X
FIDIVR source	Integer divide reversed	IE,DE,ZE,OE,UE,PE	X X X
FILD source	Integer load	IE	X X X
FIMUL source	Integer multiply	IE,DE,OE,PE	X X X
FINCSTP	Increment stack pointer	None	X X X
FINIT/FNINIT	Initialise processor	None	X X X
FIST dest	Integer store	IE,PE	X X X
FISTP dest	Integer store & pop	IE,PE	X X X
FISUB source	Integer subtract	IE,DE,OE,PE	X X X
FISUBR source	Integer subtract reversed	IE,DE,OE,PE	X X X
FLD source	Load real	IE,DE	X X X
FLD1	Load +1.0	IE	X X X
FLDCW source	Load control wd	None	X X X
FLDENV source	Load environment	None	X X X
FLDL2E	Load log (2^e)	IE	X X X
FLDL2T	Load log (2^10)	IE	X X X
FLDLG2	Load log (10^2)	IE	X X X
FLDLN2	Load log (e^2)	IE	X X X
FLDPI	Load pi	IE	X X X
FLDZ	Load +0.0	IE	X X X
FMUL dest,source	Multiply real	IE,DE,ZE,OE,UE,PE	X X X
FMULP dest,source	Multiply real & pop	IE,DE,ZE,OE,UE,PE	X X X
FNOP	No operation	None	X X X
FPATAN	Partial arctangent	UE,PE	X X X
FPREM	Partial remainder	IE,DE,UE	X X X

INSTR.	FUNCTION	FLAGS Affected	87/287/387
FPREM1	Partial remainder (IEEE)		X
FPTAN	Partial tangent	IE,PE	X X X
FRNDINT	Round to integer	IE,PE	X X X
FRSTOR source	Restore saved state	None	X X X
FSAVE/FNSAVE dest	Save state	None	X X X
FSCALE	Scale	IE,OE,UE	X X X
FSETPM	Enter protected mode	None	X X
FSIN	Sine		X
FSINCOS	Sine & cosine		X
FSQRT	Square root	IE,DE,PE	X X X
FST dest	Store real	IE,OE,UE,PE	X X X
FSTCW/FNSTCW dest	Store control wd	None	X X X
FSTENV/FNSTENV dest	Store environment	None	X X X
FSTP dest	Store real & pop	IE,OE,UE,PE	X X X
FSTSW/FNSTSW dest	Store status wd	None	X X X
FSUB dest,source	Subtract real	IE,DE,OE,UE,PE	X X X
FSUBP dest,source	Subtract real & pop	IE,DE,OE,UE,PE	X X X
FSUBR dest,source	Subtract real reversed	IE,DE,OE,UE,PE	X X X
FSUBRP dest,source	Subtract real reversed & pop	IE,DE,OE,UE,PE	X X X
FTST	Test stack top against +0.0	IE,DE	X X X
FUCOM	Unordered compare		X
FUCOMP	Unordered compare & pop		X
FUCOMPP	Unordered compare & pop twice		X
FWAIT	Wait while 8087 is busy	None	X X X
FXAM	Examine stack top	None	X X X
FXCH dest	Exchange registers	IE	X X X
FXTRACT	Extract exponent & SFificand	IE	X X X
FYL2X	Y*log (2^X)	PE	X X X
FYL2XP1	Y*log (2^X+1)	PE	X X X

LEGEND:

# =	flags affected by instruction
$ =	ignore
cnt =	count
Reg =	register
Mem =	memory
Accum =	accumulator (AL, AX, EAX)
Imm =	immediate
Deststr =	destination string
Sourcestr =	source string
Segreg =	segment register

Number PReding item indicates number of bits

EFLAGS is a 32 bit register in 80386
FLAGS (LO wd of EFLAGS) is 16 bit reg.

wd =	word
dbl =	double
lft =	left
rght =	right
arith =	arithmetic
rot =	rotate
@ =	except when task switching.

SOURCE:
Intel Microprocessor and Peripheral Handbook Volume 1, pages 2-26 to 2-30, 2-55 to 2-59, 2-85 to 2-89, 2-117 to 2-121, 3-46 to 3-53, 4-106 to 4-119

Note that some coprocessor flags are also indicated in the tables. The legend is:

IE	Invalid
UE	Underflow
PE	Precision
DE	Denormalised
ZE	Divide by zero.
OE	Overflow.

(Refer page 181).

FLAGS REGISTER:

BIT	ABBR	NAME
0	CF	Carry Flag
1		RESERVED
2	PF	Parity flag
3		RESERVED
4	AF	Auxiliary carry flag
5		RESERVED
6	ZF	Zero flag
7	SF	Sign flag
8	TF	Trap flag
9	IF	Interrupt enable
10	DF	Direction flag
11	OF	Overflow
12-13	IOPL	I/O privilege level
14	NT	Nested tank flag
15		RESERVED
16	RF	Resume flag (80386 only)
17	VM	Virtual 8086 mode (80386)
18-31		RESERVED

C

KEYBOARD CODES

INT-16h is the BIOS interrupt routine for reading the keyboard buffer, and returns the "keycode" in AX, consisting of scancode in AH and ASCII-code in AL, except for an extended key, which returns a scancode in AH and zero in AL; there are some variations on this basic plan. I have been less than satisfied with keycode summaries that I have seen in various reference books and have attempted here to produce a concise yet very thorough listing. Should you discover a code not listed, kindly let me know.

Chapter Three introduces the keyboard architecture.

The **ASCII character set** is also listed below. *370*

KEY-CODE	KEY-NAME	-keycode returned in AX- NORMAL	ALT	CTRL	SHIFT
01	Esc	011B	01F0	011B	011B
02	1 and !	0231	7800	Ignor	0221
03	2 and @	0332	7900	0300	0340
04	3 and #	0433	7A00	Ignor	0423
05	4 and $	0534	7B00	Ignor	0524
06	5 and %	0635	7C00	Ignor	0625
07	6 and ^	0736	7D00	071E	075E
08	7 and &	0837	7E00	Ignor	0826
09	8 and *	0938	7F00	Ignor	092A
0A	9 and (	0A39	8000	Ignor	0A28
0B	0 and)	0B30	8100	Ignor	0B29
0C	- and _	0C2D	8200	0C1F	0C5F
0D	= and +	0D3D	8300	Ignor	0D2B
0E	<-	0E08	0EF0	0E7F	0E08
0F	TAB	0F09	A500	9400	0F00
10	Q	1071	1000	1011	1051
11	W	1177	1100	1117	1157
12	E	1265	1200	1205	1245
13	R	1372	1300	1312	1352
14	T	1474	1400	1414	1454
15	Y	1579	1500	1519	1559
16	U	1675	1600	1615	1655
17	I	1769	1700	1709	1749
18	O	186F	1800	180F	184F
19	P	1970	1900	1910	1950
1A	[and {	1A5B	1AF0	1A1B	1A7B
1B	] and }	1B5D	1BF0	1BF0	1B7D
1C	CR	1C0D	1CF0	1C0A	1C0D
1D	CTRL	Ignore	Ignor	Ignor	Ignor
1E	A	1E61	1E00	1E01	1E41
1F	S	1F73	1F00	1F13	1F53
20	D	2064	2000	2004	2044
21	F	2166	2100	2106	2146
22	G	2267	2200	2207	2247
23	H	2368	2300	2308	2348
24	J	246A	2400	240A	244A
25	K	256B	2500	250B	254B
26	L	266C	2600	260C	264C
27	; and :	273B	27F0	Ignor	273A
28	' and "	2827	28F0	Ignor	2822
29	# and ~	2960	29F0	Ignor	297E
2A	Lft SHIFT	Ignore	Ignor	Ignor	Ignor

KEY-CODE	KEY-NAME	-keycode returned in AX- NORMAL	ALT	CTRL	SHIFT
2B	\ and |	2B5C	2BF0	2B1C	2B7C
2C	Z	2C7A	2C00	2C1A	2C5A
2D	X	2D78	2D00	2D18	2D58
2E	C	2E63	2E00	2E03	2E43
2F	V	2F76	2F00	2F16	2F56
30	B	3062	3000	3002	3042
31	N	316E	3100	310E	314E
32	M	326D	3200	320D	324D
33	, and <	332C	33F0	Ignor	333C
34	. and >	342E	34F0	Ignor	343E
35	/ and ?	352F	35F0	Ignor	353F
36	Rgt SHIFT	Ignore	Ignor	Ignor	Ignor
37	*	372A	37F0	9600	373A
38	ALT	Ignore	Ignor	Ignor	Ignor
39	SPACE	3920	3920	3920	3920
3A	CAPS LOCK	Ignore	Ignor	Ignor	Ignor
3B	F1	3B00	6800	5E00	5400
3C	F2	3C00	6900	5F00	5500
3D	F3	3D00	6A00	6000	5600
3E	F4	3E00	6B00	6100	5700
3F	F5	3F00	6C00	6200	5800
40	F6	4000	6D00	6300	5900
41	F7	4100	6E00	6400	5A00
42	F8	4200	6F00	6500	5B00
43	F9	4300	7000	6600	5C00
44	F10	4400	7100	6700	5D00
45	NUM LOCK	Ignore	Ignor	PAUSE	Ignor
46	SCRL LOCK	Ignore	Ignor	Ignor	Ignor
47	KEY PAD 7	4700	Ignor	7700	Ignor
48	KEY PAD 8	4800	Ignor	8D00	Ignor
49	KEY PAD 9	4900	Ignor	8400	Ignor
4A	KEY PAD -	4A2D	Ignor	8E00	Ignor
4B	KEY PAD 4	4B00	Ignor	7300	Ignor
4C	KEY PAD 5	Ignore	Ignor	8F00	Ignor
4D	KEY PAD 6	4D00	Ignor	7400	Ignor
4E	KEY PAD +	4E2B	Ignor	9000	Ignor
4F	KEY PAD 1	4F00	Ignor	7500	Ignor
50	KEY PAD 2	5000	Ignor	9100	Ignor
51	KEY PAD 3	5100	Ignor	7600	Ignor
52	KEY PAD 0	5200	Ignor	9200	Ignor
53	KEY PAD .	5300	Ignor	9300	Ignor
--end of PC 84-key keyboard--					
54	Alt PrScr	Ignore	SysReq	Ignor	Ignor
55	--UNDEFINED--				
56	--UNDEFINED--				
57	F11	8500	8B00	8900	8700
58	F12	8600	8C00	8A00	8800
59 -7F	--UNDEFINED--				

The NUM-LOCK key only affects keys on the numeric keypad. The 101-key extended keyboard has the "normal" function keys of the numeric-keypad separate and unaffected by NUM-LOCK:

NORMAL		NUM-LOCK		101-KEY EXTENDED
Home	4700	7	4737	4700
up-arr.	4800	8	4838	4800
PgUp	4900	9	4939	4900
-	4A2D	-	4A2D	
left-arr.	4B00	4	4B34	4B00
	ignor	5	4C35	
right-ar.	4D00	6	4D36	4D00
+	4E2B	+	4E2B	
End	4F00	1	4F31	4F00
down-arr	5000	2	5032	5000
PgDn	5100	3	5133	5100
Insert	5200	0	5230	5200
Delete	5300	.	532E	5300

CONVENTIONAL ASCII CTRL CHAR'S (decimal)

00	null	16	data line esc
01	start heading	17	device ctrl 1
02	start text	18	device ctrl 2
03	end text	19	device ctrl 3
04	end transmit	20	device ctrl 4
05	enquiry	21	neg acknowl.
06	acknowledge	22	synch idle
07	bell	23	end tran block
08	back space	24	cancel
09	horiz. tab	25	end of medium
10	line feed	26	substitute
11	vertical tab	27	escape
12	form feed	28	file separator
13	carriage ret.	29	group separat.
14	shift out	30	record separat
15	shift in	31	unit separator

ANSI CHARACTER SET:

	0	1	2	3	4	5	6	7	8	9
03				!	"	#	$	%	&	'
04	(	)	*	+	,	-	.	/	0	1
05	2	3	4	5	6	7	8	9	:	;
06	<	=	>	?	@	A	B	C	D	E
07	F	G	H	I	J	K	L	M	N	O
08	P	Q	R	S	T	U	V	W	X	Y
09	Z	[		]	^	_	`	a	b	c
10	d	e	f	g	h	i	j	k	l	m
11	n	o	p	q	r	s	t	u	v	w
12	x	y	z	{	|	}	~	•		
12									Ç	ü
13	é	â	ä	à	å	ç	ê	ë	è	ï
14	î	ì	Ä	Å	É	æ	Æ	ô	ö	ò
15	û	ù	ÿ	Ö	Ü	¢	£	¥	p	f
16	á	í	ó	ú	ñ	Ñ	ª	º	¿	_
17	x	ø	□	¡		_	_	_	†	
18	_	_	_	_	_	_	_	_	_	_
19	_	_	_	_	_	_		_	_	_
20	_	_	_	_	_	_	_	_	_	_
21	_	_	_	_	_	_	_	_	_	_
22	_	†	_	_	_	ß	_	¶	_	_
23	‰	_	_	_	_	_	_	_	°	_
24	_	‡	_	_	_	_	_	_		
25	•	_	n	™	"					

IBM CHARACTER SET:

(codes in decimal) Example 064 "@"

	0	1	2	3	4	5	6	7	8	9
03				!	"	#	$	%	&	'
04	(	)	*	+	,	-	.	/	0	1
05	2	3	4	5	6	7	8	9	:	;
06	<	=	>	?	@	A	B	C	D	E
07	F	G	H	I	J	K	L	M	N	O
08	P	Q	R	S	T	U	V	W	X	Y
09	Z	[	\	]	^	_	`	a	b	c
10	d	e	f	g	h	i	j	k	l	m
11	n	o	p	q	r	s	t	u	v	w
12	x	y	z	{	¦	}	~			
12									Ç	ü
13	é	â	ä	à	å	ç	ê	ë	è	ï
14	î	ì	Ä	Å	É	æ	Æ	ô	ö	ò
15	û	ù	ÿ	Ö	Ü	¢	£	¥	₧	ƒ
16	á	í	ó	ú	ñ	Ñ	ª	º	¿	⌐
17	¬	½	¼	¡	«	»	░	▒	▓	│
18	┤	╡	╢	╖	╕	╣	║	╗	╝	╜
19	╛	┐	└	┴	┬	├	─	┼	╞	╟
20	╚	╔	╩	╦	╠	═	╬	╧	╨	╤
21	╥	╙	╘	╒	╓	╫	╪	┘	┌	█
22	▄	▌	▐	▀	α	β	Γ	π	Σ	σ
23	µ	τ	Φ	Θ	Ω	δ	∞	ø	ε	∩
24	≡	±	≥	≤	⌠	⌡	÷	≈	°	•
25	·	√	ⁿ	²	■					

D

SOURCE LISTINGS

All of these listings are on the Companion Disk, and some are partially listed for convenience within the main text of the book. A couple of source files are listed fully within the book, so are not listed here: they are INT9.ASM and WINHULLO.*. Two files listed only in the Companion Disk are DRIVER2 and NOTHING; these are required for the second device driver Workshop.

;PCX2SCRN.COM

```
;invoke by--  PCX2SCRN <enter>
;version 20/3 has filespec DEMO.PCX inside this program.
;displays the pcx file on an cga or vga (modo 16) screen.
;
comseg segment
    org 100h
    assume DS:comseg, CS:comseg
main proc far
    jmp     start
```

```
handle      dw      2               ;file handle.
screenaddrdw        0,0A000h        ;start addr
                    ;video-RAM, current line.
screenend   dw      350*80,0A000h ;ending addr
                                    ;video-RAM.
header      db      128 dup(0)      ;pcx header read into
                                    ;here.
buffer      db 200 dup(0)  ;pcx file read into here.
bufferptr   dw      0               ;pointer into buffer.
cnt16       dw      0               ;palette register
```

```
cnt3        dw      0
cnt dw      0
colour      dw      0
bitplane    dw      0
count       dw      0
content     dw      0
lineoffset  dw      0 ;offset in video-RAM, current line.
filespec    db "temp.pcx",0 ;*****temporarily added.

MSG1        DB "Cannot open PCX file $"   ;****$ inserted
MSG2        DB      "Cannot read header $"
closemsg    db      "Cannot close PCX file $"

colourmasks         DW              00H
            DW      08H
            DW      01H
            DW      09H

start:
    mov   ah,3Dh                    ;open the file.
    mov   dx,offset filespec
    mov al,0
    int 21h
    jc  openerror
    mov handle,ax                   ;handle
    jmp short noerror
openerror:
    mov dx,offset MSG1
    mov ah,9
    int 21h
    jmp exitprog
noerror:

;***read & check the header...
    mov bx,handle                   ;filehandle
    mov cx,128
    mov dx,offset header
    mov ah,3Fh
    int 21h                         ;read file
    jc  readerror
    cmp    BYTE PTR header,10
    je     place1

readerror:
    mov dx,offset MSG2
    mov ah,9
    int 21h
    jmp exitprog

place1:
;******should put checking if mode 16 supported.
    mov ah,0
    mov al,16
    int 10h                         ;mode 16
    mov    WORD PTR cnt16,0
    jmp    SHORT place4

place2:                             ;set ega palette....
    mov   si,WORD PTR cnt16
    mov   ax,si
    shl   si,1
    add   si,ax
    mov   bx,WORD PTR cnt3
    mov   al,BYTE PTR header[bx+16][si]
    mov   cl,6
    sar   al,cl
    and   ax,3
    mov   si,ax
    mov   WORD PTR cnt,si
    shl   si,1
    mov   ax,WORD PTR colourmasks[si]
    mov   cl,2
    sub   cl,bl
    shl   ax,cl
    or    WORD PTR colour,ax
    inc   WORD PTR cnt3
place3:
    cmp   WORD PTR cnt3,3
    jl    place2

    mov ah,16           ;set palette registers...
    mov al,0            ;set individual palette register.
    mov bh,BYTE PTR colour          ;value.
    mov bl,BYTE PTR cnt16           ;which register.
    int 10h

    inc WORD PTR cnt16
place4:
    cmp WORD PTR cnt16,16
    jge place5          ;to end of outer for-loop...

    sub   ax,ax
    mov   WORD PTR colour,ax
    mov   WORD PTR cnt3,ax
    jmp   SHORT place3
place5:                             ;end of outer loop.

;***select initial colour plane...
    mov   ax,2
    mov   dx,03C4h                  ;port 03C4h
    out   dx, al

    mov   ax,1
    mov   dx,03C5h                  ;port 03C5h
    out   dx, al

    mov   ax,0
    mov   WORD PTR screenaddr,ax
    mov   dx,0A000h   ;top left byte of scrn mem
    mov   WORD PTR screenaddr+2,dx
    mov   ax,350*80
    mov   WORD PTR screenend,ax
    mov   dx,0A000h                 ;end of scrn.
    mov   WORD PTR screenend+2,dx
    sub   ax,ax
    mov   WORD PTR lineoffset,ax
```

```
    mov   WORD PTR content,ax
    mov   WORD PTR count,ax
    mov   WORD PTR bitplane,1
    mov   WORD PTR bufferptr,200

;***graphics data loop...
place6:
    mov   ax,WORD PTR screenaddr
    mov   dx,WORD PTR screenaddr+2
    cmp   WORD PTR screenend,ax
    jne   place7
    cmp   WORD PTR screenend+2,dx
    jne   place7
    jmp   place15

place7:                 ;start of the large not-end-mem loop
    cmp   WORD PTR bufferptr,200
    jne   place8
    mov   WORD PTR bufferptr,0

    mov bx, handle
    mov cx,200
    mov dx,offset buffer
    mov ah,3Fh
    int 21h                             ;read file

place8:                 ;***loop counter or data byte?
    mov   bx,WORD PTR bufferptr
    mov   al,BYTE PTR buffer[bx]
    cbw
    mov   WORD PTR count,ax
    inc   WORD PTR bufferptr
    mov   al,BYTE PTR count
    and   ax,192
    cmp   ax,192
    jne   place10

    cmp   WORD PTR bufferptr,200  ;third inner IF....
    jne   place9
    mov   WORD PTR bufferptr,0
    mov   bx, handle               ;file read...
    mov   cx,200
    mov   dx,offset buffer
    mov   ah,3Fh
    int 21h                        ;read file

place9:                            ;
    mov   bx,WORD PTR bufferptr
    mov   al,BYTE PTR buffer[bx]
    cbw
    mov   WORD PTR content,ax
    inc   WORD PTR bufferptr
    and   WORD PTR count,63
    jmp   SHORT place11
                  ;jump around the else-condition...
    nop

place10:
    mov   ax,WORD PTR count
    mov   WORD PTR content,ax
    mov   WORD PTR count,1

place11:
    mov   ax,WORD PTR count
    dec   WORD PTR count
    or    ax,ax
    jne   place12
    jmp   place6
place12:
    mov   al,BYTE PTR content
    les   bx,DWORD PTR screenaddr
    mov   si,WORD PTR lineoffset
    mov   BYTE PTR es:[bx][si],al

    inc   WORD PTR lineoffset
    cmp   WORD PTR lineoffset,80
    jne   place11
    mov   WORD PTR lineoffset,0

    cmp   WORD PTR bitplane,8
    jne   place13
    add   WORD PTR screenaddr,80
    mov   WORD PTR bitplane,1
    jmp   SHORT place14
    nop
place13:                                ;***else condition...
    shl   WORD PTR bitplane,1
place14:
    mov   ax,WORD PTR bitplane
    mov   dx,03C5h                      ;port 03C5h
    out   dx, al

    jmp   SHORT place11   ;three loops close here.
    nop

place15:                                ;***finished
    mov bx, handle
    mov ah,3Eh
    int 21h                             ;close file
    jnc  nocloseerror
    mov dx,offset closemsg
    mov ah,9
    int 21h
    jmp short exitprog
nocloseerror:
    mov ah,2            ;beep and wait for keypress....
    mov dl,07
    int 21h
    mov ah,0
    int 16h

    mov ah,0
    mov al,3
    int 10h                             ;back to text mode 3

exitprog:
```

```
     mov ax,4C00h
     int 21h              ;exit
main      ENDP
comseg ends
 END main
```

;INT8.COM B.Kauler

```
;This program demonstrates "multitasking" by using a
;resident program and the timer-interrupt.
;A resident program opens many possibilities, and can be
;made to execute at the "same" time as another program.
;This is achieved by using int08 to call the resident program.
;Int08 is generated every 55mSec, and updates the BIOS
                                        ;clock.
;Our INSTALL routine can change the interrupt-8 vector in
;the interrupt table, to divert to the RUN_TIME routine,
; which would in turn transfer control back to the proper
; BIOS routine  after doing whatever it wants.
;However, IBM considered that programmers would want to
; access the 55mSec timer, so provided int1Ch
; "USER_TIMER_INT",  which is called by int08 routine
; after it has done its own  housekeeping.
;Normally int1Ch consists of simply an IRET instruction, but
; we can divert it to our own routine, which would terminate
; with an IRET.
;Note that our RUN_TIME routine could do many other
; things; maybe display the date or time on the screen
; continuously if we wished, rather than a message, in which
; case our routine would have to access int21h, functions 2Ah
; and 2Ch. The program INT9.COM accessed the interrupt
; table, but due to the danger of an interrupt occurring while
; writing to it (which ;we got around by a CLI), IBM
; provided INT21h functions 35h and ;25h to do the job.
;  This program uses these.
;
com_seg segment
     assume  cs:com_seg,ds:com_seg,ss:com_seg
     org    100h
int8   proc   far
     jmp    install
;
;data area....
int_offset  dw    0     ;original int1Ch vector.
int_seg     dw    0           ;     /
column      db    0     ;original cursor position.
row         db    0           ;     /
message     db "MULTITASKING RESIDENT
                                  PROGRAM"
;
run_time:     ;displays message on screen.
;note; routine must be kept very short, as it is recalled every
                                  ; 55mSec.
;best to drive video ram directly.
     push   si
     push   di
     push   cx
     push   ax
     push   es
     push   ds
     push   cs
     pop    ds
     mov    ax,0b000h      ;video ram segment.
;****change this to 0B800h for colour adaptor*****
     mov    es,ax          ;     /
     mov    si,offset message
     mov    di,0           ;video offset.
     mov    ah,0f0h        ;attribute.
     mov    cx,001dh       ;loop count.
next_char: lodsb            ;display a char.
     stosw                 ;     /
loop   next_char
     pop    ds
     pop    es
     pop    ax
     pop    cx
     pop    di
     pop    si
     iret
;
install:
     mov    al,1Ch     ;get interrupt vector.
     mov    ah,35h     ;     /
     int    21h        ;     / (--> ES:BX).
     mov    int_offset,bx          ;save vector.
     mov    int_seg,es             ;     /
;note that I have saved the original vector, to show how it is
;done, though in this program there's no need to.
     mov    dx,offset run_time     ;load new vector.
     ;COM file, so DS already set okay.
     mov    al,1Ch          ;     /
     mov    ah,25h          ;     /
     int    21h                    ;     / (DS:DX-->).
     mov    dx,offset install      ;point free memory,
     int    27h                    ;leave resident.
;
int8   endp
com_seg ends
end    int8
```

;INT16.COM

```
;this is a resident program that demonstrates use of INT-16h.
;It is the basic structure only, to be used as a building block.
com_seg segment
    assume  cs:com_seg,ds:com_seg,ss:com_seg
    org    100h
main     proc   far
 jmp    install
;............................
;data area....
int16save  dw 0,0
```

```
dump        dw 0  ;scrap.
scanlines   dw 0
position    dw 0
tsrmsg      db "YES IT WORKS!!$"
;................................
runtime16:
;a little theory on interrupts-- an int
;causes 3 16-bit values to go onto the
;stack -- flags, cs, ip, with ip on top.
;interestingly, a far-call--- CALL xyz
;FAR --- puts cs & ip on stack but not
;flags.
;All BIOS routines terminate with a FAR
;IRET, which expects flags,cs,ip on
;stack.
;
;the calling program will have put a
;value in AH to select a subfunction of
;int-16, so must sort this out...
;
;You will notice some stuffing around
;with the stack in the code, as at exit
;it must be exactly as it was when
;runtime entered.
;
;What we are going to do here is call
;the original int-16h routine. the
;INSTALL portion of this program will
;have saved the old int-16h interrupt
;vector in a data area called INT16SAVE.
;A problem is that this BIOS routine is
;terminated with a FAR IRET, ---
;to make sure the stack is right for
;this, PUSHF is placed before the CALL..
;
;Have a good look in the Appendices on
;how INT-16h works.  You will see that
;it has various subfunctions, selected
;by a value in AH.  This value will
;determine what we now do...
;
      sti      ;allows interrupts.
      push ax  ;*****NOTE AX SAVED HERE****
      cmp ah,0
      je  readkey
      cmp ah,10h
      jne notreading
;............
readkey:
      pushf
      call dword ptr cs:int16save ;read key
      cmp ax,2C00h    ;test for ALT-Z
      jne nothotkey
      pop ax   ;since we pushed it above.
      jmp yesthisisit
nothotkey:
      pop dump ;get old AX off stack to variable
          ;DUMP. New AX now has keycode req
          ;-uired by main program.
      iret    ;back to main program.
;............
notreading:
      mov ah,1 ;refer to BIOS INT-16h literature.
      pushf
      call dword ptr cs:int16save  ;test key
      jz  notaltz   ;zero-flag set if no key
      cmp ax,2C00h          ;test for ALT-z
      jne notaltz
;.............
;Since it is ALT-Z, unload it from the keyboard buffer....
      mov ah,0
      pushf
      call dword ptr cs:int16save ;read char.
      pop ax
      jmp short yesthisisit
;............
notaltz:
;TSR not activated, so go on to normal int-16 handling....
      pop ax  ;get stack original condition.
      jmp dword ptr cs:int16save
          ;note this is a JMP, not a CALL.
          ;takes control back to main prog
;............
yesthisisit:
;a tsr must be very careful with regs...
;should push them all here, then when program exits,
;pop all regs,
;then back to original program...
    push ax
    push bx
    push cx
    push dx
    push bp
    push si
    push di
    push ds
    push es
;give some thought to the segment regs...
;DS requires setting....
    push cs
    pop  ds
;................................
codestarts:
    sti              ;in case you turn it off earlier.
;  ....
;  .... ;this is the guts of the TSR.
;  ....
;do something to show TSR works....
    mov ah,3         ;read cursor position,
    mov bx,0         ;display-page 0.
    int 10h          ;-->CH=starting-scan, CL=ending-scan
                     ;  DH=row, DL=column.
    mov scanlines,cx
    mov position,dx
;
    mov ah,2         ;set cursor pos.
```

```
  mov bx,0
  cmp dh,0          ;check if already on top row.
    je  disbelow
    dec dh          ;so will display msg above dos prompt.
    jmp short dismsg
disbelow:
    inc dh          ;so will display msg below dos prompt.
dismsg:
    int 10h         ;moves cursor up or down one row.
;
;...put code to display msg in here...
;
    mov ah,2        ;set cursor pos. back to where it was.
    mov bx,0
    mov dx,position
    int 10h
; ....
;...............................
;to get back to main program--
;pop all regs in reverse order to above....
  pop es
  pop ds
  pop di
  pop si
  pop bp
  pop dx
  pop cx
  pop bx
  pop ax
;In this case do not IRET back to
;main program.  Instead jump to
;original BIOS interrupt  -- this is
;because the main program invoked the
;interrupt with some intention, to read
;a key or check keyboard status, so we
;should go ahead and do this rather than
;upsetting the main program by just
;going straight back to it with IRET...
;
  jmp dword ptr cs:int16save
;
;...................................
install:
    mov   al,16h            ;get interrupt vector.
    mov   ah,35h            ;     /
    int   21h               ;     / (--> ES:BX).
    mov   int16save,bx      ;save vector.
    mov   int16save+2,es    ;     /
    mov   dx,offset runtime16   ;load new vector.
  ;COM file, so DS already set okay.
    mov   al,16h            ;     /
    mov   ah,25h            ;     /
    int   21h               ;     / (DS:DX-->).
    mov   dx,offset install ;point free memory,
    int   27h               ;leave resident.
;.......................................
main  endp
com_seg ends
        end   main
;.......................................
```

;DSK2SCRN.COM B.Kauler 1989.

```
;reads a text file from disk and displays it on the screen.
;DOS command line:  DSK2SCRN [filename]
;..............................................................
comseg  segment
     assume  cs:comseg,ds:comseg,ss:comseg
     org     100h
main   proc   far
      jmp    code_starts
;..............................................................
;disk access data here.....
fcb         db   36 dup(0)     ;file control block.
dta         db   0             ;disk transfer area(1byte only).
err_msg     db   "file access error!"
;
;program data here.....
char_pos  db  0           ;character position on the line.
;..............................................................
code_starts:
;read the DOS-command-line tail from the PSP, to a File
; Control Block (FCB) that we are creating for the file to be
; opened.....
      mov    si,5Ch        ;get addr of tail in PSP.
      mov    di,offset fcb  ;get addr of FCB.
      mov    cx,12         ;string length to move.
      cld
      rep movsb            ;mov string PSP -->FCB.
;We need to specify a Disk Transfer Address, through which
; chars are sent to and received from disk....
     mov    dx,offset dta  ;DOS function SET_DTA.
     mov    ah,1Ah         ;     /(DS:DX-->)
     int    21h            ;     /
;the filename must be at DS:DX to open the file.  We have
; the name in the FCB, so....
     mov    dx,offset fcb  ;DOS function OPEN_FILE.
     mov    ah,0Fh         ;     /(DS:DX-->)
     int    21h            ;     /
     cmp    al,0           ;test file open error.
     jnz    error
;If function 0Fh succeeds in opening the file, various relevant
;information is automatically transfered from disk into the
; FCB. the first byte of the FCB will hold the disk number
; from which the file was read, and offset 0Eh specifies the
; record-size and is set to 128, which is arbitrary, and we can
; change it and other parameters....
      mov    word ptr fcb+0Ch,0    ;current block=0.
      mov    word ptr fcb+0Eh,1    ;record size=1
      mov    fcb+20h,0             ;current record=0
;read a char from file & display it....
;note that we test here for CTRL-Z to determine the end of
; the ;file, as CTRL-Z occurs at the end of text files, however
;function 14h returns an error-code in AL that can be used to
;signal the end of file.
```

```
again: mov   dx,offset fcb
            ;DOS function SEQUENTIAL_READ.
    mov   ah,14h       ;    /
    int   21h          ;    /
    cmp   al,0         ;test if read error.
    jnz   error
    mov   al,dta       ;get the char just read.
    cmp   al,1Ah       ;is it CTRL-Z?
    je    eof
    cmp   al,09h       ;is it TAB?
    je    tab
    call  disp_char    ;display the char.
    inc   char_pos     ;update current char position.
    cmp   dta,0Ah      ;test if end of line.
    jne   again        ;not end of line--get next char.
    mov   char_pos,0   ;clear char count.
    jmp   again        ;get next char.
;.................................................................
tab:  mov   al," "
    call  disp_char    ;display a blank.
    inc   char_pos     ;update current char position.
    test  char_pos,7   ;are we at a TAB stop?
    jz    again        ;yes.
    jmp   tab
;.................................................................
eof:  mov   dx,offset fcb  ;DOS function CLOSE_FILE.
    mov   ah,10h       ;    /
    int   21h          ;    /
    mov   al,0         ;return to DOS.
    mov   ah,4Ch       ;    /
    int   21h          ;    /
;.................................................................
error: mov   dx,offset err_msg    ;display error message.
    mov   ah,9                ;    /
    int   21h                 ;    /
    mov   al,0         ;return to DOS.
    mov   ah,4Ch       ;    /
    int   21h          ;    /
;.................................................................
disp_char     proc   near
    push  bx
    mov   bx,0         ;display a char.
    mov   ah,14        ;    /
    int   10h          ;    /
    pop   bx
    ret
;.................................................................
main  endp
comseg  ends
end   main
```

;DSKSCRNB.COM B.Kauler 1989.

```
;reads a text file from disk and displays it on the screen.
;DOS command line:  DSKSCRNB <filename >CON
;This method uses standard input and standard output, with
;redirection specified on the DOS command-line tail.
;Input is redirected from the keyboard to a file, and output
;need not be redirected since standard output is the screen.
;...therefore >CON is optional.... you could as an exercise
;try >PRN for output redirection.
;.................................................................
comseg  segment
     assume  cs:comseg,ds:comseg,ss:comseg
     org    100h
main   proc   far
     jmp    code_starts
;.................................................................
;data here.....
char_pos  db  0           ;character position on the line.
;.................................................................
code_starts:
;read a character....
;note that we test for input status, as a file does not
; necessarily end with CTRL-Z.  This function sees if there is
; another character to be read, and if not returns AL=0.
again: mov   ah,0Bh      ;INPUT_STATUS.
     int   21h           ;    /
     cmp   al,0
     je    eof
;The standard input device is specified on the
;DOS command line...
     mov   ah,7          ;STANDARD_INPUT
     int   21h           ;    / (-->AL).
;process the character....
     cmp   al,1Ah        ;is it CTRL-Z?
     je    eof
     cmp   al,09h        ;is it TAB?
     je    tab
     call  disp_char     ;display the char.
     inc   char_pos      ;update current char position.
     cmp   al,0Ah        ;test if end of line.
     jne   again         ;not end of line--get next char.
     mov   char_pos,0    ;clear char count.
     jmp   again         ;get next char.
;.................................................................
tab:  mov   al," "
     call  disp_char     ;display a blank.
     inc   char_pos      ;update current char position.
     test  char_pos,7    ;are we at a TAB stop?
     jz    again         ;yes.
     jmp   tab
;.................................................................
eof:  mov   al,0         ;return to DOS.
     mov   ah,4Ch        ;    /
     int   21h           ;    /
main   endp
;.................................................................
disp_char    proc   near
;send character to the standard output device....
     mov   ah,2          ;STANDARD_OUTPUT.
     mov   dl,al         ;    /
     int   21h           ;    /
     ret
disp_char endp
```

```
;..............................................................
comseg ends
end    main
```

;DSKSCRNC.COM   B.Kauler 1989.

```
;reads a text file from disk and displays it on the screen.
;DOS command line:  DSKSCRNC [drive][path]filename
;Uses modern handles method.
;Allows path to precede filename.
;..............................................................
comseg  segment
   assume  cs:comseg,ds:comseg,ss:comseg
    org   100h
main  proc   far
    jmp   code_starts
;..............................................................
;data here.....
handle      dw  0           ;identifies file.
dta         db  0           ;Disk Transfer Area.
char_pos    db  0           ;character position on the line.
filespec    db  32 dup (0)  ;DOS command-tail goes here.
errmsg      db  "file access error!!!!$"
;..............................................................
code_starts:
;first job is to get the command-tail into FILESPEC...
    call  get_filespec
;open the file....
   mov   dx,offset filespec
   mov   al,0
   mov   ah,3Dh
   int   21h
   jc    error         ;carry-flag set if error.
   mov  handle,ax
;read a character....
again: mov    bx,handle
   mov   cx,1          ;just read one character.
   mov   dx,offset dta ;destination is DTA.
   mov   ah,3Fh        ;READ_HANDLE.
   int   21h           ;    /
   jc    error         ;carry-flag set if error.
   cmp   ax,0
   je    eof           ;end of file if AX=0.
    ;note that the file-pointer is updated by function3Fh.
;process the character....
   mov   al,dta        ;put the char in AL.
   cmp   al,1Ah        ;is it CTRL-Z?
   je    eof
   cmp   al,09h        ;is it TAB?
   je    tab
   call  disp_char     ;display the char.
   inc   char_pos      ;update current char position.
   cmp   al,0Ah        ;test if end of line.
   jne   again         ;not end of line--get next char.
   mov   char_pos,0    ;clear char count.
   jmp   again         ;get next char.
;..............................................................
tab:  mov    al," "        ;assume tab-stops every 8th column.
   call  disp_char     ;display a blank.
   inc   char_pos      ;update current char position.
   test  char_pos,7    ;are we at a TAB stop?
   jz    again         ;yes.
   jmp   tab
;..............................................................
eof:  mov    ah,3Eh        ;CLOSE_HANDLE.
   int   21h           ;    /
   jc    error
   mov   al,0          ;return to DOS.
   mov   ah,4Ch        ;    /
   int   21h           ;    /
;..............................................................
error:  mov   dx,offset errmsg ;display error message.
   mov   ah,9          ;    /
   int   21h           ;    /
   mov   al,0          ;could return an error code.
   mov   ah,4Ch
   int   21h           ;back to DOS
main   endp
;..............................................................
get_filespec   proc   near
   cld
   mov   si,082h       ;point to command-tail in PSP.
   mov   di,offset filespec ;point to destination.
read_next: lodsb
   cmp   al,0Dh        ;is char a carriage-return.
   je    end_string
   stosb
   jmp   read_next
end_string: ret
get_filespec endp
;..............................................................
disp_char     proc   near
;By default the standard output is the screen....
   mov   ah,2          ;STANDARD_OUTPUT.
   mov   dl,al         ;    /
   int   21h           ;    /
   ret
disp_char endp
;..............................................................
comseg  ends
end    main
```

;MASTREXE.ASM   B.Kauler

```
;--> MASTREXE.OBJ + SLAVEXE.OBJ + SERF.OBJ -->
;                                   MASTREXE.EXE
;A demonstration of linking .EXE files.
;..............................................................
stack1  segment stack          ;'stack' not required on the end.
     db    256   dup(0)
stack1  ends
;..............................................................
data    segment public  'data'  ;'data' useful for linker.
     extrn  data1:byte
```

```
local_data db  "this is local data",0Ah,0Dh,"$"
data   ends
;..............................................................
code    segment public  'code'   ;'code' useful for linker.
     assume  cs:code, ds:data ;tells Assembler default code &
                                              ; data
                       ;segments for the instructions to follow.
     extrn   slave_routine:near
master_routine  proc    far
     mov     ax,data          ;When prog loads, DS not set to
     mov     ds,ax            ; data segment, so do it here.
     mov     dx,offset local_data
     mov     ah,9
     int     21h              ;display a message.
;the interesting bit....
     call    slave_routine
;interesting here also....
     mov     dx,offset data1  ;DATA1 is external.
     mov     ah,9
     int     21h              ;display message.
     mov     al,0
     mov     ah,4Ch
     int     21h              ;back to DOS
master_routine  endp
code    ends
     end     master_routine
```

;SLAVE.ASM B.Kauler

```
;for use with MASTREXE.ASM, to demonstrate linking.
;LINK MASTREXE.OBJ+ SLAVE.OBJ+ SERF.OBJ -->
;                                              MASTREXE.EXE
;SLAVE contains a procedure used by MASTER.
;A few points to note --
;None of the usual preliminary directives, nor a stack
; segment, as this module is only data & code that will be
; combined with the main program.
;Note that the data segment is labeled "data" and the code
; segment is labeled "code" -- same as in the master module.
;  This ensures that LINK will combine them into one code
; segment and one data segment. 'data' and 'code' mean
; something different -- they just clarify to the LINKer which
; segments are code or data.
;Note that Microsoft & Intel have recently tended to favour
; labeling data segments with "_DATA" and code segments
; with "_TEXT", so that there is some standardisation of
; naming for linkage purposes.
;..........................................................
      public  slave_routine
;..........................................................
data    segment byte    public  'data'
      assume  ds:data   ;only used by Assembler to assemble
                   ; data references correctly. Doesn't actually
                   ;change DS.
local_mess db  "this data is in SLAVE module",0Ah,0Dh,"$"
data   ends
;..........................................................
code    segment byte    public  'code'
      assume  cs:code
;.............................
slave_routine   proc    near
      mov     dx,offset local_mess
      mov     ah,9
      int     21h      ;display message.
      ret
slave_routine   endp
;......................................................
code    ends
      end              ;no label needed here.
```

;SERF.ASM B.Kauler

```
;required for linkage demo with MASTREXE and
; SLAVEXE. contains data for use by other modules.
;note data segment given same name as other modules.
;note no code (instructions) to access local data, so no
;need for an ASSUME DS:DATA directive.
;...................................................
      public  data1
;...................................................
data    segment byte    public  'data'
data1   db      "this data is in third module",0Ah,0Dh,"$"
;more data could be put here.....
;....
data    ends
      end              ;no label
```

;OVLPARNT.COM B.Kauler

```
;This program demonstrates overlays.
;The parent and child are both .COM files in this case.
;The child is named DEMO.OVL.
;
comseg segment
     assume ds:comseg, cs:comseg, ss:comseg, es:comseg
      org 100h
main1   proc    far
      jmp     code_starts
;..................................................................
;data...
child_filespec          db "demo.ovl",0  ;put path if reqd.
child_offset            dw  0  ;address of start of child
                                              ; program.
child_segment           dw  0,0,0,0,0,0,0,0  ;      /
errflag                 db  0
message1      db "start of parent process",0Ah,0Dh,"$"
message2      db "back in parent process....$"
errmsg    db "A memory deallocation or file access ERROR
                                                  occurred$"
;..................................................................
code_starts:
```

```
;the parent program doesn't do anything, except display a
;message, load the child, transfer control to it, then
;another message upon return, then back to DOS...
    mov   dx,offset message1
    mov   ah,9
    int   21h
;The stack pointer is way out at end of the 64K segment, so
; move it in...
    mov bx,offset end_prog+126
    mov sp,bx
;...since the overlay is to load after it....
;END_PROG is a label defined at the very end of the parent
;program.  ES must point to start of PSP.
;The extra 128 bytes is for the stack-- .COM format
; automatically puts SP at the end of the segment, and we are
; here defining only as much as we think we'll need, and
; deallocating the rest of the segment.
;Function4Ah will define free memory to start from
; END_PROG+128...
    mov   bx,offset end_prog+144 ;use 144 so will be 1 para
                          ; beyond SP.
    mov   cl,4         ;convert block-size to paragraphs.
    shr   bx,cl        ;    /
    mov   ah,4Ah       ;SET_BLOCK. (ES:BX(para)-->)
    int   21h          ;    /
    jnc   nodeallocerr
    mov   errflag,1
    jmp   short errcond
nodeallocerr:
;Some shuffling, to calculate the start of the new block...
    mov   ax,es        ;note ES points to start of PSP.
    add   ax,bx
    inc   ax           ;to be sure new block beyond current
                                       ; program.
    mov   child_offset,0
    mov   child_segment,ax
;now the really interesting bit....
    call  load_ovl     ;load DEMO.OVL
;DEMO.OVL is now loaded, with CHILD_ADDRESS
; containing the starting address of the child program....
;however before we can jump to it, think about DS...
;probably the child will want to access its own data area, so...
    mov   ax,child_segment
    mov   ds,ax
;another thought... if the child is written with a RETF at the
; end, we can go to it using a far CALL, which simplifies the
; return...
    call  dword ptr cs:child_offset
;that's it, back in the parent program....
;restore original DS (=CS in .COM program)....
     push  cs
     pop   ds
;a message to acknowledge the fact.....
    mov   dx,offset message2
    mov   ah,9
    int   21h
;do we need to close the child-file? better do it...
    call unloadovl
    cmp   errflag,0
    je    backtodos
    jmp   short backtodos
errcond: mov   dx,offset errmsg
    mov   ah,9
    int   21h
    mov   errflag,1  ;flag not used in this simple prog.
backtodos:
    mov   al,0
    mov   ah,4Ch
    int   21h
main1  endp
;..............................................................
load_ovl  proc near
;now we can load the child program....
    mov   bx,offset child_segment
    mov   dx,offset child_filespec
    mov   al,3         ;method code.
    mov   ah,4Bh
    int   21h          ;EXEC
    jnc   short commonexit
error2: mov   errflag,2
commonexit:
    ret
load_ovl endp
;.........
unloadovl proc near
;wise to deallocate the memory that the overlay was
; occupying...
    mov   es,child_segment
    mov   ah,49h
    int   21h
    jnc   deallocokay
    mov   errflag,3
deallocokay: nop
     ret
unloadovl endp
;.........
end_prog:
comseg  ends
 end    main1
```

;DEMO.OVL

B.Kauler

```
;Demonstration overlay file, for use by OVLPARNT.COM
;
comseg segment
    assume ds:comseg, cs:comseg, es:comseg
     org   0           ;the overlay will not have a PSP.
main2  proc   far
     jmp   code_starts2
;..........................................................
message3 db "overlay program DEMO.OVL now
                                 executing.",0Ah,0Dh,"$"
```

```
;.............................................................
code_starts2:
    mov   dx,offset message3
    mov   ah,9
    int   21h
    ret                   ;return to parent.
main2  endp
comseg  ends
 end    main2
```

;DRIVER1.SYS B.Kauler

```
  ;simple device driver
  ;.....
code_seg  segment para   public 'code'
main_proc proc    far
    assume  cs:code_seg,es:code_seg,ds:code_seg
    org 0  ;required for device drivers.
begin:
  ;..........................................
  ;this area is the DEVICE HEADER....
next_dev   dd -1     ;no other device drivers
attribute  dw 8000h  ;character device.
strategy   dw dev_str ;addr of 1st DOS call.
interrupt  dw dev_int ;addr of 2nd DOS call.
dev_name   db "driver1$" ;name of the driver.
  ;..........................................
  ;this is the LOCAL WORKSPACE AREA....
rh_off  dw ?  ;Request Header offset.
rh_seg  dw ?  ;Request Header segment.
messages db 07h
        db "Simple character device driver"
        db 0Dh,0Ah,07h,"$"
  ;..........................................
  ;this is the STRATEGY procedure area...
dev_str:
    push  ds      ;save DS.
    push  cs      ;to avoid segment
    pop   ds      ;      override.
    mov   rh_seg,es  ;save Req.Header seg.
    mov   rh_off,bx  ;save Req.Head offset.
    pop   ds      ;restore DS.
    ret
  ;..........................................
  ;this is the INTERRUPT procedure.....
dev_int:
     push  ds     ;save registers.
     push  es     ;    /
     push  ax     ;    /
     push  bx     ;    /
     push  cx     ;    /
     push  dx     ;    /
     push  di     ;    /
     push  si     ;    /
     push  cs     ;to avoid segment
     pop   ds     ;   override.
  ;I will not assume that the second call to the
  ;driver will still have the addr. of the Req.
  ;Hdr. in ES:BX. Load it from workspace...
     mov   es,rh_seg
     mov   bx,rh_off
  ;perform branch based on the command passed in
  ;the Request Header...
     mov   al,es:[bx+2] ;get command code.
     cmp   al,0       ;check for zero.
     jne   errors
  ;perform required action...
     mov   dx,offset messages ;message
     mov   ah,9            ;to screen.
     int   21h             ;/
     mov es:word ptr [bx+3],0100h ;return status.
  ;it seems that DOS will also require to know
  ;where the driver ends....
     mov   ax,offset the_end ;end prog.
     mov es:[bx+14],ax ;break-addr for DOS.
     mov es:[bx+16],cs ;    /
     jmp finish
errors:
     mov es:word ptr [bx+3],8103h ;return status
finish:
      pop si        ;restore all reg's.
      pop di
      pop dx
      pop cx
      pop bx
      pop ax
      pop es
      pop ds
      ret
the_end:
  ;..........................................
main_proc   endp
code_seg    ends
          end   begin
  ;*****end of device driver******
  ;..........................................
```

;EXTEND

```
;NOTE: this is not on the Companion Disk!
;source for Worksheet (Extended Memory)
;Shifts seven bytes from conventional memory to extended.
;Firstly must setup the GDT... this is done with DEBUG,
; using the "E"nter command...

DEBUG
-E 2000 00 00 00 00 00 00 00 00
-E 2008 00 00 00 00 00 00 00 00
-E 2010 FF 00 00 00 00 93 00 00
-E 2018 FF 00 00 00 10 93 00 00
-E 2020 00 00 00 00 00 00 00 00
-E 2028 00 00 00 00 00 00 00 00

;now to put something into the source block...
```

```
-E 200 EE EE EE EE EE EE EE

;still within DEBUG, whip up a little program...
-A 100
mov ah,87 ;BIOS function number.
mov cx,7  ;number of bytes to copy.
mov si,2000          ;addressing of GDT.
mov dx,0  ;the following code is rough, but puts the
mov bx,cs ; 24-bit linear source address into the GDT,
shl bx,1  ; in the third descriptor.
rcl dx,1  ;( you could have course done it directly using
                                    ; "E").
shl bx,1
rcl dx,1
shl bx,1
rcl dx,1
shl bx,1
rcl dx,1
add bx,200
adc dx,0             ;we now have 24-bit addr.
mov [2014],dl
mov [2012],bx
int 15               ;go for it!
int 3

-G=100
;should return carry flag = 0 & AH = 0 if successful.
```

;C2ASM.ASM B.Kauler 1990.

```
;the skeleton .ASM module below was created by compiling a
; skeleton C program of arbitrary name filename1.c, as
; follows;
;
; add(a,b)
; int a,b;
; { int x; x=a+b; return x; }
;
;compiled with the /Fa switch to generate .ASM output, &
; the /c switch to suppress linking --
;   CL /Fa /c filename1.C , , ,   (Microsoft C v6.0)
;
;Have a look at the listing below. Note that a & b are
; defined as "int",
;which corresponds to MASM's "word", ie, 16 bits, so
; word-size values
;are passed on the stack to the .ASM routine. By default
; "add" function returns a word-size value via AX, to variable
; x.
;
;................................
INCLUDELIB      SLIBCE
_TEXT   SEGMENT  WORD PUBLIC 'CODE'
_TEXT   ENDS
_DATA   SEGMENT  WORD PUBLIC 'DATA'
_DATA   ENDS
CONST   SEGMENT  WORD PUBLIC 'CONST'
CONST   ENDS
_BSS    SEGMENT  WORD PUBLIC 'BSS'
_BSS    ENDS
DGROUP GROUP   CONST, _BSS, _DATA
    ASSUME DS: DGROUP, SS: DGROUP
EXTRN   __aNchkstk:NEAR
extrn _var1:word       ;added by me. see notes below.
;
_TEXT   SEGMENT
    ASSUME        CS: _TEXT
    PUBLIC        _add
_add    PROC NEAR
    push  bp
    mov   bp,sp
    mov   ax,2
    call  __aNchkstk  ;this is a compiler-supplied routine,
                      ; to check that
                      ;the stack has enough room
                      ;(no. bytes spec. by AX).
    mov   ax,WORD PTR [bp+6]      ;b
    add   ax,WORD PTR [bp+4]      ;a

    adc ax,_var1          ;added by me. see notes below.

    mov   sp,bp
    pop   bp
    ret
    nop
_add    ENDP
_TEXT   ENDS
END
;.....................................
;
;this basic skeleton can be used for any .ASM routine.
;here is a C program that will call the above .ASM routine --
; #include <stdio.h>
; int var1=2;
; main()
; { int x,y=3,z=5; x=add(y,z); printf("answer = %hu",x); }
;
;it defines x,y and z as 16-bit, passes y and z on the stack to
; the .ASM routine, which returns a value to x via AX
; register.
;x,y and z are local variables, however I have also included a
; global variable, "var1" -- look back at the .ASM routine to
; see how it can access a C global variable.
;if this C program is called filename2.c, & .ASM program is
; filename1,
;this is the process of compiling & linking with MS C v6.0 --
; MASM filename1;          ;filename1.asm --> filename1.obj
; CL /c filename2.c ,,,    ;filename2.c --> filename2.obj
; LINK filename2+ filename1;   ; --> filename2.EXE
;
;what if you want to pass values other than 16-bit?
;C's "long int" is the same as MASM's "doubleword", that is,
; 32 bits.
;here is a C skeleton that you can compile to .ASM for
; passing long int's;
```

```
; long int add(a,b)
; long int a,b;
; { long int x; x=a+b; return x; }
;
;as this must also return a long integer, Microsoft C does so
; in DX:AX.
;A master C program that can call such a .ASM module --
; #include <stdio.h>
; main()
; { long int x,y=3,z=5;
;    x=add(y,z); printf("answer = %lu",x); }
;
;note that "%lu" is a format specifier for x, being "long
; unsigned integer".
;.............................................................
```

;OBJECT

```
;exe format. demonstrates OOP. B.Kauler 1991
;Note that this listing is very cluttered with comments and
; suggestions.
;after basically digesting them you might like to erase them,
; to be able to more clearly see the overall program.
;
;
;..................................................
stack1      SEGMENT stack 'stack'
    db      128 DUP(0)
stack1      ENDS
;..................................................
data        SEGMENT 'data'
;     ......
;The structure SHAPES contains "variables" and also
;pointers to methods -- but note that we cannot specify the
;the address of a method, as MASM will not accept a
; forward reference from within a STRUC.
;(A solutiion is to put the STRUC definitions after the code is
; assembled, but that introduces other problems).
;The STRUC definition below is only used by Asm -- it is the
;instances that are actually assembled (BOX1, BOX2). When
;defining the instances we can initialise the fields, including
;insertion of the procedure addresses for each method.
;(Note that in the case of dynamically allocated objects, the
; pointers would have to be inserted by code, and if they are
; far pointers then the structure would have to use DD).
;Note TASM allows nested STRUCs and MASM doesn't.
;  The definition ;of BOX below shows the case for TASM,
; which is conceptually neater. the comment alongside shows
; what you would have to replace it with for MASM. Either
; way, there is a problem when you come to declare instances,
; as you cannot initialise the fields inherited from SHAPE
;(only the first field). Whatever fields have been declared in
; BOX can be initialised (in this case there's just one;
; ROUNDED).
;hence the rather messy macro (that I've called
; "instance_box").
;Note also that TASM has an "ideal mode" in which
; structure field- labels are local to that structure, thus
; allowing other structures to have identical labels -- which is
; what we ideally want for OOP --
;but the NOW override no longer works -- perhaps someone
; can find a fix for this. At the moment, structure field-labels
; are global.

SHAPES  STRUC
REDRAW          DW ?           ;dummy pointer.
                               ; **see below
VERT            DB 5
HORIZ   DB 10
SYZE    DW ?    ;near pointer to SIZE_SHAPES
                ;**see below
ROW     DB 0
COL     DB 0
PLACE   DW ?    ;near pointer to PLACE_SHAPES
                ; **see below
SHAPES  ENDS
        ;** the pointers would have to be Define
        ;Doubleword (DD) if program has multiple
                ;code segments.

;     .......
BOX STRUC
    SHAPES <>       ;TASM only.
                    ;MASM; replace with (SIZE SHAPES)
                    ; DUP(?)
ROUNDED DB 0
BOX ENDS
;     .....
;macro to create instance of BOX, with data initialisations....
;(messy, due to limitations of Asm -- have to create an
; instance of BOX then overwrite part of it with an instance
; of SHAPES)
MAKE_BOX        MACRO       ibox
ibox    BOX     < ,0>
        ;cant initialise SHAPE's inherited data here.
    ORG ibox                ;backtrack.
SHAPES  <REDRAW_BOX,,,SIZE_SHAPES,2,5,PLACE_SHAPES>
    ORG ibox+(SIZE BOX)     ;ret. location ptr to
                            ; normal position.
    ENDM

;create instances of BOX....
    MAKE_BOX    BOX1
    MAKE_BOX    BOX2

;     ......
NOW EQU [bx]
    ;es:[bx] required for multiple data segments. see below.
    ;note: TASM treats "THIS" as reserved word, so use
    ; NOW.
;     .....
data        ENDS

;.....................................................
```

```
code      SEGMENT 'code'
   ASSUME cs:code
;    ......
NOWIS    MACRO  instance_label
    mov  bx,OFFSET instance_label

;note: For multiple data segments, ES:BX must be loaded, by
; replacing the above code with the instruction below,
; however instance_label is no longer the actual address
; loaded to ES:BX but is the label of a memory location that
; contains the far address.(instance_label DD far_address).
;Extra steps are required to set up the program for this.
;    les     bx,instance_label

    ENDM
;    ......
;.........................................................
main     PROC FAR
    mov  ax,data
    mov  ds,ax
    ASSUME ds:data
;    .......
;    .....
    NOWIS BOX1
    mov  dx,0105h                  ;change row & col
    call  NOW.PLACE  ;update ROW & COL of BOX1.
    call  NOW.REDRAW               ;display the box.

;note: at this point should only call those methods belonging
; to BOX1.
;If you want to call CIRCLE1.REDRAW (for example), first
; execute
;     NOWIS CIRCLE1

;note2:     procedure calls to execute only one or two
; instructions, is very wasteful, and C++ optimises this
; situation by treating some small methods like macros,
; expanding them in-line.
;Thus, although it is not good OOP practice, you can do what
;C++ does anyway -- instead of calling PLACE, just put the
;two instructions straight in
;-- or define the method as a macro. No, don't do it.

;note3:     one thing you may have noticed in the Figure
; (textbook  hierarchy diagram of the objects) is that I created
; variable ROUNDED, attached to BOX, but I did not
; create a method for it.
;I should have, as all data must only be changed by methods
;attached to the same object.  However I left the Figure
;uncluttered as I haven't actually implemented any setting
;              of ROUNDED in this demo program.

    NOWIS           BOX2
    mov  dx,1020h                  ;row & col
    call  NOW.PLACE
    call  NOW.REDRAW               ;draws box2

    mov  ax,4C00h  ;back to DOS
    int     21h
main     ENDP
;.........................................................
PLACE_SHAPES PROC NEAR
;the new row and column coordinates are
;passed to PLACE via DX.  DH=row (0-24)
;DL=column (0-79).
    mov  NOW.ROW,dh
    mov  NOW.COL,dl

;note:      a method can call other methods, even methods
            ; belonging to other objects.  The standard rule is
            ; always use NOWIS before calling any object that
            ; is not the current one.

    ret
PLACE_SHAPES ENDP
;.........................................................
REDRAW_BOX PROC NEAR
;no parameters passed to this one.  It just
;uses ROW, COL, VERT, HORIZ
;& ROUNDED to redraw the box.
;note again that NOW override is used to
;access only the data at the currently pointed
;-to instance.
;    ......
;some code here to draw box on scrn....

;note:      don't forget when writing code that BX (or
            ; ES:BX) is/are used for the NOW override, which
            ; means that we have to save it/them if we want to
            ; use it/them for anything else.

    mov  dh,NOW.ROW
    mov  ch,0
    mov  cl,NOW.VERT

vertloop:
    mov  dl,NOW.COL
    push cx                          ;save vert loop count
    mov  ch,0
    mov  cl,NOW.HORIZ                ;horiz loop count
    push bx                          ;save NOW override

horizloop:
    push cx                          ;save horiz loop count
    mov  bh,0
    mov  ah,2                        ;set_cursor
    int  10h
    mov  cx,1
    mov  al,219                      ;ibm block-character.
    mov  bx,0003h                    ;page, colour.
    mov ah,0Ah                       ;write_char
    int  10h
    pop  cx          ;restore horiz loop count
    inc  dl          ;row no. for set_cursor
    loop horizloop                   ;next horizontal char
```

```
    pop   bx          ;restore NOW override
    pop   cx          ;restore vert loop count
    inc   dh                         ;col no. for set_cursor
    loop  vertloop                   ;next line
;   ......
    ret
REDRAW_BOX ENDP
;.........................................................
SIZE_SHAPES PROC NEAR
;perhaps this could have some parameters
;passed to it, to update VERT & HORIZ,
;then return with a pass/fail in AX.
;   ......
;   .....
    ret
SIZE_SHAPES ENDP
;.......................................................

code      ENDS
    END   main

;NOTE ON USING TURBO-DEBUGGER:
;The debugger's Watch window is particularly nice for
; viewing all the data for an object, since all you have to do is
; change to the Watch window by pressing <F6> then type
; the name of the instance you want to view, for example
; "BOX1".
```

//OOP.CPP

```
//demo OOP program, links C++ to .ASM member-function.
//to compile this file, called OOP.CPP, using Borland C++:
// BCC OOP.CPP MEMBER.ASM
//or can do it in steps....
// BCC -c OOP.CPP
// TASM /ml MEMBER
// TLINK OOP MEMBER
//*****note that this .CPP file first had to be compiled to
// produce .ASM output... see end of file.******
class box              //declaring a class called box.
{
    int row;                         //giving it some data.
    int col;
public:
    virtual void place(int ,int);
                       //declaring a method called place().
};
class circle           //declaring a class called circle.
{           int row,col;             //giving it some data.
public:
    virtual void place(int,int);
                       //declaring a method called place()
    virtual void draw();
                       //another method called draw()
};
//..........................................................
void box::place(int r,int c)
                       //definition of place() belonging to box.
{
//  row = r;           //these two lines can also be done in
//  col = c;                          //asm, as below....
    asm {
    mov si,this        //"this" equates to [bp+4]
    mov [si].row,r     //in-line assembly, can use all labels
    mov [si].col,c     //from the C++ program.
                       //"this" is the addr of current object.
      }
}

void circle::draw(void)
          //definition of draw() belonging to circle.
{                                   //does nothing.
}
    box box1;
          //instances. By declaring them here I am
    box box2;
          //making them static, and they will be
    circle circle1;
          //created in the data segment.
          //if i had declared them within main() they
          //would be automatic -- created on the
          //stack only (see below)...
//......................................................................
main()
{
 box box3;             //instance created in stack segment.
 box1.place(3,5);      //calls place() belonging to box class,
                       //with "this" set to box1.
 box *ptr;             //same thing using a pointer.
 ptr = &box1;          //required if we want this line to call
 ptr -> place(3,5);
          //various place()'s depending on entry point.
 circle1.place(1,2);   //call the .asm function.
}
//.......................................................................
//the following is anly a stub, to get the skeleton for a .asm
// module.
//Compile to produce .asm output, then remove this stub....
//See MEMBER.ASM for notes on this.
void circle::place(int r,int c)
          //definition of place() belonging to circle.
//let's say that i want this function to be written in asm, not
// inline.
//furthermore, the asm program must have access to other
// C++ functions, and the data-members of its current
// instance....
//Firstly, bit of a skeleton at the C++ level....
{   row=r; col=c;      //getting at current object's data.
    box1.place(1,2);
          //calling another function, another object.
    this->draw();      //calling a function,same object.
}
```

INDEX

COMPANION DISK ONLY £6.95

SEE OVERLEAF

COMPANION DISK SITE LICENCE:

The Companion Disk available for this book is for a single user. Each disk has a unique serial number encoded into it, to discourage copyright violation. Companies or institutions wishing to install the Companion Disk software on many PC's may find it more economical to purchase a Site Licence. Basically this entitles the institution to install unlimited copies at the site, where "site" is defined as the physical location or locations of the company or institution. "Site" is fully defined, and other conditions are clarified, in the Companion Disk Site Licence Application form, available from Karda Prints, 10 McCormick Way, Narrogin, WA 6312, AUSTRALIA. A Site Licence currently costs A$199.

A86 assembler and D86 debugger supplied on the Companion Disk are owned by Eric Isaacson. Permission is given for free individual use, to the extent of doing the exercises in this book. Further use, or regular use by any institution, will require a registration fee. Details in the documentation file A86TERMS.DOC on the Companion Disk.

CUSTOMER FEEDBACK:

The Author of "PC Architecture & Assembly Language" is a workaholic and updates the book on a regular basis. You have the opportunity to provide input to the next edition. If you find an error, please let us know. If you are an educator and would like to see some particular material included, or the current content modified, again let us know. If you have any feedback when returning the voucher, write it in the space below:

FEEDBACK:

....

....

....

....

....

Post this voucher to:

"Companion Disk Offer",
Sigma Press, 1 South Oak Lane, Wilmslow,
Cheshire SK9 6AR, England.

Above price includes postage & handling worldwide.

COMPANION DISK PURCHASE VOUCHER

Cutout and post this voucher, together with payment. (photocopy allowed)

The Companion Disk is a complete package of tools for use with this textbook: A86 Assembler, D86 Debugger, source listings of example programs and a modified version of BROWSE.COM with a hypertext database containing most of the reference material from this book. TBROWSE provides context-sensitive hypertext pop-up help at any time; BIOS/DOS services, instruction set, user guides to Assemblers & Debuggers.

(Note that the Companion Disk is NOT the Developer's Softbook Disk, described on the Companion Disk and available as a separate product)

PLEASE SEND THE COMPANION DISK FOR "PC ARCHITECTURE & ASSEMBLY LANGUAGE" 3rd EDITION. PAYMENT IS ENCLOSED.

☐ 5.25 inch

☐ 3.5 inch

NAME: .... DATE:............

ADDRESS: ....

....

WHERE PURCHASED: ....

NOTE TO STUDENTS: IF "PC ARCHITECTURE & ASSEMBLY LANGUAGE" IS OFFICIALLY PRESCRIBED AT YOUR EDUCATIONAL INSTITUTION, IT MAY HAVE A SITE LICENCE, IN WHICH CASE IT IS NOT NECESSARY TO PLACE THIS ORDER.

Price shown overleaf. Includes Postage & handling. Subject to change. Cheque or money order only, payable to Sigma Press. Overseas orders must pay by international money order or bank draft in British Pounds Sterling, payable at a British bank. Post this voucher with payment to: "Companion Disk Offer", Sigma Press, 1 South Oak Lane, Wilmslow, Cheshire SK9 6AR, England.

CONTENTS OF THE COMPANION DISK ARE NOT GUARANTEED TO BE EXACTLY AS DESCRIBED. NO LIABILITY IS ACCEPTED FOR ANY DISCREPANCY BETWEEN DESCRIPTION AND CONTENT, NOR FOR UNEXPECTED BEHAVIOUR OF PROGRAMS & SOURCE LISTINGS, NOR FOR NON-ARRIVAL OF ORDERED DISKS AFTER DISPATCH FROM PUBLISHER.